The HYMNAL for YOUTH

All things praise Thee, Lord most high:
Heaven and earth, and sea and sky,
All were for Thy glory made,
That Thy greatness thus displayed,
Should all worship bring to Thee;
All things praise Thee: Lord, may we.

— *George W. Conder.*

1948
THE WESTMINSTER PRESS
PHILADELPHIA

Published July, 1941
Second Printing, January, 1942
Third Printing, February, 1943
Fourth Printing, March, 1944
Fifth Printing, February, 1945
Sixth Printing, September, 1945
Seventh Printing, March, 1946
Eighth Printing, March, 1947
Ninth Printing, November, 1947
Tenth Printing, October, 1948

PRINTED IN THE UNITED STATES OF AMERICA

PREFACE

THE very nature of man makes him reach out for a closer fellowship with God. That is one reason why man has always worshiped. But the ways in which man worships change from time to time, and the forms of worship services vary. *The Hymnal for Youth* is issued, therefore, to make available many worship materials which have made their appearance since the forerunner of this book, *The Church School Hymnal for Youth*, was published in 1928.

The basic purpose of this hymnal coincides with the objectives of the church program for youth: the full surrender of one's self to God as he is revealed in Jesus Christ, the Saviour; the manifestation of a Christlike love for all people; and the identification of one's self with the fellowship of Christ's followers throughout the world. Although this hymnal has been prepared primarily for use in young people's groups in the church, it may also be used by adult organizations and in general church services.

In compiling *The Hymnal for Youth* the four basic tests that for many years have been used to measure the quality of a hymn were employed. These tests briefly stated are:

1. Does the hymn have a distinctly Christian message?
2. Is the hymn good literature?
3. Is the tune good music?
4. Is the music singable?

Some well-known hymns are not included in this book, either because they do not carry a clear and convincing Christian message or because they fail in one of the other three measurements. The hymns that are found in this hymnal have been used helpfully among young people. Some tunes are arranged in lower keys in order to make them singable for young men as well as young women. As far as possible the words conform with original and correct texts. In a few instances lines, and even stanzas, not in keeping with Christian thought have been changed or eliminated.

Not all the special features of this new hymnal can be mentioned, but the following comments will call attention to a number of features which, it is hoped, will make the book a useful source book: Consciousness of the universal character of the Christian Church and of the contributions which many nationalities have made to its worship has led to the inclusion of hymns that originated in such countries as ancient Greece, ancient Rome, Wales, Switzerland, Denmark, France, Austria, Russia, the Netherlands, Germany, Bohemia, England. Negro spirituals also add to the enrichment of the hymn collection. Some of the famous composers whose works are found in the book are Bach, Beethoven, Grieg, Haydn, Handel, Mendelssohn, Palestrina, Schumann, Sibelius. The types of hymn tunes to be found in this hymnal include plain songs, tunes from the Scottish and Genevan Psalters, carols, chorals, folk songs, and modern hymns. Thirty themes or subjects are listed in the table of contents, which indicates the wide range of hymns. The Topical Index contains listings of hymns under nearly two hundred different topics, thus increasing the usability of this hymnal. In recognition of a growing trend in church music, descants have been added to a number of hymns. Use of these descants by organ, choir, or congregation will add a musical quality that will greatly enhance the singing of the hymns.

The section entitled "Suggestions for Worship" will be found invaluable for those who plan worship programs and conduct worship services. Five typical worship programs are provided, with numerous choices in the several parts of the program, thus affording a wide variety in the preparation for worship services over an extended period of time. The section containing prayers is unusual in that it contains prayers expressing the thoughts of young people, the well-known prayers of the Church, and prayers in the form of litanies. The quotations from religious literature are in keeping with themes frequently used for worship services.

This book would not be complete without a word of tribute to and appreciation of Calvin W. Laufer, D.D., Editor of *The Church School Hymnal for Youth*, and, until his death, editor and chairman of the Committee for *The Hymnal for Youth*. Dr. Laufer's enthusiasm for the finest type of church music and his spirit of devoted service to the young people of the Church are contained in this new hymnal. It is deeply regretted that his death made impossible his completion of the work to which he gave initial leadership.

Many workers with young people, including pastors, organists, choir directors, directors of religious education, and Sunday School teachers have given valuable advice and counsel regarding the contents of this book. Their assistance is deeply appreciated. This hymnal is offered, therefore, with the hope that it will meet the religious needs of youth, that it will serve the purpose of the Church, and that it will lead to a deeper devotion to Jesus Christ.

RUTH E. BEISWINGER.
HAZEL R. BROWNSON.
MARIE C. DIETER.
S. FRANKLIN MACK.
JEAN W. STEELE.
FRANK D. GETTY, *Chairman.*
LAWRENCE CURRY, *Musical Editor.*

DESCANTS AND INSTRUMENTAL MUSIC

THE descant has a long and interesting musical history. It sprang from that period, about the year A.D. 1000, when music was freeing itself from the bonds of unison singing and experiments in two-part music (diaphony) were being made. The counterpart to the main melody of any piece was called the "descant." Since then the descant has come a long way.

Intrinsically the descant is more than a mere obbligato. If it is worthy the name, it will enhance and beautify the original tune by contrast and by reinforcement of the important harmonies of the hymn. No two descants are quite alike. Some are sustained and slow-moving like the one to "Nicaea," Hymn 32. Others are independent melodic lines that reinforce the hymn tune by their very strength and virility; for example, "Sine Nomine," Hymn 290.

These melodies are best used as contrast portions in the hymn-singing. They lose their effectiveness if sung to every stanza. It is therefore recommended that they be sung to alternate stanzas or just to the final stanza.

There are several effective ways of using the descant: (1) It may be sung by a few high sopranos, with the remainder of the soprano section singing the hymn tune. (2) It may be sung by a solo voice, accompanied by the chorus singing or humming the hymn. (3) For the most rousing effect of all, the high voices (sopranos and tenors) should sing the descant and the low voices (altos and basses) the hymn tune in unison. This two-part combination, when supported by full organ or piano accompaniment is most inspiring.

In this hymnal the following hymns have descants: 32, 40, 70, 74, 93, 119, 120, 122 (first and second tunes), 290.

THE instrumental music has been chosen for its practical use in every type of service. Each piece represents a different mood and all of them will be found invaluable as preludes, interludes, offertories, or postludes in the worship service. Here will be found the lyric strains of Mendelssohn, the virile strength of Brahms, the quiet devotion of Schumann, and the unfathomable depths of Beethoven.

It should be noted that the music here included has not been simplified. With one or two exceptions, the composer's original notes remain unaltered. The difficulty of the music was carefully considered before including it. A glance at the content of the section will reveal its musical worth. It is the hope of the committee that real reverence and inspiration may be derived from contact with some of the great music of the masters.

ACKNOWLEDGMENTS

THE committee wishes to express its gratitude to all those who have granted permission for the use of copyrighted materials. Material that is not in the public domain carries with it notice of copyright. Painstaking search has been made to determine what hymns, tunes, and quotations in the worship aids are copyrighted, and thanks are due to all those who have aided in this task. If any material has inadvertently been used without due credit, correction will be made in future editions.

CONTENTS

	PAGE		PAGE
Preface	3	Alphabetic Index of Tunes	13
Descants and Instrumental Music	5	Metrical Index of Tunes	15
Acknowledgments	6	Topical Index	17
Index of First Lines	9	The Lord's Prayer	25
Index of Chants and Responses	12	The Commandments	25
Index of Instrumental Music	12	The Apostles' Creed	25

THE HYMNS

I. WORSHIP AND PRAISE

	HYMNS		HYMNS
Adoration and Thanksgiving	1–18	Evening Hymns	22–31
Morning Hymns	19–21		

II. GOD

The Holy Trinity	32–35	God's World	42–49
God's Eternity and Power	36–41	God's Love and Care	50–59

III. JESUS CHRIST

The Birth of Jesus	60–82	The Resurrection	102–109
The Life and Ministry of Jesus	83–94	The Everliving Christ	110–126
The Crucifixion	95–101		

IV. THE HOLY SPIRIT 127–131

V. THE SCRIPTURES 132–136

VI. THE CHURCH AND THE SACRAMENTS

The Church	137–143	The Lord's Supper	145–149
Baptism	144		

VII. LIVING THE CHRISTIAN LIFE

Prayer and Hope	150–165	Discipleship and Service	196–209
Consecration	166–177	Faith and Trust	210–216
Purity and Self-Control	178–187	Loyalty and Courage	217–237
Love and Obedience	188–195		

VIII. THE KINGDOM OF GOD ON EARTH

	HYMNS
Missions and World Fellowship	238–250
The Neighborhood	251–261
The Home and School	262–266
The Nation	267–276
World Friendship and Peace	277–288

IX. ETERNAL LIFE 289–293

CHANTS AND RESPONSES

	NUMBERS
Opening Sentences	294–297
Prayer Responses	298–301
Responses to Scripture	302–303
Chants and General Responses	304–310
Offertory Responses	311–314
Closing Sentences	315–317
Amens	318–323

INSTRUMENTAL MUSIC

Numbers 324–336

WORSHIP MATERIALS

	PAGES
Suggestions for Worship	308–317
Readings from Scripture	318–338
Prayers and Collects	340–360
Poetry and Prose for Worship	361–381

INDEX OF FIRST LINES

HYMN

A king might miss the guiding star . . 71
A mighty Fortress is our God 38
Abide with me: fast falls the eventide 293
All beautiful the march of days. . . . 46
All creatures of our God and King . . 13
All glory, laud, and honor 90
All hail the power of Jesus' Name. . . 122
All people that on earth do dwell . . . 1
All praise to Thee, my God, this night. 26
Ancient of Days, who sittest throned in glory 34
Angels, from the realms of glory . . . 69
As with gladness men of old 77
At length there dawns the glorious day 288
At Thy feet, our God and Father . . . 7
Awake, my soul, and with the sun . . 21
Away in a manger 75

Backward we look, O God of all our days 59
Be strong 229
Be Thou my Vision, O Lord of my heart 115
Believe not those who say 227
Beneath the cross of Jesus 173
Blest be the tie that binds 141
Bread of the world in mercy broken. . 146
Break Thou the bread of life 133
Breathe on me, Breath of God 130
Brightly beams our Father's mercy . . 206
By roads that wound uphill and down. 88

Christ for the world we sing 250
Christ of the Upward Way 230
"Christ the Lord is risen today" 104
Christian, rise and act thy creed . . . 259
Come, all ye shepherds, ye children of earth 78
Come, Holy Ghost, our souls inspire . 129
Come, let us join with faithful souls . . 255
Come, Thou Almighty King 33
Come, Thou long-expected Jesus . . . 62
Come, ye faithful, raise the strain . . 108
Come, ye thankful people, come . . . 18
Crown Him with many crowns 120

Dare to be brave, dare to be true . . . 223
Day is dying in the west. 30
Dear Father, whom we cannot see . . 287

HYMN

Dear Lord and Father of mankind . . 150
Dear Lord, who sought at dawn of day 160
Draw Thou my soul, O Christ 164

Fairest Lord Jesus 119
Faith of our fathers! living still . . . 224
Father, in Thy mysterious presence kneeling 52
Father, lead me day by day 183
Father of lights, in whom there is no shadow 12
Father of mercies, in Thy Word . . . 135
Fight the good fight with all thy might . 228
Fling out the banner! let it float . . . 246
For all the saints who from their labors rest 290
For the beauty of the earth 42
For the bread, which Thou hast broken 145
From homes of quiet peace. 265
From ocean unto ocean 241

Give of your best to the Master . . . 176
Glorious things of thee are spoken . . 139
Go, labor on: spend, and be spent . . 249
God is Love; His mercy brightens . . 58
God of grace and God of glory 236
God of our fathers, known of old . . . 270
God of our fathers, whose almighty hand 271
God of our life, through all the circling years 39
God of our youth, to whom we yield . 179
God of the earth, the sky, the sea. . . 49
God of the nations, hear our call . . . 247
God of the nations, near and far . . . 277
God save America! New world of glory 273
God send us men whose aim 'twill be . 276
God, that madest earth and heaven . . 24
God the Omnipotent! King, who ordainest 285
God, who touchest earth with beauty . 178
Goin' to lay down my burden 286
Good Christian men, rejoice 80
Great Master, touch us with Thy skillful hands 186

Hail, gladdening Light, of His pure glory poured 31
Hail the glorious golden city 251

INDEX OF FIRST LINES

HYMN

Hail to the brightness of Zion's glad morning 245
Hail to the Lord's Anointed 61
Hark! hark, my soul! angelic songs are swelling 289
Hark! the herald angels sing 68
Hark, what a sound, and too divine for hearing 116
Have Thine own way, Lord 162
He leadeth me: O blessèd thought . . 54
He who would valiant be 233
Heralds of Christ who bear the King's commands 235
Here, O my Lord, I see Thee face to face 149
Holy Father, bless us 27
Holy Father, God of might 163
Holy, holy, holy! Lord God Almighty . 32
Holy Spirit, Truth divine 128
How firm a foundation, ye saints of the Lord 210

I am trusting Thee, Lord Jesus . . . 215
I bind my heart this tide 205
I feel the winds of God today. 181
I heard the voice of Jesus say 216
I know not how that Bethlehem's Babe 213
I know that my Redeemer lives. . . . 184
I look to Thee in every need 51
I love Thy Kingdom, Lord. 140
I love to tell the story. 193
I name Thy hallowed Name 152
I need Thee every hour 155
I think when I read that sweet story of old 144
I would be true, for there are those who trust me 180
Immortal Love, forever full 208
In Christ there is no East or West . . 243
In the cross of Christ I glory 95
Into the woods my Master went . . . 100
It came upon the midnight clear . . . 64
I've found a Friend; oh, such a Friend 190

Jesus, and shall it ever be 218
Jesus calls us: o'er the tumult 198
Jesus Christ is risen today 103
Jesus, I live to Thee 292
Jesus, Lover of my soul 151
Jesus, Saviour, pilot me 157
Jesus shall reign where'er the sun . . . 248
Jesus, the very thought of Thee . . . 194
Jesus, Thou divine Companion 200
Jesus, Thou Joy of loving hearts . . . 147
Joy to the world! the Lord is come . . 65
Joyful, joyful, we adore Thee. 6

HYMN

Just as I am, Thine own to be 171
Just as I am, without one plea 170

Lead on, O King Eternal 226
Let all the world in every corner sing . 16
Let there be light, Lord God of Hosts. . 278
Let us with a gladsome mind. 41
Lift up your heads, ye mighty gates. . 92
Light of the world, we hail Thee . . . 281
Lord and Saviour, true and kind . . . 264
Lord, I want to be a Christian in-a my heart 217
Lord of all being, throned afar 56
Lord, speak to me, that I may speak . 196
"Lord, Thy glory fills the heaven" . . 10
Lord, we come with hearts aflame. . . 207
Love divine, all loves excelling 153

March on, O soul, with strength . . . 234
Men and children everywhere 5
'Mid all the traffic of the ways 165
More about Jesus would I know . . . 126
More love to Thee, O Christ 191
My country, 't is of thee 267
My faith looks up to Thee 211
My God, I thank Thee, who hast made . 11
My Jesus, as Thou wilt 172
My life, dear Lord, I give to Thee . . 199
My Master was so very poor 87

Nearer, my God, to Thee 156
No distant Lord have I 113
Not alone for mighty empire 274
Now in the days of youth 169
Now praise we great and famous men . 269
Now thank we all our God. 17
Now the day is over 29
Now to heaven our prayer ascending . 159

O beautiful for spacious skies. 272
O brother man, fold to thy heart thy brother 260
O come, all ye faithful. 74
O come, O come, Emmanuel 63
O God, beneath Thy guiding hand . . 275
O God of love, O King of peace. . . . 279
O happy home, where Thou art loved the dearest. 262
O Jesus, I have promised 174
O Jesus, Prince of life and truth . . . 182
O Jesus, Thou art standing. 201
O Light, from age to age the same . . 143
O little town of Bethlehem 66
O Love that wilt not let me go 192
O Master, let me walk with Thee . . . 166

INDEX OF FIRST LINES

HYMN

O Master Workman of the race. . . . 85
O sacred Head, now wounded 99
O say, can you see, by the dawn's early light 268
O sing a song of Bethlehem 89
O Son of Man, our Hero strong and tender 114
O Son of Man, Thou madest known. . 197
O Son of Man, who walked each day . 112
O sons and daughters, let us sing . . . 107
O Thou Eternal Christ of God 93
O Thou, in all Thy might so far . . . 110
O Thou whose feet have climbed life's hill 263
O Thou whose glory shone like fire . . 142
O Thou whose gracious presence blessed 266
O where are kings and empires now . . 137
O Word of God incarnate 132
O worship the King all-glorious above 36
O Zion, haste, thy mission high fulfilling 240
Of the Father's love begotten 35
Once to every man and nation 221
Onward, Christian soldiers 231
Open my eyes, that I may see 189
Our God, our Help in ages past. . . . 40

Praise God from whom all blessings flow 2
Praise the Lord, His glories show . . . 15
Praise the Lord: ye heavens, adore Him 8
Praise to God, immortal praise 14
Praise to the Lord, the Almighty, the King of creation 9
Prayer is the soul's sincere desire . . . 161

Rejoice, the Lord is King 123
Rejoice, ye pure in heart. 124
Ride on! ride on in majesty 94
Ring out, wild bells, to the wild sky. . 282
Rise up, O men of God 258
Rock of Ages, cleft for me 154

Saviour, again to Thy dear Name we raise 23
Saviour, Thy dying love 195
Shepherd of tender youth 121
Shepherds! shake off your drowsy sleep 81
Silent night! holy night 73
Soldiers of Christ, arise 220
Sow the seed beside all waters 244
Spirit of God, descend upon my heart 127
Spring has now unwrapped the flowers. 47
Stand up, stand up for Jesus 225
Steal away, steal away, steal away to Jesus 209
Still, still with Thee, when purple morning breaketh 53

HYMN

Strong Son of God, immortal Love . . 212
Sun of my soul, Thou Saviour dear . . 25
Sunset and evening star 291

Take my life, and let it be 175
Take Thou our minds, dear Lord . . . 168
Teach me, O Lord, Thy holy way. . . 188
Teach us, O Lord, true brotherhood . . 256
Temper my spirit, O Lord 185
That cause can neither be lost nor stayed 237
The body, Lord, is ours to keep. . . . 187
The Church's one Foundation 138
The day of resurrection 102
The day Thou gavest, Lord, is ended . . 22
The fathers built this city 252
The first Nowell the angel did say . . 70
The God of Abraham praise 37
The heavens declare Thy glory 45
The heavens declare Thy glory, Lord . 134
The hidden years at Nazareth 83
The King of love my Shepherd is . . . 57
The light of God is falling 254
The Lord be with us as we walk . . . 28
The Lord's my Shepherd, I'll not want . 148
The morning light is breaking 239
The spacious firmament on high . . . 44
The Spirit breathes upon the Word . . 136
The strife is o'er, the battle done . . 105
The sun is on the land and sea 20
The voice of God is calling 202
The whole wide world for Jesus. . . . 242
There is a green hill far away 97
There's a light upon the mountains . . 118
There's a song in the air 79
There's a wideness in God's mercy . . 50
These things shall be: a loftier race . 283
Thine is the glory. 106
This is my Father's world 43
This is the day the Lord hath made. . 3
Thou art the Way: to Thee alone . . 214
Thou didst leave Thy throne and Thy kingly crown 167
Thy home is with the humble, Lord . 131
Thy Kingdom come, O Lord 280
'Tis midnight; and on Olive's brow . 98
To the knights in the days of old . . . 232
Truehearted, wholehearted, faithful and loyal 177
Turn back, O man, forswear thy foolish ways 284

Wake, awake, for night is flying . . . 117
Watchman, tell us of the night 60
We are climbing Jacob's ladder 219
We bear the strain of earthly care . . 111
We plow the fields, and scatter 55

INDEX OF FIRST LINES

HYMN

We praise Thee, O God, our Redeemer, Creator 4
We thank Thee, Lord, Thy paths of service lead 203
We three kings of Orient are 76
We would be building; temples still undone 204
We would see Jesus, lo! His star is shining 84
"Welcome, happy morning!" 109
Were you there when they crucified my Lord 101
We've a story to tell to the nations . . 238
What a Friend we have in Jesus . . . 158
What Child is this, who, laid to rest. . 72

HYMN

When, His salvation bringing. 91
When I survey the wondrous cross . . 96
When morning gilds the skies 19
When the golden evening gathered . . 86
When the great sun sinks to his rest. . 48
When thy heart, with joy o'erflowing . 257
When wilt Thou save the people . . . 261
Where cross the crowded ways of life . 253
While by my sheep I watched at night . 82
While shepherds watched their flocks by night 67
Who is on the Lord's side 222

Ye servants of God, your Master proclaim 125

INDEX OF CHANTS AND RESPONSES

NUMBER

All things come of Thee, O Lord . . . 314
Amens 318–323
Bless Thou the gifts our hands have brought 311
Enter into His gates with thanksgiving 295
Ere we part, O God our Father . . . 317
Glory be to God on high 309
Glory be to the Father 307, 308
God be in my head, and in my understanding 310
God be with you till we meet again . . 315
Hear our prayer, O Lord 300, 301
Holy, holy, holy, Lord of Hosts . . . 305
Let all mortal flesh keep silence . . . 296

NUMBER

Let the words of my mouth 298
Lord, have mercy, have mercy upon us 303
Lord, have mercy upon us 304
Now may the light that shone in Jesus Christ our Lord 316
O Thou who hearest every heartfelt prayer 299
Our Father which art in heaven . . . 306
Seek ye the Lord while He may be found 294
The Lord is in His holy temple 297
Thy word have I hid in my heart . . . 302
Thy work, O God, needs many hands . 312
We give Thee but Thine own 313

INDEX OF INSTRUMENTAL MUSIC

NUMBER

Bach, J. S.: "Nun Ruhen Alle Wälder" (Innsbruck) 334
Beethoven: Theme from Adagio, "Concerto for Piano No. 5," Op. 73 . . . 325
Beethoven: Theme from Andante con Moto, "Appassionata Sonata," Op. 57 333
Brahms: Principal Theme of the Last Movement, " Symphony No. 1," Op. 68 326
Chopin: From "Nocturne," Op. 37, No. 1 329
Chopin: From "Nocturne," Op. 15, No. 3 324

NUMBER

Gounod: From "Marche Romaine" 335
Mendelssohn: Theme from "Andante con Variazioni," Op. 82 332
Mendelssohn: Arr. from Adagio, "Sonata No. 1 for Organ," Op. 65 . . . 330
Schubert: Tr. from "Impromptu in A Flat," Op. 142 327
Schumann: Arr. from "The Poet Speaks," "Kinderscenen," Op. 15 . . 328
Verdi: From Triumphal March, "Aida" 336
Wagner: From Prelude to "Parsifal" . 331

ALPHABETIC INDEX OF TUNES

Aberystwyth 151
Ach Gott und Herr . . 269
Adeste Fideles . . 74, 210
Agape 145
Agni 185
All Saints New . . 182, 288
All the World 16
America 267
Amesbury 85
Ancient of Days . . 12, 34
Angelic Songs 240
Angel's Story 174
Antioch 65
Ar Hyd Y Nos . . 24, 159
Arlington 3
Armageddon 222
Armentrout 27
Arthur's Seat 234
Aurelia 138
Austrian Hymn . 139, 251
Azmon 111

Barnard 176
Beatitudo 135
Beecher 153
Benediction 316
Besançon Carol . . . 81
Bethany 156
Bethlehem 83
Bethlehem Road . . . 71
Bradford. 184
Bread of Life 133
Brookfield 197
Bullinger . . 178, 215, 257

Cannons 279
Canonbury . 21, 196, 311
Carol 64
Charterhouse 114
Chenies 45
Christmas 67
Christmas Song . . . 79
Commonwealth . . . 261
Conisborough 186
Consolation 53
Coronation 122
Covert 179
Creation 44

Crossing the Bar . . . 291
Crucifer 244
Cushman 84
Cwm Rhondda 236

Dalehurst 28
Dare to Be Brave . . 223
Darwall's 148th. . . . 123
Dennis 141
Depauw 283
Deus Tuorum Militum 282
Diademata 120, 169
Divinum Mysterium . 35
Dix 42, 77
Dolut 187
Dominus Regit Me . . 57
Duke Street . . 248, 275
Dundee (French) . . 161

Easter Hymn. 103
Ein' Feste Burg . . . 38
Ellacombe 255
Ellers 23
Empaytaz 129
Eucharistic Hymn . . 146
Evan 148
Evening Praise 30
Eventide 293
Exeter 213

Faben 8
Fealty 205
Federal Street 218
Festal Song 227, 258
Field 203
Finlandia 204
Follow the Gleam . . 232
Forest Green 46
Friend 190

Galilee 198
Germany 253
God Be in My Head . 310
God Be with You . . 315
God's Plan 237
Gratitude 59
Greenland 254
Greensleeves 72

Hall 168
Hamburg 96
Handel 106
Hanna. 163
Harold 229
Have Thine Own Way. 162
He Leadeth Me. . . . 54
Hendon 175
Henley 52
Hermas 109
Hursley 25
Hyfrydol . . . 10, 62, 274
Hymn to Joy 6

I Love to Tell the Story 193
I Want to Be a Christian 217
In Babilone 50
In Dulci Jubilo 80

Jacob's Ladder 219
Jewett 172
Jüngst 82
Just as I Am 171

Kings of Orient . . . 76
Kingsfold 89
Kirby Bedon 121
Kommet Ihr Hirten . 78
Kremser 4

Lake Enon (Mercersburg) 292
Lancashire . . . 102, 226
Lanier 100
Lasst Uns Erfreuen . 13
Laudes Domini . . . 19
Leoni 37
Lest We Forget . . . 270
Littlefield 199
Llanfair 15, 104
Llewellyn 287
Lluelyn 113
Lobe den Herren . . . 9
Louvan 56
Love Divine [Le Jeune] 200
Lower Lights 206

Lyne 183
Lyons 36, 125

Manoah 312
Margaret 167
Marion 124
Marlow 256
Martyn 151
Maryton 166
Materna 272
Meditation 97
Melrose 276
Mendelssohn 68
Mercy 128
Merrial 29
Message 238
Miles Lane 122
Monkland 41
More About Jesus . . 126
More Love to Thee . . 191
Morecambe . 127, 149, 299
Mount Holyoke . . . 118
Mount Vernon 181
Mueller 75
Munich 132
My Master [Day] . . 87

Naomi 131
National Hymn . 235, 271
Need 155
Nicaea 32
Nun Danket 17

O Filii et Filiae . . . 107
O Jesu 51
Old Hundredth . . . 1, 2
Old 124th 284
Olive's Brow 98
Olivet 211
Open My Eyes 189
Orientis Partibus . . . 264
Ortonville 136

Palestrina 105
Park 20
Passion Chorale . . . 99
Patmos 252
Peek 180
Pentecost . . 228, 249, 278
Percival Smith 93
Picardy 296
Pilgrims [Smart] . . . 289
Pilot 157
Pleyel's Hymn 14
Posen 259

Quebec 88, 147

Rathbun 95
Regent Square 69
Rest 150, 266
Rimington 188
Rock of Ages 5
Russian Hymn . . 273, 285

St. Agnes . . 165, 194, 277
St. Anne 40, 137
St. Asaph 7
St. Athanasius 207
St. Catherine 224
St. Cecilia 280
St. Christopher . . . 173
St. Chrysostom 49
St. Clement 22
St. Crispin 212
St. Drostane 94
St. Dunstan's 233
St. Edith 201
St. Edmund 164
St. George's, Windsor 18, 60
St. Gertrude 231
St. James 214
St. Kevin 108
St. Louis 66
St. Magnus 263
St. Margaret 192
St. Peter 243
St. Stephen 143
St. Theodulph 90
St. Thomas 140
St. Venantius 48
Salve Domine 281
Sandon 39
Sarum 290
Schönster Herr Jesu . 119
Schumann 313
Serenity 110, 208
Sine Nomine 290
Slane 115
Soldau 112
Soldiers of Christ . . . 220
Solothurn 142
Something for Jesus . 195
Steal Away 209
Stille Nacht 73
Stirewalt 160
Stockwell, New . . . 86
Study War No More . 286
Stuttgart 58, 317
Sundown 31
Sursum Corda 230
Swabia 152
Sweet Story 144

Tallis' Canon 26
Tempus Adest Floridum 47
Tennent 241
Terra Beata 43
The First Nowell . . . 70
The Star-spangled Banner 268
The Whole Wide World 242
Ton-Y Botel 221
Toplady 154
Tours 61, 91
Trentham 130, 265
Trinity (Italian Hymn) 33, 250
Truehearted 177
Truro 92

Uxbridge 134, 247

Veni Emmanuel . . . 63
Vox Dilecti 216

Wachet auf 117
Waltham 246
Webb . . . 202, 225, 239
Welwyn . . . 116, 260, 262
Wentworth 11
Were You There . . . 101
Wesley 245
What a Friend 158
Wir Pflügen 55
Woodworth 170

METRICAL INDEX OF TUNES

S. M.

Dennis 141
Festal Song . 227, 258
Lake Enon (Mercersburg) . . . 292
Lluelyn 113
St. Thomas . . . 140
Schumann 313
Soldiers of Christ . 220
Swabia 152
Trentham . . 130, 265

S. M. with Refrain

Marion 124

S. M. D.

Diademata . . 120, 169
Terra Beata . . . 43

C. M.

Antioch 65
Arlington 3
Azmon 111
Beatitudo 135
Bradford 184
Christmas 67
Coronation 122
Dalehurst 28
Dundee (French) . 161
Evan 148
Exeter 213
Manoah 312
Marlow 256
Meditation 97
Miles Lane 122
Naomi 131
Ortonville 136
St. Agnes . 165, 194, 277
St. Anne 40, 137
St. James 214
St. Magnus . . . 263
St. Peter 243
St. Stephen . . . 143
Serenity . . . 110, 208

C. M. D.

All Saints New 182, 288
Amesbury 85
Bethlehem 83
Carol 64
Ellacombe 255
Forest Green . . . 46
Kingsfold 89
Materna 272
Mount Vernon . . 181
Percival Smith . . 93
Vox Dilecti 216

L. M.

Brookfield 197
Cannons 279
Canonbury . 21, 196, 311
Depauw 283
Deus Tuorum Militum 282
Duke Street . 248, 275
Empaytaz 129
Federal Street . . 218
Germany 253
Hamburg 96
Hursley 25
Littlefield 199
Louvan 56
Maryton 166
Melrose 276
My Master [Day] . 87
Old Hundredth . . 1, 2
Olive's Brow . . . 98
Pentecost 228, 249, 278
Quebec 88, 147
Rimington 188
St. Crispin 212
St. Drostane . . . 94
St. Venantius . . . 48
Soldau 112
Solothurn 142
Stirewalt 160
Tallis' Canon . . . 26
Truro 92
Uxbridge . . . 134, 247
Waltham 246
Woodworth 170

L. M. with Refrain

More About Jesus . 126

L. M. D.

Creation 44
He Leadeth Me . 54

2. 10. 10. 10.

Harold 229

5. 4. 5. 4. D.

Have Thine Own Way 162

5. 6. 8. 5. 5. 8.

Schönster Herr Jesu 119

6. 4. 6. 4. with Refrain

Need 155

6. 4. 6. 4. D.

Bread of Life . . . 133

6. 4. 6. 4. 6. 6. 4.

More Love to Thee 191

6. 4. 6. 4. 6. 6. 6. 4.

Bethany 156
St. Edmund . . . 164
Something for Jesus 195

6. 4. 6. 4. 10. 10.

Sursum Corda . . 230

6. 5. 6. 5.

Armentrout 27
Merrial 29

6. 5. 6. 5. D. with Refrain

Hermas 109
St. Gertrude . . . 231

6. 5. 6. 5. 6. 5. D.

Armageddon . . . 222

6. 5. 6. 5. 6. 6. 6. 5.

St. Dunstan's . . 233

6. 6. 4. 6. 6. 6. 4.

America 267
Kirby Bedon . . . 121
Olivet 211
Trinity (Italian Hymn) . . . 33, 250

6. 6. 6. 6.

St. Cecilia 280

6. 6. 6. 6. 6. 6.

Laudes Domini . . 19

6. 6. 6. 6. D.

Jewett 172

6. 6. 6. 6. 8. 8.

Arthur's Seat . . . 234
Darwall's 148th . . 123

6. 6. 6. 6. 12. 12.

Christmas Song . . 79

6. 6. 7. 9. 7. 8. 5. 5.

In Dulci Jubilo . . 80

6. 6. 8. 4. D.

Leoni 37

6. 7. 6. 7. 6. 6. 6. 6.

Nun Danket . . . 17

6. 7. 7. 7. D.

Fealty 205

7. 6. 7. 6. D.

Angel's Story . . . 174
Aurelia 138
Chenies 45
Greenland 254
Lancashire . . 102, 226
Munich 132
Passion Chorale . . 99
St. Edith (St. Hilda) 201
St. Kevin 108
St. Theodulph . . 90
Salve Domine . . 281
Tempus Adest Floridum 47
Tennent 241
Tours 61, 91
Webb . . 202, 225, 239

7. 6. 7. 6. D. with Refrain

I Love to Tell the Story 193
The Whole Wide World 242
Wir Pflügen . . . 55

7. 6. 7. 6. 8. 8. 8. 5.

Commonwealth . . 261

7. 6. 8. 6. D.

Patmos 252

7. 6. 8. 6. 8. 6. 8. 6.

St. Christopher . . 173

7. 7. 7. 5.

Hanna 163

7. 7. 7. 7.

Lyne 183
Mercy 128
Monkland 41
Orientis Partibus . 264
Pleyel's Hymn . . 14
Posen 259

7. 7. 7. 7. with Alleluias

Easter Hymn . . . 103
Llanfair 15, 104

7. 7. 7. 7. 4. with Refrain

Evening Praise . . 30

7. 7. 7. 7. 5. 7. with Refrain

Rock of Ages . . . 5

7. 7. 7. 7. 7.

Hendon 175

7. 7. 7. 7. 7. 7.

Dix 42, 77
Pilot 157
St. Athanasius . . 207
Toplady 154

7. 7. 7. 7. D.

Aberystwyth . . . 151
Martyn 151
St. George's, Windsor 18, 60

7. 7. 7. 7. D. with Refrain

Mendelssohn . . . 68

METRICAL INDEX OF TUNES

8. 4. 8. 4. 8. 4.

Park 20
Wentworth 11

8. 4. 8. 4. 8. 8. 8. 4.

Ar Hyd Y Nos 24, 159

8. 5. 8. 3.

Bullinger . . . 215, 257

8. 5. 8. 5.

Bullinger 178

8. 6. 8. 6. 7. 6. 8. 6.

St. Louis 66

8. 6. 8. 6. 8. 8.

O Jesu 51

8. 6. 8. 8. 6.

Llewellyn 287
Rest 150, 266

8. 7. 8. 7.

Ach Gott und Herr. 269
Agape 145
Dominus Regit Me 57
Galilee 198
Rathbun 95
Stuttgart . . 58, 317

8. 7. 8. 7. with Refrain

Greensleeves . . . 72
Lower Lights . . . 206
Regent Square . . 69

8. 7. 8. 7. 6. 6. 6. 6. 7.

Ein' Feste Burg . . 38

8. 7. 8. 7. 8. 7.

Cwm Rhondda . . 236
Picardy 296

8. 7. 8. 7. 8. 7. Iambic

Bethlehem Road . 71

8. 7. 8. 7. 8. 7. 7.

Divinum Mysterium 35

8. 7. 8. 7. D.

Austrian Hymn 139, 251
Barnard 176
Beecher 153
Crucifer 244
Faben 8
Friend 190
Hyfrydol . 10, 62, 274
Hymn to Joy . . . 6
In Babilone. . . . 50
Love Divine [Le Jeune] 200
Mount Holyoke . . 118
St. Asaph 7
Ton-Y-Botel . . . 221
What a Friend . . 158

8. 7. 9. 8. with Refrain

Besançon Carol . . 81

8. 7. 11. 8. 7. 11.

Stockwell, New . . 86

8. 8. 4. 4. 8. 8. 6. with Alleluias

Lasst Uns Erfreuen 13

8. 8. 8. with Alleluias

O Filii et Filiae . . 107

8. 8. 8. 4. with Alleluias

Palestrina 105

8. 8. 8. 5.

Jacob's Ladder . . 219

8. 8. 8. 6.

Just as I Am . . . 171

8. 8. 8. 6. with Refrain

Kings of Orient . . 76

8. 8. 8. 8. 6.

St. Margaret . . . 192

8. 8. 8. 8. 8. 5.

Dolut 187

8. 8. 8. 8. 8. 8.

Covert 179
Lest We Forget . . 270
St. Catherine . . . 224
St. Chrysostom . . 49
Veni Emmanuel . 63

8. 10. 9. 10. with Refrain

Dare to Be Brave . 223

9. 8. 8. 9.

God Be with You . 315

9. 8. 9. 8.

Eucharistic Hymn 146
St. Clement . . . 22

9. 9. 10. 10.

God's Plan 237

10. 4. 6. 6. 6. 6. 10. 4.

All the World . . . 16

10. 4. 10. 4. 10. 10.

Sandon 39

10. 8. 8. 7. 7. with Refrain

Message 238

10. 10. 10. 4.

Sarum 290
Sine Nomine . . . 290

10. 10. 10. 10.

Conisborough . . . 186
Ellers 23
Eventide 293
Field 203
Gratitude 59
Hall 168
Morecambe 127, 149, 299
National Hymn 235, 271
Slane 115

10. 10. 10. 10. 4.

Kommet Ihr Hirten 78

10. 10. 10. 10. 10.

Old 124th 284

10. 10. 10. 10. 10. 10.

Finlandia 204
Sundown 31

10. 10. 11. 11.

Lyons 36, 125

10. 11. 11. 11.

Handel 106

11. 10. 11. 9.

Russian Hymn . . 285

11. 10. 11. 10.

Ancient of Days. 12, 34
Charterhouse . . . 114
Consolation 53
Cushman 84
Henley 52
Peek 180
Russian Hymn . . 273
Welwyn . 116, 260, 262
Wesley 245

11. 10. 11. 10. with Refrain

Angelic Songs . . . 240
Pilgrims [Smart] . 289
Truehearted . . . 177

11. 11. 11. 11.

Adeste Fideles . . 210
Mueller 75

11. 12. 12. 10.

Nicaea 32

12. 11. 12. 11.

Kremser 4

12. 12. 12. 12.

Benediction 316

14. 14. 4. 7. 8.

Lobe den Herren . 9

Irregular

Adeste Fideles . . 74
Agni 185
Crossing the Bar . 291
Follow the Gleam . 232
God Be in My Head 310
I Want to Be a Christian 217
Jüngst 82
Lanier 100
Margaret 167
Open My Eyes . . 189
Steal Away . . . 209
Stille Nacht . . . 73
Study War No More 286
Sweet Story . . . 144
The Star-spangled Banner. 268
Wachet auf . . . 117
Were You There . 101

Irregular, with Refrain

The First Nowell . 70

TOPICAL INDEX

No.

Adoration

All people that on earth . . 1
Ancient of Days 34
Come, Thou Almighty King 33
Day is dying in the west . . 30
Glory be to God 309
Glory be to the Father . 307, 308
Hail, gladdening Light . . . 31
Holy, holy, holy! Lord God 32
Holy, holy, holy, Lord of Hosts 305
Joyful, Joyful, we adore . . 6
"Lord, Thy glory fills" . . 10
Men and children everywhere 5
Praise the Lord 8
Praise to the Lord 9
We praise Thee, O God . . 4

Anniversaries

God of our life 39
God of the nations, hear . . 247
Now praise we great . . . 269
O Light, from age to age . . 143
O Thou whose glory 142
Our God, our Help 40
Rejoice, ye pure 124
We praise Thee, O God . . 4

Aspiration

Breathe on me 130
Dear Lord, who sought . . 160
Draw Thou my soul 164
God, who touchest 178
Holy Father, God of might . 163
I look to Thee 51
I name Thy hallowed . . . 152
I need Thee 155
I would be true 180
Just as I am, Thine 171
More love to Thee 191
Nearer, my God 156
O Master, let me walk . . . 166
O Son of Man, who walked 112
Open my eyes 189
Spirit of God, descend . . . 127
Take my life, and let . . . 175

Assurance

A mighty Fortress 38
God of our life 39
How firm a foundation . . 210
I heard the voice 216
I know that my Redeemer . 184

No.

Assurance — *Continued*

No distant Lord 113
Strong Son of God 212
The King of love 57
The Lord's my Shepherd . . 148
There's a wideness 50
Thy home is with 131

Atonement

I know not how 213
In the cross of Christ . . . 95
Into the woods 100
Just as I am, without . . . 170
My Master was so 87
Rock of Ages 154
There is a green hill 97
When I survey 96

Baptism

I am trusting Thee 215
I think when I read 144
Just as I am, without . . . 170
Spirit of God, descend . . . 127

Bible, The . . . 132–136

How firm a foundation . . 210
I love to tell 193
The heavens declare Thy glory 45

Bread of Life

Break Thou the bread of life 133
For the bread, which Thou . 145
Jesus, Thou Joy of 147
See also "The Bible"

Brotherhood

Come, let us join with . . . 255
In Christ there is no East . 243
Let there be light 278
O brother man, fold 260
Rise up, O men of God . . 258
Teach us, O Lord, true . . 256
The fathers built this city . 252
The light of God is 254
These things shall be . . . 283
Thy Kingdom come, O Lord 280
When thy heart, with joy . 257

Calmness

Dear Lord and Father of . . 150
God of our life 39

No.

Calmness —*Continued*

I am trusting Thee 215
I look to Thee 51
Jesus, the very thought . . 194

Cheerfulness

As with gladness 77
Awake, my soul, and . . . 21
For the beauty of the earth . 42
Let us with a gladsome. . . 41
Rejoice, the Lord is King. . 123
Rejoice, ye pure 124

Children, Christ's Love for

I think when I read 144
When, His salvation bringing 91

Christ:

Advent of

Come, Thou long-expected . 62
Hail to the Lord's Anointed 61
O come, O come, Emmanuel 63
Watchman, tell us of the . . 60

Advocate, The

Immortal Love, forever . . 208
No distant Lord 113
O Love that wilt not . . . 192
O Son of Man, who walked 112
Strong Son of God 212
We bear the strain 111

Ascension of

All hail the power 122
Crown Him with many . . 120
Fairest Lord Jesus 119
Hail to the Lord's Anointed 61
Rejoice, the Lord is King . 123
Rejoice, ye pure 124
Ye servants of God 125

Beauty of

Fairest Lord Jesus 119
Jesus, the very thought . . 194
Jesus, Thou Joy of 147
My Master was so 87
O Son of Man, who walked 112

Birth and Infancy of . 60–82

Boyhood and Youth of

O sing a song of Bethlehem 89

No.

Christ — *Continued*

Boyhood and Youth of (*Continued*)

The hidden years 83
We would see Jesus 84

Call of

I heard the voice 216
Jesus calls us 198
O Jesus, Prince of life . . . 182
O Jesus, Thou art standing 201
We bear the strain 111

Conqueror, The

A mighty Fortress 38
Hail to the Lord's Anointed 61
Jesus shall reign 248
Light of the world 281
O Jesus, Prince of life . . . 182
O Thou Eternal Christ . . 93
Rejoice, the Lord is King . 123
Ride on! ride on 94
The strife is o'er 105
Ye servants of God 125

Divine, The

I know not how 213
I know that my Redeemer . 184
Jesus, Thou divine 200
Joy to the world 65
Love divine, all loves . . . 153
O come, all ye faithful . . . 74
O Thou Eternal Christ . . 93
Thou didst leave 167

Epiphany

A king might miss 71
As with gladness 77
Good Christian men, rejoice 80
We three kings 76
What Child is this 72

Exaltation of . . . 116–126

Example of

By roads that wound . . . 88
Christ of the Upward Way 230
Immortal Love, forever . . 208
O Master Workman 85
O Son of Man, our Hero . . 114
O Thou whose feet 263
Thou art the Way 214
We would see Jesus 84

Founder of the Church, The

Glorious things of thee . . 139
O Light, from age to age . . 143
O Thou whose glory 142
O where are kings 137
The Church's one 138

Friend, The

Beneath the cross 173
I know that my Redeemer . 184

No.

Christ — *Continued*

Friend, The (*Continued*)

Immortal Love, forever . . 208
I've found a Friend 190
Jesus, Lover of my soul . . 151
No distant Lord 113
O Jesus, I have promised . 174
O Jesus, Thou art standing 201
O Son of Man, who walked 112
The King of love 57
There is a green hill 97
We bear the strain 111
What a Friend we have . . 158

Guide, Our

Christ of the Upward Way . 230
I need Thee 155
Jesus calls us 198
Jesus, Saviour, pilot me . . 157
Jesus, Thou divine 200
My life, dear Lord 199
O Jesus, I have promised . 174
O Son of Man, who walked 112
Saviour, again to Thy . . . 23
Shepherd of tender youth . . 121
Thou art the Way 214
We thank Thee, Lord . . . 203

Humility of

Love divine, all loves . . . 153
My Master was so 87
O Master Workman 85
There's a wideness 50
Thou didst leave 167
Thy home is with 131

King, Our

All hail the power 122
Be Thou my Vision 115
Crown Him with many . . 120
Hail to the Lord's Anointed 61
Hark! the herald angels . . 68
Heralds of Christ 235
Jesus Christ is risen 103
Jesus shall reign 248
Joy to the world 65
Lead on, O King 226
Lift up your heads 92
O worship the King 36
Rejoice, the Lord is King . 123

Lamb of God, The

Crown Him with many . . 120
Just as I am, without . . . 170
My faith looks up 211

Leader, Our

He leadeth me 54
Jesus, Saviour, pilot me . . 157
Lead on, O King 226
My faith looks up 211
O Jesus, I have promised . 174

No.

Christ — *Continued*

Leader Our, (*Continued*)

Take Thou our minds . . . 168
The King of love 57
Thou art the Way 214
We thank Thee, Lord . . . 203

Life and Ministry of . 83–89

Light, Our

Fairest Lord Jesus 119
Hail, gladdening Light . . . 31
Lift up your heads 92
Light of the world 281
O Thou whose glory 142
Watchman, tell us of the . . 60

Love of

By roads that wound . . . 88
I think when I read 144
Immortal Love, forever . . 208
In Christ there is no East . 243
I've found a Friend 190
Jesus, Lover of my soul . . 151
Love divine, all loves . . . 153
My Master was so 87
No distant Lord 113
O Jesus, Thou art standing 201
O Love that wilt not . . . 192
O Son of Man, our Hero . . 114
The King of love 57
We bear the strain 111
We would see Jesus 84
What a Friend we have . . 158
When, His salvation bringing 91
When I survey 96
When the golden evening . 86

Master, The

Great Master, touch us . . 186
My Master was so 87
O Jesus, I have promised . 174
O Master, let me walk . . . 166
O Master Workman 85
O Son of Man, Thou madest 197
O Thou whose feet 263
Ye servants of God 125

Ministry of 84–89

Miracles of

By roads that wound . . . 88
We would see Jesus 84
When the golden evening . 86

Name of

All hail the power 122
Hail to the Lord's Anointed 61
Ye servants of God 125

Nativity of 60–82

Passion, His . . . 95–101

TOPICAL INDEX

No.

Christ — *Continued*

Patience of

O Jesus, Thou art standing . 201
O Love that wilt not . . . 192
O Master, let me walk . . 166
Thou didst leave 167

Praise to

All glory, laud, and honor . 90
All hail the power 122
Crown Him with many . . 120
Fairest Lord Jesus 119
Hail to the Lord's Anointed 61
Jesus shall reign 248
Jesus, the very thought . . 194
Jesus, Thou Joy of . . . 147
More about Jesus 126
O Son of Man, our Hero . . 114
O Thou Eternal Christ . . 93
Rejoice, the Lord is King . 123
Rejoice, ye pure 124
Saviour, again to Thy . . . 23
When morning gilds 19
Ye servants of God 125

Presence, His

Be Thou my Vision 115
Immortal Love, forever . . 208
Jesus. Thou Joy of 147
No distant Lord 113
O Son of Man, who walked 112
O Thou in all Thy might . 110
We bear the strain 111
We thank Thee, Lord . . . 203

Resurrection of . . 102–109

Saviour, Our

Beneath the cross 173
Christ for the world 250
I am trusting Thee 215
I bind my heart 205
I heard the voice 216
I know not how 213
I know that my Redeemer . 184
Joy to the world 65
Lord and Saviour 264
My faith looks up 211
O Zion, haste 240
Rock of Ages 154
Silent night 73
Sow the seed 244
Sun of my soul 25
Thou art the Way 214
We've a story to tell . . . 238
What a Friend we have . . 158
When, His salvation bringing 91
While shepherds watched . 67

Second Coming of

Hail to the Lord's Anointed 61
Hark, what a sound 116

No.

Christ — *Continued*

Second Coming of (*Continued*)

Light of the world 281
There's a light upon 118
Wake, awake, for night . . 117

Shepherd, Our

Shepherd of tender youth . 121
The King of love 57

Son of God, The

Crown Him with many . . 120
Fairest Lord Jesus 119
Hail to the Lord's Anointed 61
I know not how 213
Strong Son of God 212
Ye servants of God 125

Son of Man, The

All glory, laud, and honor . 90
Fairest Lord Jesus 119
O Son of Man, our Hero . . 114
O Son of Man, Thou madest 197
O Son of Man, who walked 112

Sympathy of

By roads that wound . . . 88
I heard the voice 216
Immortal Love, forever . . 208
I've found a Friend 190
Jesus, Thou divine 200
No distant Lord 113
O Son of Man, who walked 112
We bear the strain 111
What a Friend we have . . 158
When the golden evening . 86

Teacher, Our

O Master, let me walk . . . 166
O Son of Man, Thou madest 197
O Thou whose feet 263
Open my eyes 189
Take Thou our minds . . . 168
Teach me, O Lord, Thy holy 188
Teach us, O Lord, true . . 256

Triumphal Entry, His 90–94

Way, The

Christ of the Upward Way . 230
Fight the good fight 228
I know that my Redeemer . 184
Jesus calls us 198
O Thou whose feet 263
O Word of God 132
Teach me, O Lord, Thy holy 188
Thou art the Way 214

Christmas 60–82

Church, The . . . 137–143

No.

Citizenship, Christian

Be strong 229
Christian, rise and act . . . 259
Faith of our fathers 224
I would be true 180
My life, dear Lord 199
Now praise we great . . . 269
Now to heaven our prayer . 159
O beautiful for spacious . . 272
Once to every man 221
Rise up, O men of God . . 258
Soldiers of Christ, arise . . 220
Teach us, O Lord, true . . 256
That cause can neither . . 237
The fathers built this city . 252
The light of God is 254
When thy heart, with joy . 257

College

Believe not those who say. . 227
I know that my Redeemer . 184
Lord and Saviour 264
O Thou whose feet 263
Take Thou our minds . . . 168
Thou art the Way 214

Comfort

Breathe on me 130
Dear Lord and Father of . . 150
God is Love 58
He leadeth me 54
Holy Spirit, Truth divine . 128
No distant Lord 113
O Son of Man, our Hero . . 114
O Son of Man, who walked 112
O Thou, in all Thy might . 110
Spirit of God, descend . . . 127
The King of love 57
The Lord's my Shepherd . . 148
Thy home is with 131
We bear the strain 111

Communion, Holy 145–149

Comradeship

Blest be the tie 141
Come, let us join with . . . 255
I bind my heart 205
Jesus, Thou divine 200
No distant Lord 113
O brother man, fold 260
Teach us, O Lord, true . . 256
The light of God is 254
These things shall be . . . 283
When thy heart, with joy . 257
Where cross the crowded . . 253

Confession

All praise to Thee 26
Awake, my soul, and . . . 21
Beneath the cross 173
I am trusting Thee 215
Jesus, Lover of my soul . . 151

No.

Confession — *Continued*
Just as I am, without . . . 170
More love to Thee 191
O Jesus, Thou art standing 201
Rock of Ages 154
Temper my spirit 185
When I survey 96

Confidence
A mighty Fortress 38
Be strong 229
Christ of the Upward Way . 230
Faith of our fathers 224
Fling out the banner . . . 246
God of our fathers, whose . 271
God of our life 39
Hail to the brightness . . . 245
How firm a foundation . . 210
I am trusting Thee 215
I know not how 213
In the cross of Christ . . . 95
Lead on, O King 226
Our God, our Help 40
That cause can neither . . 237
Truehearted, wholehearted . 177

Conflict with Sin
Be strong 229
Christ of the Upward Way . 230
Christian, rise and act . . . 259
Dare to be brave 223
Fight the good fight 228
March on, O soul 234
Now in the days 169
Once to every man 221
Rise up, O men of God . . 258
Soldiers of Christ, arise . . 220
Stand up, stand up 225
To the knights 232
Where cross the crowded . . 253
Who is on the Lord's . . . 222

Consecration
Beneath the cross 173
Draw Thou my soul 164
Holy Father, God of might . 163
I bind my heart 205
Jesus, I live to Thee . . . 292
Just as I am, Thine 171
Lord, I want to be 217
Lord, we come with 207
My life, dear Lord 199
Now in the days 169
O Jesus, I have promised . 174
Take my life, and let . . . 175
Take Thou our minds . . . 168
The body, Lord 187
Thou didst leave 167
To the knights 232
Who is on the Lord's . . . 222

Country, Our . . . 267–276

No.

Courage and Loyalty 210–237
A mighty Fortress 38
God send us men 276
I feel the winds of God . . 181
I would be true 180
Lord, we come with 207
Not alone for mighty . . . 274
O Jesus, Prince of life . . . 182
Rise up, O men of God . . 258
We thank Thee, Lord . . . 203
We would be building . . . 204

Creed
Ancient of Days 34
Christian, rise and act . . . 259
Come, Thou Almighty King 33
Holy, holy, holy! Lord God 32

Death
Abide with me 293
At length there dawns . . . 288
For all the saints 290
Hark! hark, my soul . . . 289
He leadeth me 54
Jesus, I live to Thee 292
Jesus, Saviour, pilot me . . 157
Sunset and evening star . . 291

Decision
Beneath the cross 173
Christ of the Upward Way . 230
Faith of our fathers 224
Great Master, touch us . . 186
Holy Father, God of might . 163
I bind my heart 205
I would be true 180
Just as I am, Thine 171
Just as I am, without . . . 170
Lord, I want to be 217
Lord, we come with 207
My Jesus, as Thou 172
My life, dear Lord 199
Now in the days 169
O Jesus, I have promised . 174
O Master, let me walk . . . 166
Take my life, and let . . . 175
Take Thou our minds . . . 168
Teach me, O Lord, Thy holy 188
Temper my spirit 185
To the knights 232
Who is on the Lord's . . . 222

Discipleship . . . 150–209

Duty, Daily
Awake, my soul, and . . . 21
Father, lead me 183
God, that madest 24
I would be true 180
Light of the world 281
My life, dear Lord 199
Now in the days 169

No.

Duty, Daily — *Continued*
Take Thou our minds . . . 168
The light of God is 254

Easter 102–109

Education
Believe not those who say . 227
Lord and Saviour 264
Lord, speak to me 196
O Thou whose feet 263
Take Thou our minds . . . 168
Teach me, O Lord, Thy holy 188
Teach us, O Lord, true . . 256
Thou art the Way 214

Epiphany
As with gladness 77
Silent night 73
We three kings 76
What Child is this 72

Eternal Life . . . 289–293

Evangelistic Services
Brightly beams our Father's 206
Crown Him with many . . 120
Draw Thou my soul 164
Fairest Lord Jesus 119
Give of your best 176
Have Thine own way . . . 162
I am trusting Thee 215
I heard the voice 216
I know that my Redeemer . 184
I need Thee 155
In the cross of Christ . . . 95
I've found a Friend 190
Jesus calls us 198
Jesus, Lover of my soul . . 151
Just as I am, without . . . 170
Lord, I want to be 217
More love to Thee 191
O Jesus, Thou art standing 201
O Love that wilt not . . . 192
Praise to the Lord 9
Saviour, Thy dying love . . 195
Spirit of God, descend . . . 127
Stand up, stand up 225
Take my life, and let . . . 175
There is a green hill . . . 97
We are climbing Jacob's . . 219
When I survey 96
Who is on the Lord's . . . 222

Evening Hymns . . . 22–31

Faith 210–216

See also "Confidence"

Faithfulness 217–237

Family, The
From homes of quiet . . . 265

TOPICAL INDEX

No.

Family, The — *Continued*

O happy home 262
O Thou whose gracious . . 266

Farewell Services

Blest be the tie 141
Father, lead me 183
Fight the good fight 228
Holy Father, bless 27
I need Thee 155
Jesus, Saviour, pilot me . . 157
Nearer, my God. 156
Praise to the Lord 9
What a Friend we have . . 158

Fellowship

Blest be the tie 141
Dear Lord and Father of . 150
In Christ there is no East . 243
Jesus, Thou divine 200
Let us with a gladsome . . 41
Men and children everywhere 5
O brother man, fold 260
Teach us, O Lord, true . . 256
We thank Thee, Lord . . . 203
When thy heart, with joy . 257
Where cross the crowded . . 253

Following Christ

See "Christ, Our Guide"
"Christ, Our Leader"
"Christ, the Way"
"Consecration"
"Courage and Loyalty"
"Discipleship"

Forgiveness

Dear Lord and Father of . . 150
God is Love 58
Hail to the Lord's Anointed 61
Holy Father, God of might 163
I heard the voice 216
I've found a Friend 190
Jesus, Lover of my soul . . 151
Joyful, joyful, we adore . . 6
Rock of Ages 154
There is a green hill 97
What a Friend we have . . 158
When the golden evening . 86

Friendship

See "Comradeship"
"Fellowship"

Future Life, The . 289–293

Giving 311–314

God:

Being, His

A mighty Fortress 38
God is Love 58
Holy Father, God of might . 163

No.

God — *Continued*

Being, His (*Continued*)

I look to Thee 51
Joyful, joyful, we adore . . 6
Let us with a gladsome . . 41
Lord of all being 56
"Lord, Thy glory fills" . . 10
O Thou, in all Thy might . 110
Of the Father's love 35
Our God, our Help 40
The God of Abraham . . . 37

Care, His 49–59

Creator, The

God of the earth 49
God, that madest 24
Let us with a gladsome . . 41
O worship the King 36
The heavens declare Thy glory 45
The spacious firmament . . 44
This is my Father's 43
We praise Thee, O God . . 4

Defender, Our

A mighty Fortress 38
God of our life 39
I look to Thee 51
O worship the King 36
Praise to the Lord 9
The King of love 57

Eternity and Power, His

A mighty Fortress 38
Holy, holy, holy! Lord God 32
Joyful, joyful, we adore . . 6
"Lord, Thy glory fills" . . 10
O Thou, in all Thy might . 110
Our God, our Help 40
The God of Abraham . . . 37
We praise Thee, O God . . 4

Fatherhood and Care, His

God is Love 58
God of our life 39
He leadeth me 54
Holy Father, God of might . 163
I look to Thee 51
Let us with a gladsome . . 41
Lord of all being 56
No distant Lord 113
O Thou, in all Thy might . 110
Praise to the Lord 9
The King of love 57
The Lord's my Shepherd . . 148
There's a wideness 50
We plow the fields 55

Grace of

God is Love 58
God of grace 236
God, who touchest 178

No

God — *Continued*

Grace of (*Continued*)

Here, O my Lord 149
Let us with a gladsome . . 41
Love divine, all loves . . . 153
O beautiful for spacious skies 272

Greatness of

All people that on earth . . 1
God of the earth 49
Of the Father's love 35
Praise God from whom . . 2

Guidance, His

Backward we look 59
Father of lights 12
God of our fathers, known . 270
God of our fathers, whose . 271
God of our life 39
Great Master, touch us . . 186
Have Thine own way . . . 162
He leadeth me 54
Holy Father, God of might 163
I look to Thee 51
Lead on, O King 226
O God, beneath Thy . . . 275
We praise Thee, O God . . 4

Kingdom of, The

I love Thy kingdom 140
Lead on, O King 226
O Son of Man, Thou madest 197
Rise up, O men of God . . 258
Teach us, O Lord, true . . 256
The light of God is 254
Thy Kingdom come, O Lord 280

Nature, in . . 13, 14, 42–49

Presence of

Abide with me 293
Breathe on me 130
Dear Lord and Father of . . 150
Father, in Thy mysterious . 52
Father of lights 12
God of our life 39
Holy Father, bless 27
Holy Father, God of might 163
I look to Thee 51
O Thou, in all Thy might . 110
Praise to the Lord 9
Spirit of God, descend . . . 127
Still, still with Thee 53
The Lord be with us . . . 28
Thy home is with 131
When the golden evening . 86
Ye servants of God 125

Purpose of

Father, lead me 183
God of the nations, hear . . 247
O Zion, haste 240
Of the Father's love 35

TOPICAL INDEX

No.

God — *Continued*

Purpose of (*Continued*)

That cause can neither . . . 237
The light of God is 254
The voice of God 202
There's a light upon 118
These things shall be . . . 283
Thy Kingdom come, O Lord 280
We would be building . . . 204
When wilt Thou save . . . 261

Refuge, Our

A mighty Fortress 38
God is Love 58
He who would valiant . . . 233
I look to Thee 51
Nearer, my God 156
O Love that wilt not . . . 192
Our God, our Help 40

Shepherd, The

Shepherd of tender youth . 121
The King of love 57
The Lord's my Shepherd . . 148

Triune

All creatures of our God . . 13
Ancient of Days 34
Come, Holy Ghost 129
Come, Thou Almighty King 33
Holy, holy, holy! Lord God 32
Of the Father's love 35
Praise God from whom . . 2
The God of Abraham . . . 37

Good Friday 95–101

Good Will

At length there dawns . . . 288
Heralds of Christ 235
I bind my heart 205
I would be true 180
In Christ there is no East . 243
Let there be light 278
Lord, I want to be 217
O brother man, fold 260
O God of love 279
O Master, let me walk . . . 166
Ring out, wild bells 282
When thy heart, with joy . 257
Where cross the crowded . . 253

Gratitude

All creatures of our God . . 13
Come, ye thankful 18
For the beauty of the earth 42
Joyful, joyful, we adore . . 6
Let us with a gladsome . . 41
My God, I thank Thee . . 11
Now thank we all 17
Praise God from whom . . 2
Praise to God, immortal . . 14
We thank Thee, Lord . . . 203

No.

Guidance

Be Thou my Vision 115
Christ of the Upward Way . 230
Come, Holy Ghost 129
Draw Thou my soul 164
Father, lead me 183
God of our fathers, whose . 271
God of our life 39
Have Thine own way 162
He leadeth me 54
Holy Spirit, Truth divine . 128
I feel the winds of God . . 181
Jesus calls us 198
Jesus, Saviour, pilot me . . 157
Lead on, O King 226
My faith looks up 211
My Jesus, as Thou 172
Now in the days 169
O God, beneath Thy 275
O Master, let me walk . . . 166
O Son of Man, Thou madest 197
Teach me, O Lord, Thy holy 188
Thou art the Way 214
We thank Thee, Lord . . . 203

Happiness

As with gladness 77
Come, ye faithful 108
For the beauty of the earth 42
God, who touchest 178
Jesus Christ is risen 103
Jesus, Thou Joy of 147
Joy to the world 65
Joyful, joyful, we adore . . 6
Let all the world 16
Let us with a gladsome . . 41
Light of the world 281
Rejoice, the Lord is King . 123
The first Nowell 70
The strife is o'er 105
The sun is on the land . . . 20
There's a song in the air . . 79
We thank Thee, Lord . . . 203

Harvest

All beautiful the march . . 46
Come, ye thankful 18
Praise the Lord, His glories 15
Praise to God, immortal . . 14
We plow the fields 55

Holy Scriptures

See "The Bible"

Holy Spirit, The . 127–131

Holy Trinity, The

All creatures of our God . . 13
Ancient of Days 34
Come, Holy Ghost 129
Come, Thou Almighty King 33
Holy, holy, holy! Lord God 32
Of the Father's love 35

No.

Holy Trinity, The — *Continued*

Praise God from whom . . 2
The God of Abraham . . . 37

Home, The

Blest be the tie 141
From homes of quiet . . . 265
O happy home 262
O Thou whose feet 263
O Thou whose glory 142
O Thou whose gracious . . 266

Hope

Believe not those who say . 227
Blest be the tie 141
Here, O my Lord 149
I am trusting Thee 215
I look to Thee 51
Jesus, Lover of my soul . . 151
Now to heaven our prayer . 159
O Master, let me walk . . . 166
Our God, our Help 40
That cause can neither . . 237

Humility

Beneath the cross 173
Holy Father, God of might . 163
I would be true 180
Lord, I want to be 217
My Master was so 87
O Master, let me walk . . . 166
Take Thou our minds . . . 168
Thy home is with 131
When I survey 96

Immortal Life . . . 289–293

Intercession

Christ for the world 250
Dear Lord, who sought . . 160
Not alone for mighty . . . 274
Now to heaven our prayer . 159
O Zion, haste 240
The whole wide world . . . 242
When thy heart, with joy . 257
When wilt Thou save . . . 261

International Peace 277–288

Invitation

See "Christ, Call of"

Invocation and Praise 1–18

See also "Prayer and Hope"

Jesus, Name of

See "Christ, Name of"

Joy

As with gladness 77
Awake, my soul, and 21
Come, ye faithful 108
Fairest Lord Jesus 119
For the beauty of the earth 42

TOPICAL INDEX

No.

Joy — *Continued*

Hail to the brightness . . . 245
Jesus, the very thought . . 194
Jesus, Thou Joy of 147
Joy to the world 65
Joyful, joyful, we adore . . 6
Let us with a gladsome . . 41
Love divine, all loves . . . 153
My God, I thank Thee . . 11
O come, all ye faithful . . . 74
O Love that wilt not . . . 192
O Son of Man, our Hero . . 114
Rejoice, the Lord is King . 123
Rejoice, ye pure 124
This is my Father's 43

Kingdom of God on Earth

See "God, The Kingdom of"

Labor Day

Be strong 229
Believe not those who say . 227
Go, labor on 249
O Master Workman 85
O Son of Man, Thou madest 197
We plow the fields 55
We thank Thee, Lord . . . 203

Life Everlasting . . 289–293

Light of the World, Christ

See "Christ, Our Light"

Lord's Supper, The 145–149

Love and Obedience

See "Consecration"
"Discipleship"

Loyalty and Courage

See "Courage and Loyalty"

Meditation

Abide with me 293
Breathe on me 130
Dear Lord and Father of . 150
Draw Thou my soul 164
Have Thine own way . . . 162
I look to Thee 51
I need Thee 155
Just as I am, without . . . 170
My Jesus, as Thou 172
Spirit of God, descend . . . 127
Thy home is with 131

Memorial Day

For all the saints 290
God of our fathers, known . 270
God of our fathers, whose . 271
God of our life 39
Goin' to lay down 286

Memorial Day — *Continued*

Now praise we great . . . 269
O beautiful for spacious skies 272
That cause can neither . . 237
When wilt Thou save . . . 261

Ministry of Christ . 84–89

Missions 238–261

Morning

Awake, my soul, and . . . 21
Father of lights 12
Holy, holy, holy! Lord God 32
Light of the world 281
Take Thou our minds . . . 168
The sun is on the land . . . 20
Wake, awake, for night . . 117
When morning gilds 19

National and International 267–288

From ocean unto ocean . . 241
God of the nations, hear . . 247

Nativity, The 60–82

Neighborhood . . . 251–261

New Year

At length there dawns . . . 288
Glorious things of thee . . . 139
God of our life 39
I feel the winds of God . . 181
O where are kings 137

Obedience

See "Consecration"
"Courage and Loyalty"
"Discipleship"

Offertory

All things come of 314
Bless Thou the gifts 311
Praise God from whom . . 2
Thy work, O God, needs . . 312
We give Thee but Thine . . 313

Opening of Service

See "Adoration,"
"Invocation and Praise"

Out Doors

See "God, in Nature"

Palm Sunday 90–94

Pardon

See "Forgiveness"

Peace:

International . . 277–288

Peace — *Continued*

Spiritual

Be Thou my Vision 115
Breathe on me 130
Dear Lord and Father of . 150
Father, lead me 183
He leadeth me 54
Holy Father, bless 27
Jesus, the very thought . . 194
Saviour, again to Thy . . . 23
Spirit of God, descend . . . 127
The Lord be with us . . . 28
The Lord's my Shepherd . 148

Penitence

See "Confession"

Perseverance

See "Consecration"
"Courage and Loyalty"
"Discipleship"
"Service"

Prayer and Hope 150–169

See also "Discipleship"

Providence

See "God, His Fatherhood and Care"

Purity and Self-Control 178–187

Rally Day

At length there dawns . . . 288
Backward we look 59
Be strong 229
Christ of the Upward Way . 230
Dare to be brave 223
I feel the winds of God . . 181
Let all the world 16
Lord, we come with . . . 207
Now in the days 169
O Son of Man, our Hero . . 114
Onward, Christian 231
Rise up, O men of God . . 258
Stand up, stand up 225
To the knights 232

Rejoicing

See "Joy"

Repentance and Faith

See "Confession"
"Confidence"
"Consecration"
"Faith"

Resurrection, The . 102–109

Salvation

I am trusting Thee 215
I heard the voice 216

No.

Salvation — *Continued*

I know not how 213
In the cross of Christ . . . 95
Jesus, Lover of my soul . . 151
Just as I am, without . . . 170
More about Jesus 126
My faith looks up 211
O Love that wilt not . . . 192
Rock of Ages 154
Saviour, Thy dying love . . 195
The Church's one 138
There is a green hill 97
There's a wideness 50
What a Friend we have . . 158

School, The

See "College"

Scriptures, The

See "The Bible"

Self-Control

Backward we look 59
Be strong 229
Christ of the Upward Way . 230
Faith of our fathers 224
God of our youth 179
God, who touchest 178
Great Master, touch us . . 186
He who would valiant . . . 233
I bind my heart 205
I feel the winds of God . . 181
I know that my Redeemer . 184
I would be true 180
Now in the days 169
O Jesus, Prince of life . . . 182
Strong Son of God 212
Temper my spirit 185
The body, Lord 187

Service 166–209

Social Progress . . 251–261
276–288

Spring

See "God, in Nature"

Steadfastness

See "Courage and Loyalty"

Stewardship:

Of Life

See "Consecration"
"Discipleship"
"Service"

Of Substance

All things come of 314
Bless Thou the gifts 311
Thy work, O God, needs . . 312
We give Thee but Thine . . 313

No.

Summer

See "God, in Nature"

Temperance

See "Self-Control"

Thanksgiving

All creatures of our God . . 13
All people that on earth . . 1
At Thy feet 7
Come, ye faithful 108
Come, ye thankful 18
For the beauty of the earth 42
Joyful, joyful, we adore . . 6
Let all the world 16
Let us with a gladsome . . 41
Men and children everywhere 5
My God, I thank Thee . . 11
Now praise we great . . . 269
Now thank we all 17
O God, beneath Thy . . . 275
O worship the King 36
Praise God from whom . . 2
Praise to God, immortal . . 14
Praise to the Lord 9
We plow the fields 55
We thank Thee, Lord . . . 203
When I survey 96
When thy heart, with joy . 257

Trust and Confidence

See "Assurance"
"Christ, the Conqueror"
"Confidence"

Victorious Living

A mighty Fortress 38
All hail the power 122
Ancient of Days 34
Be Thou my Vision 115
Beneath the cross 173
Christ of the Upward Way . 230
Dare to be brave 223
Fight the good fight 228
God send us men 276
Have Thine own way . . . 162
He who would valiant . . . 233
I am trusting Thee 215
I know that my Redeemer . 184
I would be true 180
In the cross of Christ . . . 95
Jesus, I live to Thee 292
Just as I am, Thine 171
Lord, I want to be 217
March on, O soul 234
'Mid all the traffic 165
My Jesus, as Thou 172
My life, dear Lord 199
O Jesus, Prince of life . . . 182

No.

Victorious Living — *Continued*

O Love that wilt not 192
O Son of Man, Thou madest 197
Once to every man 221
Onward, Christian 231
Rise up, O men of God . . 258
Soldiers of Christ, arise . . 220
Stand up, stand up 225
Take my life, and let . . . 175
Take Thou our minds . . . 168
Temper my spirit 185
That cause can neither . . 237
Thine is the glory 106
Truehearted, wholehearted . 177
We bear the strain 111
We would be building . . . 204
Who is on the Lord's . . . 222

Voice of Jesus

See "Christ, Call of"

Walking with God

Holy Father, God of might . 163
O Master, let me walk . . . 166
O Son of Man, who walked 112
O Thou whose feet 263
Teach me, O Lord, Thy holy 188
We thank Thee, Lord . . . 203
Where cross the crowded . 253
See also "God, Presence of"

Winter

See "God, in Nature"

Word of God

See "The Bible"

Work

See "Brotherhood"
"Discipleship"
"Service"

World, The

See "Brotherhood"
"Fellowship"
"God, in Nature"
"God, the Creator"
"God, The Kingdom of"
"Missions"
"Peace, International"

Zeal

See "Courage and Loyalty"

Zion

See "The Church"

THE LORD'S PRAYER

OUR FATHER WHO ART IN HEAVEN, HALLOWED BE THY NAME. THY KING DOM COME. THY WILL BE DONE ON EARTH, AS IT IS IN HEAVEN. GIVE US THIS DAY OUR DAILY BREAD. AND FORGIVE US OUR DEBTS, AS WE FORGIVE OUR DEBTORS. AND LEAD US NOT INTO TEMPTATION, BUT DELIVER US FROM EVIL: FOR THINE IS THE KINGDOM, AND THE POWER, AND THE GLORY, FOR EVER. AMEN.

THE COMMANDMENTS

GOD spake all these words, saying, I am the LORD thy God, which have brought thee out of the land of Egypt, out of the house of bondage.

I. Thou shalt have no other gods before me.

II. Thou shalt not make unto thee any graven image, or any likeness of any thing that is in heaven above, or that is in the earth beneath, or that is in the water under the earth; thou shalt not bow down thyself to them, nor serve them: for I, the LORD thy God, am a jealous God, visiting the iniquity of the fathers upon the children unto the third and fourth generation of them that hate me; and showing mercy unto thousands of them that love me, and keep my commandments.

III. Thou shalt not take the name of the LORD thy God in vain: for the LORD will not hold him guiltless that taketh his name in vain.

IV. Remember the Sabbath Day, to keep it holy. Six days shalt thou labor, and do all thy work: but the seventh day is the Sabbath of the LORD thy God; in it thou shalt not do any work, thou, nor thy son, nor thy daughter, thy manservant, nor thy maid-servant, nor thy cattle, nor thy stranger that is within thy gates: for in six days the LORD made heaven and earth, the sea, and all that in them is, and rested the seventh day; wherefore the LORD blessed the Sabbath Day and hallowed it.

V. Honor thy father and thy mother; that thy days may be long upon the land which the LORD thy God giveth thee.

VI. Thou shalt not kill.

VII. Thou shalt not commit adultery.

VIII. Thou shalt not steal.

IX. Thou shalt not bear false witness against thy neighbor.

X. Thou shalt not covet thy neighbor's house, thou shalt not covet thy neighbor's wife, nor his manservant, nor his maidservant, nor his ox, nor his ass, nor any thing that is thy neighbor's.

HEAR also the words of our Lord Jesus, how He saith: Thou shalt love the Lord thy God with all thy heart, and with all thy soul, and with all thy mind. This is the first and great commandment. And the second is like unto it, Thou shalt love thy neighbour as thyself. On these two commandments hang all the law and the prophets.

THE APOSTLES' CREED

I BELIEVE in GOD THE FATHER Almighty, Maker of heaven and earth: And in JESUS CHRIST his only Son, our Lord; who was conceived by the Holy Ghost, born of the Virgin Mary, suffered under Pontius Pilate, was crucified, dead, and buried; he descended into hell *; the third day he rose again from the dead; he ascended into heaven, and sitteth on the right hand of God the Father Almighty; from thence he shall come to judge the quick and the dead.

I believe in the HOLY GHOST; the holy Catholic Church; the communion of saints; the forgiveness of sins; the resurrection of the body; and the life everlasting. Amen.

* *i. e.* Continued in the state of the dead, and under the power of death, until the third day.

HYMNS

ADORATION AND THANKSGIVING

All People That on Earth Do Dwell **1**

OLD HUNDREDTH L. M.

From Psalm 100
William Kethe, 1561

Louis Bourgeois, 1551
(English Form of Final Line)

1. All peo - ple that on earth do dwell,
2. Know that the Lord is God in - deed;
3. O en - ter then His gates with praise,
4. For why? the Lord our God is good,

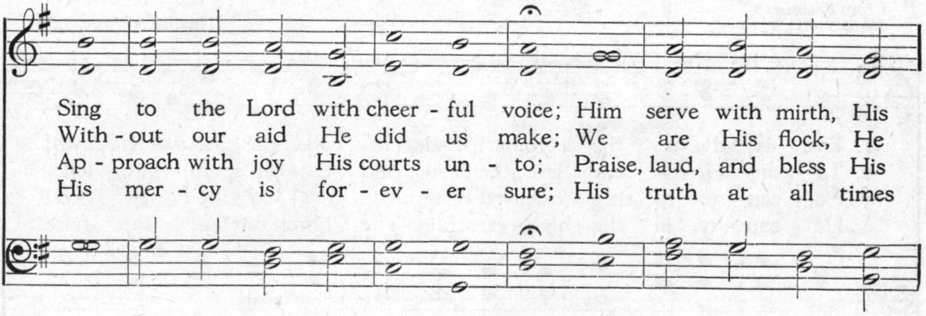

Sing to the Lord with cheer - ful voice; Him serve with mirth, His
With - out our aid He did us make; We are His flock, He
Ap - proach with joy His courts un - to; Praise, laud, and bless His
His mer - cy is for - ev - er sure; His truth at all times

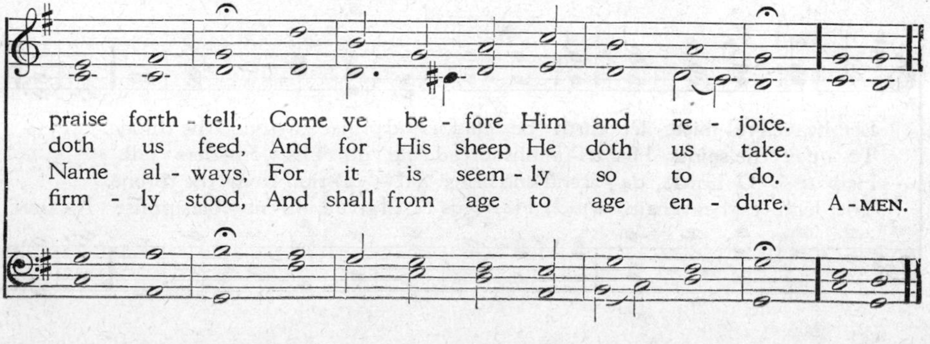

praise forth - tell, Come ye be - fore Him and re - joice.
doth us feed, And for His sheep He doth us take.
Name al - ways, For it is seem - ly so to do.
firm - ly stood, And shall from age to age en - dure. A - MEN.

2 The Doxology

OLD HUNDREDTH (Altered Rhythm) L. M.

Thomas Ken, 1692 — Louis Bourgeois, 1551

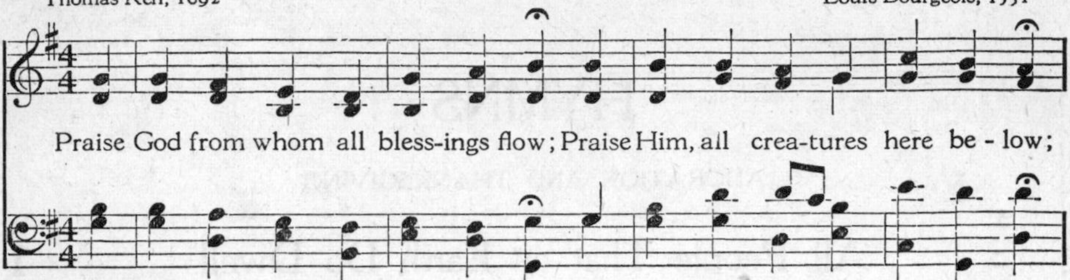
Praise God from whom all bless-ings flow; Praise Him, all crea-tures here be - low;

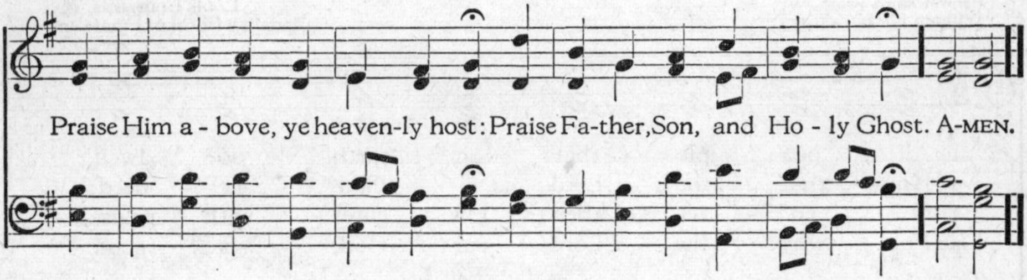
Praise Him a - bove, ye heaven-ly host: Praise Fa-ther, Son, and Ho - ly Ghost. A-MEN.

3 This Is the Day the Lord Hath Made

ARLINGTON C. M.

From Psalm 118
Isaac Watts, 1719 — Thomas A. Arne, 1762

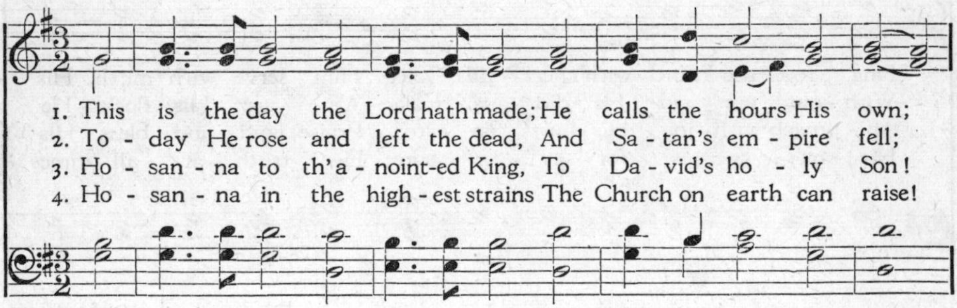
1. This is the day the Lord hath made; He calls the hours His own;
2. To - day He rose and left the dead, And Sa - tan's em - pire fell;
3. Ho - san - na to th' a - noint-ed King, To Da - vid's ho - ly Son!
4. Ho - san - na in the high - est strains The Church on earth can raise!

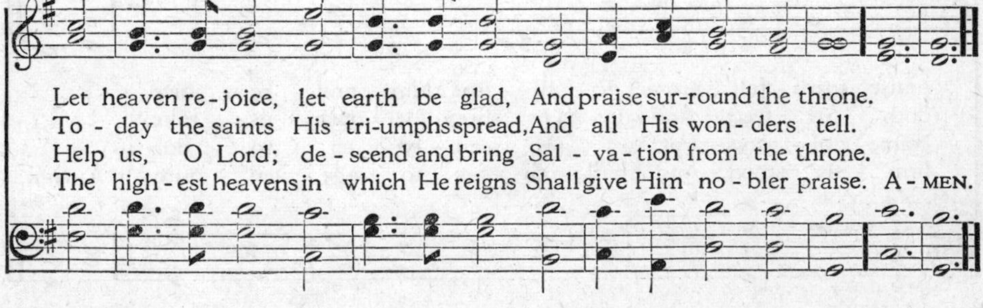
Let heaven re - joice, let earth be glad, And praise sur-round the throne.
To - day the saints His tri-umphs spread, And all His won - ders tell.
Help us, O Lord; de - scend and bring Sal - va - tion from the throne.
The high - est heavens in which He reigns Shall give Him no - bler praise. A - MEN.

We Praise Thee, O God

KREMSER 12. 11. 12. 11.

Old Netherlands Melody in
The Collection, by Adrianus Valerius, 1625
Arr. by Eduard Kremser (1838-1914)
Julia Cady Cory, 1902
1. We praise Thee, O God, our Re - deem - er, Cre - a - tor,
2. We wor - ship Thee, God of our fa - thers, we bless Thee;
3. With voi - ces u - nit - ed our prais - es we of - fer,
In grate - ful de - vo - tion our trib - ute we bring.
Through life's storm and tem - pest our Guide hast Thou been.
To Thee, God e - ter - nal, glad an - thems we raise.
We lay it be - fore Thee, we kneel and a - dore Thee,
When per - ils o'er - take us, es - cape Thou wilt make us,
Thy strong arm will guide us, our God is be - side us,
We bless Thy ho - ly Name, glad prais - es we sing.
And with Thy help, O Lord, life's bat - tles we win.
To Thee, our great Re - deem - er, for - ev - er be praise. A - MEN.

Words used by permission of Julia Cady Cory.

5 Men and Children Everywhere

ROCK OF AGES 7. 7. 7. 7. 5. 7. with Refrain

John J. Moment, 1930

Ancient Hebrew Melody
Arr. by Charlotte Mathewson Lockwood

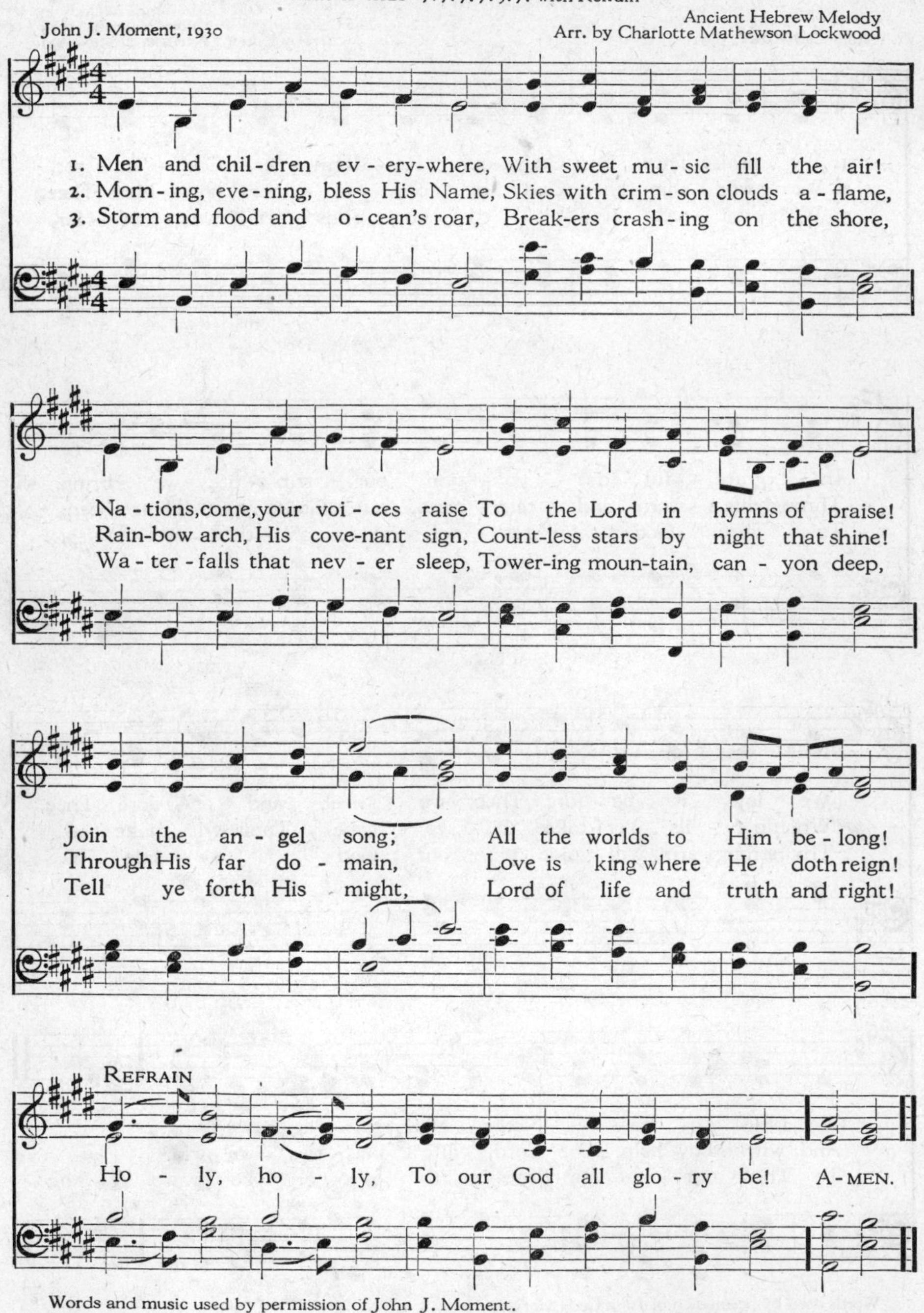
1. Men and chil-dren ev-ery-where, With sweet mu-sic fill the air!
2. Morn-ing, eve-ning, bless His Name, Skies with crim-son clouds a-flame,
3. Storm and flood and o-cean's roar, Break-ers crash-ing on the shore,
Na-tions, come, your voi-ces raise To the Lord in hymns of praise!
Rain-bow arch, His cove-nant sign, Count-less stars by night that shine!
Wa-ter-falls that nev-er sleep, Tower-ing moun-tain, can-yon deep,
Join the an-gel song; All the worlds to Him be-long!
Through His far do-main, Love is king where He doth reign!
Tell ye forth His might, Lord of life and truth and right!
REFRAIN
Ho-ly, ho-ly, To our God all glo-ry be! A-MEN.

Joyful, Joyful, We Adore Thee

HYMN TO JOY 8.7.8.7.D.

Henry van Dyke, 1907

Ludwig van Beethoven, 1824
Arr. by Edward Hodges (1796–1867)

1. Joy - ful, joy - ful, we a - dore Thee, God of glo - ry, Lord of love;
2. All Thy works with joy sur-round Thee, Earth and heaven re - flect Thy rays,
3. Thou art giv - ing and for - giv - ing, Ev - er bless - ing, ev - er blest,
4. Mor - tals, join the might - y cho - rus Which the morn - ing stars be - gan;

Hearts un - fold like flowers be - fore Thee, Prais - ing Thee their Sun a - bove.
Stars and an - gels sing a - round Thee, Cen - ter of un - bro - ken praise.
Well - spring of the joy of liv - ing, O - cean depth of hap - py rest!
Fa - ther love is reign - ing o'er us, Broth - er love binds man to man.

Melt the clouds of sin and sad - ness, Drive the dark of doubt a - way;
Field and for - est, vale and moun - tain, Bloom - ing mead - ow, flash - ing sea,
Thou our Fa - ther, Christ our Broth - er, All who live in love are Thine;
Ev - er sing - ing, march we on - ward, Vic - tors in the midst of strife,

Giv - er of im - mor - tal glad - ness, Fill us with the light of day.
Chant - ing bird and flow - ing foun - tain, Call us to re - joice in Thee.
Teach us how to love each oth - er, Lift us to the Joy di - vine.
Joy - ful mu - sic lifts us Sun - ward In the tri - umph song of life. A - MEN.

7 At Thy Feet, Our God and Father

ST. ASAPH 8.7.8.7.D.

James D Burns, 1861 — William S. Bambridge, 1872

1. At Thy feet, our God and Father, Who hast blest us all our days,
2. Je - sus, for Thy love most ten - der, On the cross for sin - ners shown,
3. Ev - ery day will be the bright - er When Thy gra - cious face we see;
We with grate - ful hearts would gath - er, To be - gin this hour with praise:
We would praise Thee, and sur - ren - der All our hearts to be Thine own:
Ev - ery bur - den will be light - er When we know it comes from Thee.
Praise for light so bright - ly shin - ing On our steps from heaven a - bove;
With so blest a Friend pro - vid - ed, We up - on our way would go,
Spread Thy love's broad ban - ner o'er us, Give us strength to serve and wait,
Praise for mer - cies dai - ly twin - ing Round us gold - en cords of love.
Sure of be - ing safe - ly guid - ed, Guard - ed well from ev - ery foe.
Till the glo - ry breaks be - fore us Through the Cit - y's o - pen gate. A - MEN.

Praise the Lord: Ye Heavens, Adore Him

FABEN 8. 7. 8. 7. D.

From Psalm 148
Stanzas 1 and 2, *Foundling Hospital Collection*, 1796
Stanza 3, Edward Osler, 1836

John H. Willcox, 1849

1. Praise the Lord: ye heavens, a - dore Him; Praise Him, an - gels, in the height;
2. Praise the Lord, for He is glo - rious; Nev - er shall His prom - ise fail:
3. Wor - ship, hon - or, glo - ry, bless - ing, Lord, we of - fer un - to Thee;

Sun and moon, re - joice be - fore Him; Praise Him, all ye stars and light.
God hath made His saints vic - to - rious; Sin and death shall not pre - vail.
Young and old, Thy praise ex - press - ing, In glad hom - age bend the knee.

Praise the Lord, for He hath spo - ken; Worlds His might - y voice o - beyed:
Praise the God of our sal - va - tion; Hosts on high, His power pro - claim;
All the saints in heaven a - dore Thee; We would bow be - fore Thy throne:

Laws which nev - er shall be bro - ken For their guid - ance hath He made.
Heaven and earth and all cre - a - tion, Laud and mag - ni - fy His Name.
As Thine an - gels serve be - fore Thee, So on earth Thy will be done. A-MEN.

9 Praise to the Lord

LOBE DEN HERREN 14. 14. 4. 7. 8.
Joachim Neander, 1680
Trans. by Catherine Winkworth, 1863
Stralsund Gesangbuch, 1665
Harmonized by J. F. Ohl
1. Praise to the Lord, the Al-might-y, the King of cre-a-tion!
2. Praise to the Lord, who o'er all things so won-drous-ly reign-eth,
3. Praise to the Lord, who doth pros-per thy work and de-fend thee;
4. Praise to the Lord! O let all that is in me a-dore Him!
O my soul, praise Him, for He is thy health and sal-va-tion!
Shel-ters thee un-der His wings, yea, so gen-tly sus-tain-eth!
Sure-ly His good-ness and mer-cy here dai-ly at-tend thee!
All that hath life and breath, come now with prais-es be-fore Him!
All ye who hear, Now to His tem-ple draw near;
Hast thou not seen How thy de-sires e'er have been
Pon-der a-new What the Al-might-y can do,
Let the A-men Sound from His peo-ple a-gain:
Praise Him in glad ad-o-ra-tion!
Grant-ed in what He or-dain-eth?
If with His love He be-friend thee!
Glad-ly for aye we a-dore Him.
A-MEN.

Lord, Thy Glory Fills the Heaven

10

HYFRYDOL 8.7.8.7.D.
Richard Mant, 1837
Rowland Hugh Prichard (1811–1887)
1. "Lord, Thy glo - ry fills the heav - en; Earth is with its full - ness stored;
2. Ev - er thus, in God's high prais - es, Breth-ren, let our tongues u - nite,
3. "Lord, Thy glo - ry fills the heav - en; Earth is with its full - ness stored;
Un - to Thee be glo - ry giv - en, Ho - ly, ho - ly, ho - ly Lord!"
While our thought His great - ness rais - es, And our love His gifts ex - cite;
Un - to Thee be glo - ry giv - en, Ho - ly, ho - ly, ho - ly Lord!"
Heaven is still with glo - ry ring - ing; Earth takes up the an - gels' cry,
With His ser - aph train be - fore Him, With His ho - ly Church be - low,
Thus Thy glo - rious Name con - fess - ing, We a - dopt the an - gels' cry,
"Ho - ly, ho - ly, ho - ly" sing - ing, "Lord of Hosts, the Lord Most High."
Thus con - spire we to a - dore Him, Bid we thus our an - them flow.
"Ho - ly, ho - ly, ho - ly," bless - ing Thee, the Lord of Hosts Most High! A - MEN.

11 My God, I Thank Thee

WENTWORTH 8. 4. 8. 4. 8. 4.

Adelaide A. Procter, 1858 — Frederick C. Maker, 1876

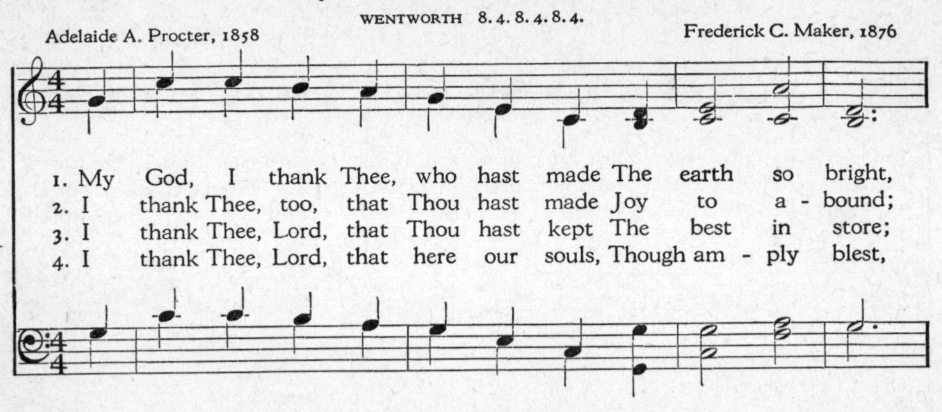
1. My God, I thank Thee, who hast made The earth so bright,
2. I thank Thee, too, that Thou hast made Joy to a - bound;
3. I thank Thee, Lord, that Thou hast kept The best in store;
4. I thank Thee, Lord, that here our souls, Though am - ply blest,

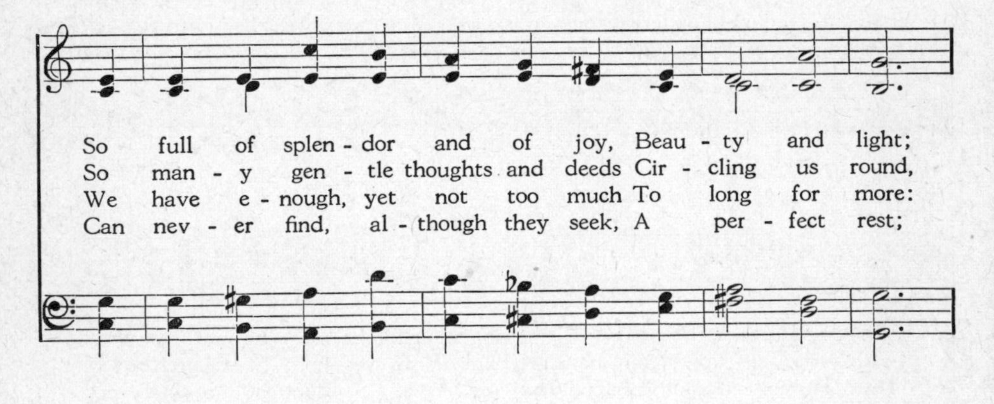
So full of splen - dor and of joy, Beau - ty and light;
So man - y gen - tle thoughts and deeds Cir - cling us round,
We have e - nough, yet not too much To long for more:
Can nev - er find, al - though they seek, A per - fect rest;

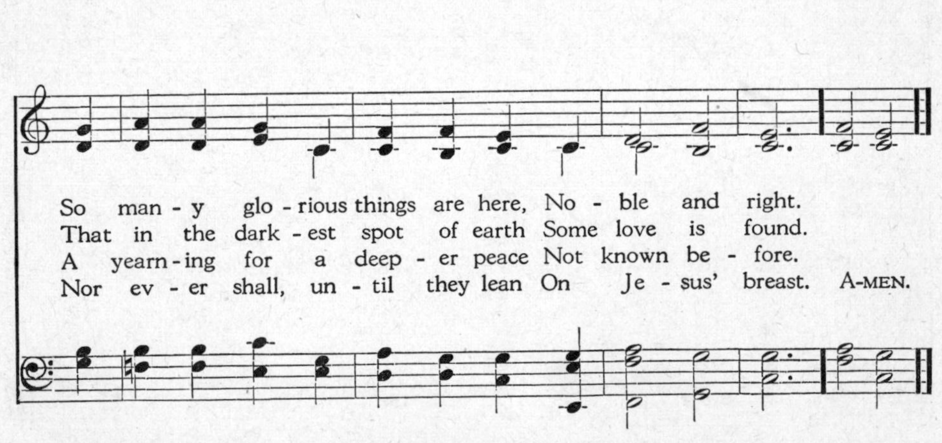
So man - y glo - rious things are here, No - ble and right.
That in the dark - est spot of earth Some love is found.
A yearn - ing for a deep - er peace Not known be - fore.
Nor ev - er shall, un - til they lean On Je - sus' breast. A-MEN.

Father of Lights

12

ANCIENT OF DAYS 11. 10. 11. 10.

Elizabeth Wilson and Helen Thoburn, 1913

J. Albert Jeffery, 1886

1 Fa - ther of lights, in whom there is no shad - ow,
2 Glad for the cause that binds our lives to - geth - er,
3 Light of the world, through whom we know the Fa - ther!
4 Thou art the Christ! To Thee we own al - le - giance.
Giv - er of ev - ery good and per - fect gift!
Through Thee u - nit - ed, wor - ship - ing as one:
Pour out up - on us Thine a - bid - ing love,
May our de - vo - tion sweep from sea to sea,
With one ac - cord we seek Thy ho - ly pres - ence,
Glad for the crown - ing gift that Thou hast giv - en,
That we may know its depth and height and splen - dor,
Ev - en as we, the gift from Thee re - ceiv - ing,
Glad - ly our hearts to Thee in praise we lift.
Send - ing, to light the world, Thine on - ly Son.
That heaven may come to earth from heaven a - bove.
Joy - ful - ly min - is - ter that gift for Thee.
A - MEN.

13 All Creatures of Our God and King

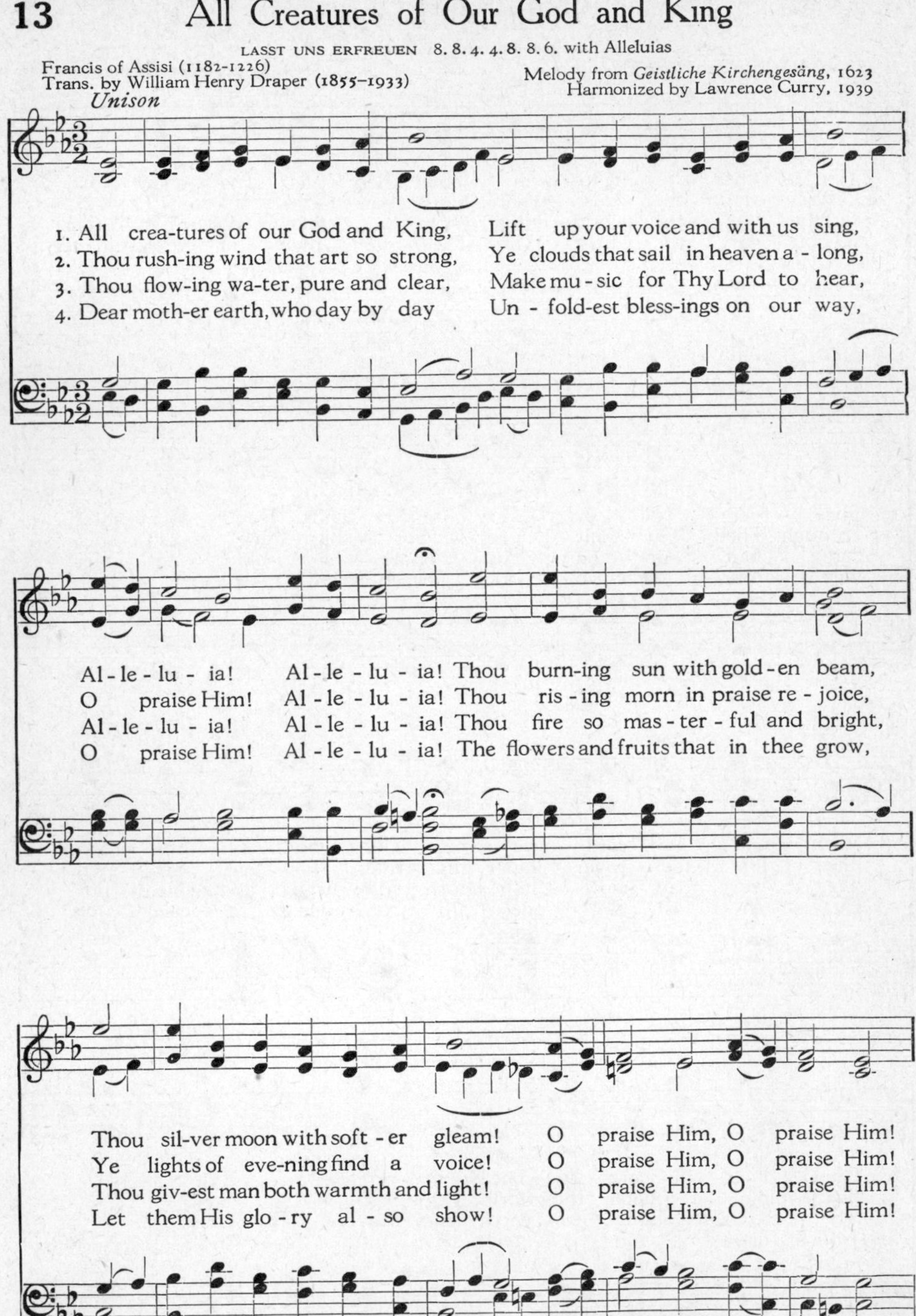
LASST UNS ERFREUEN 8. 8. 4. 4. 8. 8. 6. with Alleluias
Francis of Assisi (1182-1226)
Trans. by William Henry Draper (1855–1933)
Melody from Geistliche Kirchengesäng, 1623
Harmonized by Lawrence Curry, 1939
Unison
1. All crea-tures of our God and King, Lift up your voice and with us sing,
2. Thou rush-ing wind that art so strong, Ye clouds that sail in heaven a - long,
3. Thou flow-ing wa-ter, pure and clear, Make mu - sic for Thy Lord to hear,
4. Dear moth-er earth, who day by day Un - fold-est bless-ings on our way,
Al - le - lu - ia! Al - le - lu - ia! Thou burn-ing sun with gold - en beam,
O praise Him! Al - le - lu - ia! Thou ris - ing morn in praise re - joice,
Al - le - lu - ia! Al - le - lu - ia! Thou fire so mas - ter - ful and bright,
O praise Him! Al - le - lu - ia! The flowers and fruits that in thee grow,
Thou sil-ver moon with soft - er gleam! O praise Him, O praise Him!
Ye lights of eve-ning find a voice! O praise Him, O praise Him!
Thou giv-est man both warmth and light! O praise Him, O praise Him!
Let them His glo - ry al - so show! O praise Him, O praise Him!

All Creatures of Our God and King (Concluded)

Al - le - lu - ia! Al - le - lu - ia! Al - le - lu - - - - ia! A-MEN.

5. And all ye men of tender heart,
Forgiving others, take your part.
O sing ye! Alleluia!
Ye who long pain and sorrow bear,
Praise God and on Him cast your care!
O praise Him! Alleluia!

6. Let all things their Creator bless,
And worship Him in humbleness.
O praise Him! Alleluia!
Praise, praise the Father, praise the Son,
And praise the Spirit, Three in One!
O praise Him! Alleluia!

Praise to God, Immortal Praise **14**

PLEYEL'S HYMN 7.7.7.7.

Anna L. Barbauld, 1772
Doxology Added, Charles Wesley, 1740

Arr. from Ignaz J. Pleyel, 1790

1. Praise to God, im - mor - tal praise, For the love that crowns our days:
2. Flocks that whit - en all the plain, Yel - low sheaves of rip - ened grain,
3. All that spring with boun-teous hand Scat - ters o'er the smil - ing land;
4. These to Thee, our God, we owe, Source whence all our bless-ings flow;
5. Sing we to our God a - bove Praise e - ter - nal as His love;

Boun-teous Source of ev - ery joy, Let Thy praise our tongues em - ploy.
Clouds that drop their fat-tening dews, Suns that tem-perate warmth dif-fuse;
All that lib - eral au - tumn pours From her rich o'er-flow - ing stores—
And for these our souls shall raise Grate-ful vows and sol - emn praise.
Praise Him, all ye heaven-ly host, Fa - ther, Son, and Ho - ly Ghost. A-MEN.

15 Praise the Lord, His Glories Show

LLANFAIR 7. 7. 7. 7. with Alleluias
From Psalm 150
Henry Francis Lyte, 1834
Robert Williams, 1817
Harmonized by Lawrence Curry, 1940
1. Praise the Lord, His glo - ries show, Al - - le - lu - ia!
2. Earth to heaven, and heaven to earth, Al - - le - lu - ia!
3. Praise the Lord, His mer - cies trace, Al - - le - lu - ia!
Saints with - in His courts be - low, Al - - le - lu - ia!
Tell His won - ders, sing His worth, Al - - le - lu - ia!
Praise His prov - i - dence and grace, Al - - le - lu - ia!
An - gels round His throne a - bove, Al - - le - lu - ia!
Age to age and shore to shore, Al - - le - lu - ia!
All that He for man hath done, Al - - le - lu - ia!
All that see and share His love. Al - - le - lu - ia!
Praise Him, praise Him ev - er - more! Al - - le - lu - ia!
All He sends us through His Son. Al - - le - lu - ia! A-MEN.

My God and King! 16

ALL THE WORLD 10. 4. 6. 6. 6. 6. 10. 4.
George Herbert (1593-1632)
Robert G. McCutchan, 1934
1. Let all the world in ev - ery cor - ner sing, "My God and King!" The heavens are not too high, His praise may thith - er fly; The earth is not too low, His prais - es there may grow. Let all the world in ev - ery cor - ner sing, "My God and King!"
2. Let all the world in ev - ery cor - ner sing, "My God and King!" The Church with psalms must shout, No door can keep them out: But more than all the heart Must bear the lar - gest part. Let all the world in ev - ery cor - ner sing, "My God and King!"
1.
2.

17 Now Thank We All Our God

NUN DANKET 6. 7. 6. 7. 6. 6. 6. 6.
Martin Rinkart, c. 1636
Trans. by Catherine Winkworth, 1858
Johann Crüger, 1648
1. Now thank we all our God With heart and hands and voi - ces,
2. O may this boun - teous God Through all our life be near us,
3. All praise and thanks to God The Fa - ther now be giv - en,
Who won-drous things hath done, In whom His world re - joi - ces;
With ev - er - joy - ful hearts And bless - ed peace to cheer us;
The Son, and Him who reigns With Them in high - est heav - en,
Who, from our moth - ers' arms, Hath blessed us on our way
And keep us in His grace, And guide us when per - plexed,
The one e - ter - nal God, Whom earth and heaven a - dore;
With count - less gifts of love, And still is ours to - day.
And free us from all ills In this world and the next.
For thus it was, is now, And shall be ev - er - more.
A-MEN.

Come, Ye Thankful People, Come

18

ST. GEORGE'S, WINDSOR 7.7.7.7.D.

Henry Alford, 1844; Alt.

George J. Elvey, 1859

1. Come, ye thank-ful peo - ple, come, Raise the song of har - vest home:
2. All the world is God's own field, Fruit un - to His praise to yield;
3. For the Lord our God shall come, And shall take His har - vest home;
4. E - ven so, Lord, quick - ly come To Thy fi - nal har - vest home;
All is safe - ly gath - ered in, Ere the win - ter storms be - gin;
Wheat and tares to - geth - er sown, Un - to joy or sor - row grown:
From His field shall in that day All of - fen - ses purge a - way;
Gath - er Thou Thy peo - ple in, Free from sor - row, free from sin;
God, our Mak - er, doth pro - vide For our wants to be sup - plied:
First the blade, and then the ear, Then the full corn shall ap - pear:
Give His an - gels charge at last In the fire the tares to cast,
There, for - ev - er pu - ri - fied, In Thy pres - ence to a - bide:
Come to God's own tem - ple, come, Raise the song of har - vest home.
Lord of har - vest, grant that we Whole-some grain and pure may be.
But the fruit - ful ears to store In His gar - ner ev - er - more.
Come, with all Thine an - gels, come, Raise the glo - rious har - vest home.
A-MEN.

19 When Morning Gilds the Skies

LAUDES DOMINI 6. 6. 6. 6. 6. 6.

From the German, c. 1800
Trans. by Edward Caswall, 1853, 1858

Joseph Barnby, 1868

1. When morn - ing gilds the skies, My heart a - wak - ing cries
2. Let earth's wide cir - cle round In joy - ful notes re - sound
3. Be this, while life is mine, My can - ti - cle di - vine,
May Je - sus Christ be praised: A - like at work and prayer
May Je - sus Christ be praised: Let air and sea and sky,
May Je - sus Christ be praised: Be this th'e - ter - nal song,
To Je - sus I re - pair; May Je - sus Christ be praised!
From depth to height, re - ply, May Je - sus Christ be praised!
Through all the a - ges long, May Je - sus Christ be praised! A-MEN.

20 The Sun Is on the Land and Sea

PARK 8. 4. 8. 4. 8. 4.

Louis F. Benson, 1897

Lawrence Curry, 1939

Unison
1. The sun is on the land and sea, The day be - gun;
2. Thy love was ev - er in our view, Like stars, by night;
3. We do not know what grief or care The day may bring:
4. All glo - ry to the Fa - ther be, With Christ the Son,

The Sun Is on the Land and Sea (Concluded)

Our morn-ing hymn be-gins with Thee, Blest Three in One;
Thy gifts are ev-ery morn-ing new, O God of light;
The heart shall find some glad-ness there That loves its King;
And, Ho-ly Spir-it, un-to Thee, For-ev-er One;
Harmony
Our praise shall rise con-tin-ual-ly Till day is done.
Thy mer-cy, like the heav-ens' blue, Fills all our sight.
The life that serves Thee ev-ery-where Can al-ways sing.
All glo-ry to the Trin-i-ty While a-ges run! A-MEN.

Alternative tune, "Wentworth," number 11.

Awake, My Soul, and with the Sun 21

CANONBURY L. M.

Thomas Ken, 1692 (Text of 1709) Arr. from Robert A. Schumann, 1839

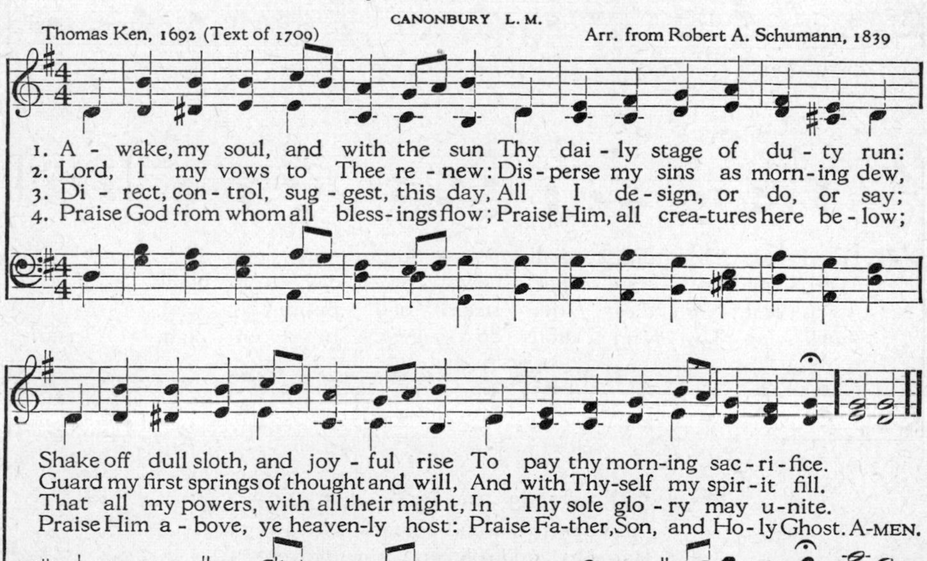
1. A-wake, my soul, and with the sun Thy dai-ly stage of du-ty run:
2. Lord, I my vows to Thee re-new: Dis-perse my sins as morn-ing dew,
3. Di-rect, con-trol, sug-gest, this day, All I de-sign, or do, or say;
4. Praise God from whom all bless-ings flow; Praise Him, all crea-tures here be-low;
Shake off dull sloth, and joy-ful rise To pay thy morn-ing sac-ri-fice.
Guard my first springs of thought and will, And with Thy-self my spir-it fill.
That all my powers, with all their might, In Thy sole glo-ry may u-nite.
Praise Him a-bove, ye heaven-ly host: Praise Fa-ther, Son, and Ho-ly Ghost. A-MEN.

22 The Day Thou Gavest, Lord, Is Ended

ST. CLEMENT 9. 8. 9. 8.
John Ellerton, 1870
Clement C. Scholefield, 1874
1. The day Thou gav - est, Lord, is end - ed, The dark - ness
2. We thank Thee that Thy Church un - sleep - ing, While earth rolls
3. As o'er each con - ti - nent and is - land The dawn leads
4. The sun that bids us rest is wak - ing Our breth - ren
falls at Thy be - hest; To Thee our morn - ing hymns as -
on - ward in - to light, Through all the world her watch is
on an - oth - er day, The voice of prayer is nev - er
'neath the west - ern sky, And hour by hour fresh lips are
cend - ed, Thy praise shall hal - low now our rest.
keep - ing, And rests not now by day or night.
si - lent, Nor dies the strain of praise a - way.
mak - ing Thy won - drous do - ings heard on high. A - MEN.

5. So be it, Lord; Thy throne shall never,
Like earth's proud empires, pass away;
But stand, and rule, and grow forever,
Till all Thy creatures own Thy sway.

Saviour, Again to Thy Dear Name We Raise 23

ELLERS 10. 10. 10. 10.
John Ellerton, 1866 (Text of 1868)
Edward J. Hopkins, 1869
1. Saviour, again to Thy dear Name we raise
With one accord our parting hymn of praise;
We stand to bless Thee ere our worship cease;
Then, lowly kneeling, wait Thy word of peace.
2. Grant us Thy peace upon our homeward way;
With Thee began, with Thee shall end the day:
Guard Thou the lips from sin, the hearts from shame,
That in this house have called upon Thy Name.
3. Grant us Thy peace, Lord, through the coming night;
Turn Thou for us its darkness into light;
From harm and danger keep Thy children free,
For dark and light are both alike to Thee.
4. Grant us Thy peace throughout our earthly life,
Our balm in sorrow, and our stay in strife;
Then, when Thy voice shall bid our conflict cease,
Call us, O Lord, to Thine eternal peace.
A-MEN.

24 God, That Madest Earth and Heaven

AR HYD Y NOS 8. 4. 8. 4. 8. 8. 8. 4.
Reginald Heber (1783–1826)
William Mercer, 1864
Welsh Traditional Melody
Harmonized by L. O. Emerson, 1906
1. God, that mad - est earth and heav - en, Dark - ness and light;
2. And when morn a - gain shall call us To run life's way,
3. Ho - ly Fa - ther, throned in heav - en, All - ho - ly Son,
Who the day for toil hast giv - en, For rest the night;
May we still, what - e'er be - fall us, Thy will o - bey.
Ho - ly Spir - it, free - ly giv - en, Blest Three in One,
May Thine an - gel guards de - fend us, Slum - ber sweet Thy mer - cy send us;
From the power of e - vil hide us, In the nar - row path - way guide us,
Grant Thy grace, we now im - plore Thee, Till we cast our crowns be - fore Thee,
Ho - ly dreams and hopes at - tend us, This live - long night.
Nor Thy smile be e'er de - nied us The live - long day.
And in wor - thier strains a - dore Thee, While a - ges run.
A-MEN.

Sun of My Soul, Thou Saviour Dear

HURSLEY L. M.

Katholisches Gesangbuch, Vienna, c. 1774
Arr. by William Henry Monk, 1861

John Keble, 1820

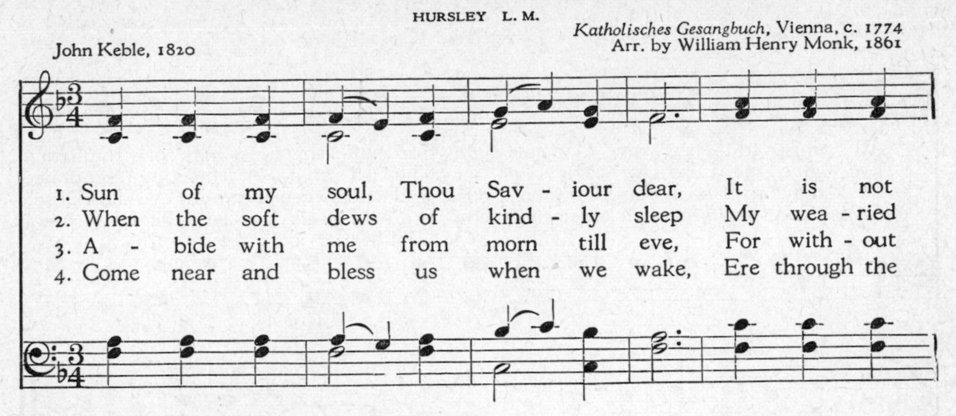
1. Sun of my soul, Thou Sav - iour dear, It is not
2. When the soft dews of kind - ly sleep My wea - ried
3. A - bide with me from morn till eve, For with - out
4. Come near and bless us when we wake, Ere through the

night if Thou be near; O may no earth - born
eye - lids gen - tly steep, Be my last thought, how
Thee I can - not live; A - bide with me when
world our way we take, Till in the o - cean

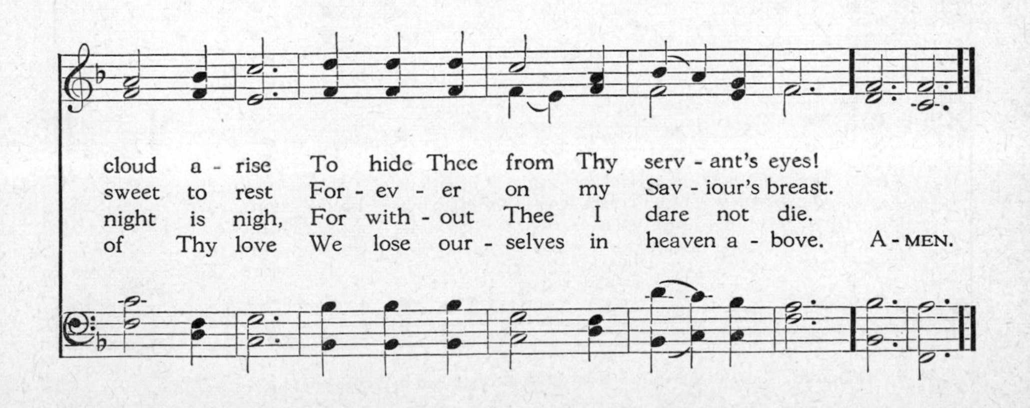
cloud a - rise To hide Thee from Thy serv - ant's eyes!
sweet to rest For - ev - er on my Sav - iour's breast.
night is nigh, For with - out Thee I dare not die.
of Thy love We lose our - selves in heaven a - bove. A - MEN.

26 All Praise to Thee, My God, This Night
TALLIS' CANON L. M.
Thomas Ken (1637–1711)
(Text of 1709)
Thomas Tallis (c. 1520-1585)
1. All praise to Thee, my God, this night, For all the bless-ings of the light;
2. For - give me, Lord, for Thy dear Son, The ill that I this day have done;
3. O may my soul on Thee re - pose, And with sweet sleep mine eye - lids close;
4. Praise God, from whom all bless-ings flow; Praise Him, all crea-tures here be - low;
Keep me, O keep me, King of kings, Be-neath Thine own al-might-y wings.
That with the world, my - self, and Thee, I, ere I sleep, at peace may be.
Sleep that may me more vig-orous make To serve my God when I a - wake.
Praise Him a - bove, ye heaven-ly host; Praise Fa - ther, Son, and Ho - ly Ghost. A-MEN.
27 Holy Father, Bless Us
ARMENTROUT 6. 5. 6. 5.
Calvin W. Laufer, 1921
Calvin W. Laufer, 1921
1. Ho - ly Fa - ther, bless us As the day we close,
2. All the day Thy pres - ence Made our hearts to burn,
3. So to - night we pray Thee Leave us not a - lone;
4. Grant to us in slum - ber To be ver - y near,
5. When at length the dawn - ing Sweeps the night a - way,
And the night's re - fresh - ing Grant us in re - pose.
As we heard Thy coun - sel, Felt Thy love's con - cern.
But through light and shad - ow Keep us as Thine own.
In Thy good - ness quell - ing Need - less doubt and fear.
Help us rise tri - um - phant, Wor - thy of the day. A-MEN.

28 The Lord Be with Us

DALEHURST C. M.

John Ellerton, 1870 — Arthur Cottman, 1874

1. The Lord be with us as we walk A - long our home-ward road;
2. The Lord be with us till the night En - fold our day of rest;
3. The Lord be with us through the hours Of slum - ber calm and deep,
In si - lent thought or friend - ly talk Our hearts be near to God.
Be He of ev - ery heart the Light, Of ev - ery home the Guest.
Pro - tect our homes, re - new our powers, And guard us while we sleep. A-MEN.

29 Now the Day Is Over

MERRIAL 6. 5. 6. 5.

Sabine Baring-Gould, 1865 — Joseph Barnby, 1868

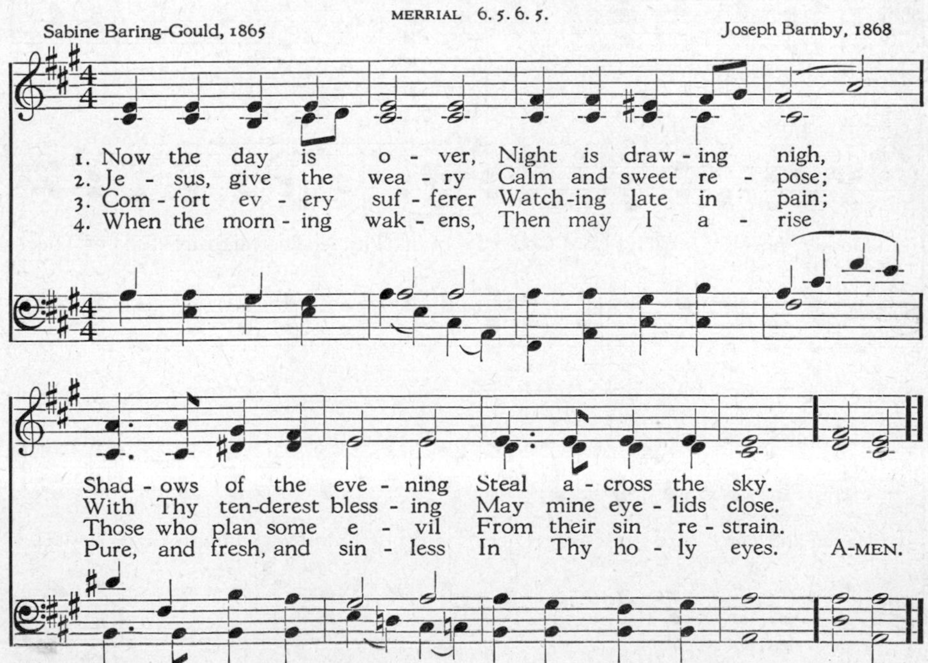

1. Now the day is o - ver, Night is draw - ing nigh,
2. Je - sus, give the wea - ry Calm and sweet re - pose;
3. Com - fort ev - ery suf - ferer Watch-ing late in pain;
4. When the morn - ing wak - ens, Then may I a - rise
Shad - ows of the eve - ning Steal a - cross the sky.
With Thy ten-derest bless - ing May mine eye - lids close.
Those who plan some e - vil From their sin re - strain.
Pure, and fresh, and sin - less In Thy ho - ly eyes. A-MEN.

30 Day Is Dying in the West

EVENING PRAISE 7. 7. 7. 7. 4. with Refrain

Mary Ann Lathbury, 1877

William F. Sherwin, 1877

1. Day is dy - ing in the west; Heaven is touch-ing earth with rest: Wait and wor-ship while the night Sets her eve - ning lamps a - light Through all the sky.
2. Lord of life, be-neath the dome Of the u - ni-verse, Thy home, Gath-er us who seek Thy face To the fold of Thy em-brace, For Thou art nigh.
3. While the deep-ening shad-ows fall, Heart of Love, en - fold - ing all, Through the glo-ry and the grace Of the stars that veil Thy face, Our hearts as - cend.
4. When for-ev - er from our sight Pass the stars, the day, the night, Lord of an - gels, on our eyes Let e - ter - nal morn-ing rise, And shad - ows end.
Refrain
Ho - ly, ho - ly, ho - ly! Lord God of Hosts! Heaven and earth are full of Thee! Heaven and earth are prais - ing Thee, O Lord Most High!
A-men.

Words and music used by permission of Chautauqua Institution, Chautauqua, New York.

Hail, Gladdening Light
31
SUNDOWN 10. 10. 10. 10. 10. 10.
From Greek Service Book
Trans. by John Keble, 1834
John H. Gower, 1890
Voices in unison
1. Hail, glad-dening Light, of His pure glo - ry poured, Who is im - mor-tal Fa-ther,
2. The lights of eve - ning now a-round us shine; We hymn Thy blest hu-man-i -
Voices in harmony
heaven - ly, blest, High - est and ho - liest—Je - sus Christ our Lord!
ty di - vine; Wor-thiest art Thou at all times to be sung,
p Unison
Now are we come to the sun's hour of rest; All times are or - dered
By grate-ful hearts, with un - de - fil - ed tongue, Son of our God, Giv -
cresc.
Harmony f
in Thy Word a-lone, There-fore the day and night Thy glo - ries own.
er of life, a-lone! There-fore shall all the worlds Thy glo - ries own. A-MEN.

32 Holy, Holy, Holy! Lord God Almighty!

NICAEA 11. 12. 12. 10.

Reginald Heber (1783–1826)

John B. Dykes, 1861
Descant by Donald D. Kettring, 1940

Descant
2.–4. Ho - ly, ho - ly, ho - - - - - - ly,
ho - ly, ho - ly, ho - - - - ly,
ho - ly, ho - ly, ho - - - - - - ly,
1. Ho - ly, ho - ly, ho - ly! Lord God Al - might - y!
2. Ho - ly, ho - ly, ho - ly! All the saints a - dore Thee,
3. Ho - ly, ho - ly, ho - ly! Though the dark - ness hide Thee,
4. Ho - ly, ho - ly, ho - ly! Lord God Al - might - y!
Ear - ly in the morn - ing our song shall rise to Thee;
Cast - ing down their gold - en crowns a - round the glass - y sea;
Though the eye of sin - ful man Thy glo - ry may not see,
All Thy works shall praise Thy Name, in earth and sky and sea;
Ho - ly, ho - ly, ho - ly! Mer - ci - ful and Might - y!
Cher - u - bim and ser - a - phim fall - ing down be - fore Thee,
On - ly Thou art ho - ly; there is none be - side Thee
Ho - ly, ho - ly, ho - ly! Mer - ci - ful and Might - y!

Holy, Holy, Holy! Lord God Almighty! (Concluded)

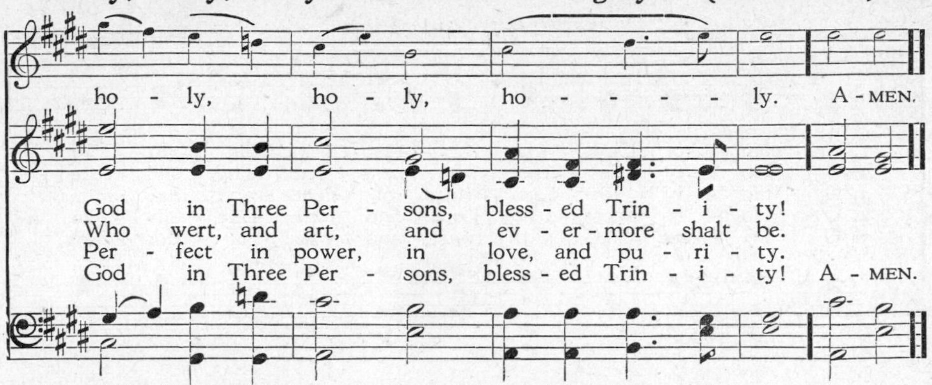
ho - ly, ho - ly, ho - - - - - ly. A - MEN.
God in Three Per - sons, bless - ed Trin - i - ty!
Who wert, and art, and ev - er - more shalt be.
Per - fect in power, in love, and pu - ri - ty.
God in Three Per - sons, bless - ed Trin - i - ty! A - MEN.

Come, Thou Almighty King

33

TRINITY (ITALIAN HYMN) 6. 6. 4. 6. 6. 6. 4.

Anon., c. 1757 — Felice de Giardini, 1769

1. Come, Thou Al - might - y King, Help us Thy Name to sing,
2. Come, Thou In - car - nate Word, Gird on Thy might - y sword,
3. Come, Ho - ly Com - fort - er, Thy sa - cred wit - ness bear
4. To the great One in Three E - ter - nal prais - es be,

Help us to praise: Fa - ther, all - glo - ri - ous, O'er all vic -
Our prayer at - tend: Come, and Thy peo - ple bless, And give Thy
In this glad hour: Thou who al - might - y art, Now rule in
Hence ev - er - more! His sov - ereign maj - es - ty May we in

to - ri - ous, Come, and reign o - ver us, An - cient of Days.
word suc - cess; Spir - it of ho - li - ness, On us de - scend.
ev - ery heart, And ne'er from us de - part, Spir - it of power.
glo - ry see, And to e - ter - ni - ty Love and a - dore. A - MEN.

34 Ancient of Days, Who Sittest Throned in Glory

ANCIENT OF DAYS 11.10.11.10.
William C. Doane, 1886
J. Albert Jeffery, 1886
1. An - cient of Days, who sit - test throned in glo - ry;
2. O Ho - ly Fa - ther, who hast led Thy chil - dren
3. O Ho - ly Je - sus, Prince of Peace and Sav - iour,
4. O Ho - ly Ghost, the Lord and the Life - Giv - er,
5. O Tri - une God, with heart and voice a - dor - ing,
To Thee all knees are bent, all voi - ces pray;
In all the a - ges, with the fire and cloud,
To Thee we owe the peace that still pre - vails,
Thine is the quick - ening power that gives in - crease;
Praise we the good - ness that doth crown our days;
Thy love has blest the wide world's won - drous sto - ry
Through seas dry - shod, through wea - ry wastes be - wil - dering;
Still - ing the rude wills of men's wild be - hav - ior,
From Thee have flowed, as from a pleas - ant riv - er,
Pray we that Thou wilt hear us, still im - plor - ing
With light and life since E - den's dawn - ing day.
To Thee, in rev - erent love, our hearts are bowed.
And calm - ing pas - sion's fierce and storm - y gales.
Our plen - ty, wealth, pros - per - i - ty, and peace.
Thy love and fa - vor, kept to us al - ways.
A - MEN.

Of the Father's Love Begotten

DIVINUM MYSTERIUM 8. 7. 8. 7. 8. 7. 7.

Aurelius Clemens Prudentius (348–413)
Trans. by John Mason Neale, 1854, and
Henry Williams Baker, 1859

Medieval Plain Song, Mode V
Arr. and Harmonized by Winfred Douglas, 1917, 1940

Unison

1. Of the Fa-ther's love be - got - ten, Ere the worlds be - gan to be,
2. O ye heights of heaven a - dore Him; An - gel hosts, His prais - es sing;
3. Christ, to Thee with God the Fa - ther, And, O Ho - ly Ghost, to Thee,

He is Al - pha and O - me - ga, He the Source, the End - ing He,
Powers, do - min - ions, bow be - fore Him, And ex - tol our God and King;
Hymn and chant and high thanks-giv - ing And un - wea - ried prais - es be:

Of the things that are, that have been, And that fu - ture
Let no tongue on earth be si - lent, Ev - ery voice in
Hon - or, glo - ry, and do - min - ion, And e - ter - nal

years shall see, Ev - er - more and ev - er - more!
con - cert ring, Ev - er - more and ev - er - more!
vic - to - ry, Ev - er - more and ev - er - more! A - MEN.

36 O Worship the King All-glorious Above

LYONS 10. 10. 11. 11.
From Psalm 104
Robert Grant, 1833
Arr. from J. Michael Haydn (1737–1806)
1. O wor - ship the King all - glo - rious a - bove,
2. O tell of His might, O sing of His grace,
3. The earth with its store of won - ders un - told,
4. Thy boun - ti - ful care what tongue can re - cite?
5. Frail chil - dren of dust, and fee - ble as frail,
O grate - ful - ly sing His pow - er and His love;
Whose robe is the light, whose can - o - py space.
Al - might - y, Thy power hath found - ed of old;
It breathes in the air, it shines in the light;
In Thee do we trust, nor find Thee to fail;
Our Shield and De - fend - er, the An - cient of Days,
His char - iots of wrath the deep thun - der - clouds form,
Hath stab - lished it fast by a change - less de - cree,
It streams from the hills, it de - scends to the plain,
Thy mer - cies how ten - der, how firm to the end,
Pa - vil - ioned in splen - dor, and gird - ed with praise.
And dark is His path on the wings of the storm.
And round it hath cast, like a man - tle, the sea.
And sweet - ly dis - tills in the dew and the rain.
Our Mak - er, De - fend - er, Re - deem - er, and Friend! A - MEN.

The God of Abraham Praise

LEONI 6. 6. 8. 4. D.
Daniel Ben Judah, Fourteenth Century
Revised Version of the Yigdal
Hebrew Melody
1. The God of Abra - ham praise, All prais - ed be His Name,
2. His spir - it flow - eth free, High sur - ging where it will:
3. He hath e - ter - nal life Im - plant - ed in the soul;
Who was, and is, and is to be, And still the same!
In proph - et's word He spoke of old— He speak - eth still.
His love shall be our strength and stay, While a - ges roll.
The one e - ter - nal God, Ere aught that now ap - pears;
Es - tab - lished is His law, And change - less it shall stand,
Praise to the liv - ing God! All prais - ed be His Name,
The First, the Last: be - yond all thought His time - less years!
Deep writ up - on the hu - man heart, On sea, or land.
Who was, and is, and is to be, And still the same! A - MEN.

38 A Mighty Fortress Is Our God

EIN' FESTE BURG 8. 7. 8. 7. 6. 6. 6. 6. 7.

Martin Luther, 1529
Trans. by Frederick H. Hedge, 1853
Martin Luther, 1529
May be sung in unison
1. A might-y For-tress is our God, A Bul-wark nev-er fail-ing;
2. Did we in our own strength con-fide, Our striv-ing would be los-ing;
3. And though this world, with dev-ils filled, Should threat-en to un-do us;
4. That word a-bove all earth-ly powers, No thanks to them, a-bid-eth;
Our Help-er He a-mid the flood Of mor-tal ills pre-vail-ing:
Were not the right Man on our side, The Man of God's own choos-ing:
We will not fear, for God hath willed His truth to tri-umph through us:
The Spir-it and the gifts are ours Through Him who with us sid-eth:
For still our an-cient Foe Doth seek to work us woe; His craft and power are great,
Dost ask who that may be? Christ Je-sus, it is He; Lord Sab-a-oth His Name,
The Prince of Dark-ness grim, We trem-ble not for him; His rage we can en-dure,
Let goods and kin-dred go, This mor-tal life al-so; The bod-y they may kill:
And, armed with cru-el hate, On earth is not his e-qual.
From age to age the same, And He must win the bat-tle.
For lo! his doom is sure, One lit-tle word shall fell him.
God's truth a-bid-eth still, His King-dom is for-ev-er. A-MEN.

39 God of Our Life, Through All the Circling Years

SANDON 10. 4. 10. 4. 10. 10.
Hugh T. Kerr, 1916
Charles Henry Purday (1799–1885)
1. God of our life, through all the cir - cling years, We trust in Thee;
2. God of the past, our times are in Thy hand; With us a - bide.
3. God of the com - ing years, through paths un-known We fol - low Thee;
In all the past, through all our hopes and fears, Thy hand we see.
Lead us by faith to hope's true Prom - ised Land; Be Thou our Guide.
When we are strong, Lord, leave us not a - lone; Our Ref - uge be.
With each new day, when morn - ing lifts the veil,
With Thee to bless, the dark - ness shines as light,
Be Thou for us in life our Dai - ly Bread,
We own Thy mer - cies, Lord, which nev - er fail.
And faith's fair vi - sion chan - ges in - to sight.
Our heart's true Home when all our years have sped.
A-MEN.

Words used by permission of Hugh T. Kerr.

40 Our God, Our Help in Ages Past

ST. ANNE C. M.

From Psalm 90
Isaac Watts, 1719

William Croft (1678–1727)
Supplement to the New Version, 1708
Descant by Donald D. Kettring, 1940

Descant
1. Our God, our Help in ages past, Our Hope for years to come,
2. Before the hills in order stood, Or earth received her frame,
3. A thousand ages in Thy sight Are like an evening gone;
4. Time, like an ever-rolling stream, Bears all its sons away;
5. Our God, our Help in ages past, Our Hope for years to come,
Our Shelter from the stormy blast, And our eternal Home:
From everlasting Thou art God, To endless years the same.
Short as the watch that ends the night Before the rising sun.
They fly forgotten, as a dream Dies at the opening day.
Be Thou our Guard while troubles last, And our eternal Home. A-MEN.

41 Let Us with a Gladsome Mind

MONKLAND 7.7.7.7.

From Psalm 136
John Milton, 1623; Alt.

Melody from *Hymn Tunes of the United Brethren*, 1824
Arr. by John B. Wilkes, 1861

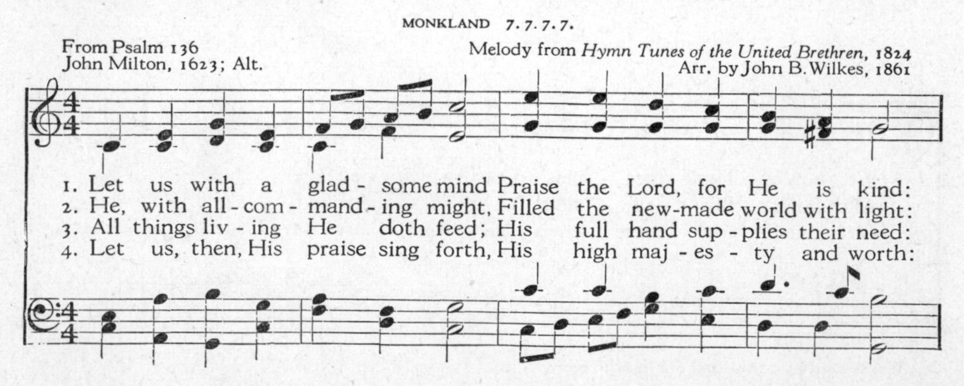
1. Let us with a gladsome mind Praise the Lord, for He is kind:
2. He, with all-commanding might, Filled the new-made world with light:
3. All things living He doth feed; His full hand supplies their need:
4. Let us, then, His praise sing forth, His high majesty and worth:

Let Us with a Gladsome Mind (Concluded)

For His mer-cies aye en-dure, Ev-er faith-ful, ev-er sure.
For His mer-cies aye en-dure, Ev-er faith-ful, ev-er sure.
For His mer-cies aye en-dure, Ev-er faith-ful, ev-er sure.
For His mer-cies aye en-dure, Ev-er faith-ful, ev-er sure. A-MEN.

For the Beauty of the Earth 42

DIX 7.7.7.7.7.7.
Folliott S. Pierpoint, 1864; Alt.
Arr. from Conrad Kocher, 1838
1. For the beau-ty of the earth; For the glo-ry of the skies;
2. For the won-der of each hour Of the day and of the night,
3. For the joy of hu-man love, Broth-er, sis-ter, par-ent, child,
4. For Thy Church that ev-er-more Lift-eth ho-ly hands a-bove,
For the love which from our birth O-ver and a-round us lies:
Hill and vale, and tree and flower, Sun and moon, and stars of light:
Friends on earth, and friends a-bove; For all gen-tle thoughts and mild:
Of-fering up on ev-ery shore Her pure sac-ri-fice of love:
Lord of all, to Thee we raise This our hymn of grate-ful praise.
Lord of all, to Thee we raise This our hymn of grate-ful praise.
Lord of all, to Thee we raise This our hymn of grate-ful praise.
Lord of all, to Thee we raise This our hymn of grate-ful praise. A-MEN.

43 This Is My Father's World

TERRA BEATA S. M. D.
Maltbie D. Babcock, 1901
Franklin L. Sheppard, 1915
1. This is my Fa - ther's world, And to my lis - tening ears,
2. This is my Fa - ther's world, The birds their car - ols raise,
3. This is my Fa - ther's world, O let me ne'er for - get
All na - ture sings, and round me rings The mu - sic of the spheres.
The morn - ing light, the lil - y white, De - clare their Mak - er's praise.
That though the wrong seems oft so strong, God is the Rul - er yet.
This is my Fa - ther's world: I rest me in the thought
This is my Fa - ther's world: He shines in all that's fair;
This is my Fa - ther's world: The bat - tle is not done;
Of rocks and trees, of skies and seas; His hand the won - ders wrought.
In the rus-tling grass I hear Him pass, He speaks to me ev-ery-where.
Je - sus who died shall be sat - is - fied, And earth and heaven be one. A-MEN.

The Spacious Firmament on High

CREATION · L. M. D.

Joseph Addison, 1712 — Arr. from Franz Joseph Haydn, 1798

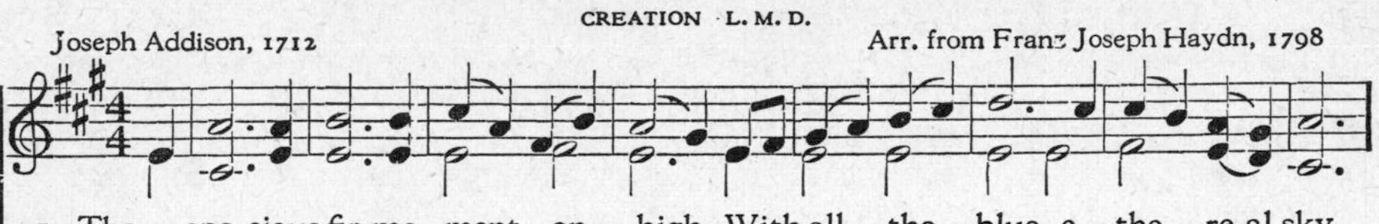

1. The spa-cious fir-ma - ment on high, With all the blue e - the - re-al sky,
2. Soon as the eve-ning shades pre - vail, The moon takes up the won - drous tale,
3. What though in sol-emn si - lence all Move round this dark ter - res - tri-al ball?

And span-gled heavens, a shin-ing frame, Their great O - rig - i - nal pro - claim:
And night-ly to the lis - tening earth Re - peats the sto - ry of her birth;
What though no re-al voice nor sound A - midst their ra - diant orbs be found?

Th' un-wea - ried sun, from day to day, Does his Cre - a - tor's power dis - play,
Whilst all the stars that round her burn, And all the plan - ets in their turn,
In rea - son's ear they all re - joice, And ut - ter forth a glo - rious voice;

And pub - lish - es to ev - ery land The work of an al-might-y hand.
Con-firm the ti - dings as they roll, And spread the truth from pole to pole.
For - ev - er sing-ing, as they shine, "The Hand that made us is di-vine." A-MEN.

45 The Heavens Declare Thy Glory

CHENIES 7. 6. 7. 6. D.

Psalm 19
Thomas R. Birks, 1874

Timothy R. Matthews, 1855

1. The heavens de - clare Thy glo - ry, The fir - ma - ment Thy power;
2. The sun with roy - al splen - dor Goes forth to chant Thy praise;
3. How per - fect, just, and ho - ly The pre - cepts Thou hast given;
4. All heaven on high re - joi - ces To do its Mak - er's will;
Day un - to day the sto - ry Re - peats from hour to hour;
And moon-beams soft and ten - der Their gen - tler an - them raise;
Still mak - ing wise the low - ly, They lift the thoughts to heaven:
The stars with sol - emn voi - ces Re - sound Thy prais - es still;
Night un - to night re - ply - ing, Pro - claims in ev - ery land,
O'er ev - ery tribe and na - tion That mu - sic strange is poured,
How pure, how soul - re - stor - ing Thy gos - pel's heaven - ly ray,
So let my whole be - hav - ior, Thoughts, words, and ac - tions, be,
O Lord, with voice un - dy - ing, The won - ders of Thy hand.
The song of all cre - a - tion, To Thee, cre - a - tion's Lord.
A bright - er ra - diance pour - ing Than noon of bright - est day.
O Lord, my Strength, my Sav - iour, One cease - less song to Thee. A-MEN.

All Beautiful the March of Days

FOREST GREEN C. M. D.

Frances Whitmarsh Wile, 1912

English Traditional Melody
Arr. by R. Vaughan Williams, 1906

1. All beau - ti - ful the march of days, As sea - sons come and go;
2. O'er white ex - pans - es spar - kling pure The ra - diant morns un - fold;
3. O Thou from whose un - fath - omed law The year in beau - ty flows,

The Hand that shaped the rose hath wrought The crys - tal of the snow;
The sol - emn splen - dors of the night Burn bright-er through the cold;
Thy - self the vi - sion pass - ing by In crys - tal and in rose,

Hath sent the hoar - y frost of heaven, The flow - ing wa - ters sealed,
Life mounts in ev - ery throb-bing vein, Love deep - ens round the hearth,
Day un - to day doth ut - ter speech, And night to night pro-claim,

And laid a si - lent love - li - ness On hill and wood and field.
And clear - er sounds the an - gel hymn, "Good will to men on earth."
In ev - er - chan - ging words of light, The won - der of Thy Name. A-MEN.

Words used by permission of Dorothy M. W. Bean.
Music from *The English Hymnal*. Used by permission of Oxford University Press.

47 Spring Has Now Unwrapped the Flowers

TEMPUS ADEST FLORIDUM 7. 6. 7. 6. D.
Piae Cantiones, 1582
Trans. in The Oxford Book of Carols, 1928
Fourteenth Century (?) Melody
Arr. by Ernest MacMillan
1. Spring has now un-wrapped the flowers, Day is fast re - viv - ing,
2. Herb and plant that, win - ter long, Slum-bered at their lei - sure,
3. Earth puts on her dress of glee; Flowers and grass - es hide her;
4. Through each won - der of fair days God Him - self ex - press - es;
Life in all her grow - ing powers Toward the light is striv - ing:
Now be - stir - ring, green and strong, Find in growth their pleas - ure:
We go forth in char - i - ty— Broth - ers all be - side her;
Beau - ty fol - lows all His ways, As the world He bless - es:
Gone the i - ron touch of cold, Win - ter time and frost time,
All the world with beau - ty fills, Gold the green en - han - cing;
For, as man this glo - ry sees In th'a - wak - ening sea - son,
So, as He re - news the earth, Art - ist with - out ri - val,
Seed - lings, work - ing through the mold, Now make up for lost time.
Flowers make glee a - mong the hills, Set the mead-ows dan - cing.
Rea - son learns the heart's de - crees, Hearts are led by rea - son.
In His grace of glad new birth We must seek re - viv - al.

Words used by permission of Oxford University Press. One stanza omitted with their consent.
Music used by permission of Ernest MacMillan.

NOTE: A spring carol, the tune of which Neale used for his version of the Christmas legend "Good King Wenceslaus." The carol as printed here is in its original and proper setting.

When the Great Sun Sinks to His Rest 48

ST. VENANTIUS L. M.
Maltbie D. Babcock, 1901
Rouen Church Melody
May be sung in unison
1. When the great sun sinks to his rest,
2. And when the stars— the day - light fled—
3. Or if in sol - emn for - est shades
4. Not in the sa - cred shrines a - lone,
His gold - en glo - ries thrill - ing me,
In ser - ried, shin - ing ranks I see,
The calm of na - ture steals o'er me,
Which chime their sum - mons un - to me,
And voice - less long - ings stir my breast,
Fill - ing the splen - did vault o'er - head,
And si - lence all my soul per - vades,
Would I look up - ward to Thy throne,
Then teach me, Lord, to wor - ship Thee.
Then teach me, Lord, to wor - ship Thee.
Then teach me, Lord, to wor - ship Thee.
But ev - ery - where would wor - ship Thee.
A - - MEN.

49 God of the Earth, the Sky, the Sea!

ST. CHRYSOSTOM 8. 8. 8. 8. 8. 8.

Samuel Longfellow, 1864 — Joseph Barnby, 1872

1. God of the earth, the sky, the sea! Mak - er of all a - bove, be - low! Cre - a - tion lives and moves in Thee, Thy pres - ent life through all doth flow. We give Thee thanks, Thy Name we sing, Al - might - y Fa - ther, heaven - ly King.
2. Thy love is in the sun - shine's glow, Thy life is in the quick - ening air; When light - nings flash and storm winds blow, There is Thy power; Thy law is there. We give Thee thanks, Thy Name we sing, Al - might - y Fa - ther, heaven - ly King.
3. We feel Thy calm at eve - ning's hour, Thy gran - deur in the march of night; And, when Thy morn - ing breaks in power, We hear Thy word, "Let there be light." We give Thee thanks, Thy Name we sing, Al - might - y Fa - ther, heaven - ly King.
A - MEN.

There's a Wideness in God's Mercy 50

IN BABILONE 8. 7. 8. 7. D.
Dutch Traditional Melody
Frederick W. Faber, 1854
Harmonized by Julius Röntgen (1855–1933)
May be sung in unison
1. There's a wide-ness in God's mer-cy, Like the wide-ness of the sea;
2. For the love of God is broad-er Than the meas-ure of man's mind;
There's a kind-ness in His jus-tice, Which is more than lib-er-ty.
And the heart of the E-ter-nal Is most won-der-ful-ly kind.
There is no place where earth's sor-rows Are more felt than up in heaven;
If our love were but more sim-ple, We should take Him at His word;
There is no place where earth's fail-ings Have such kind-ly judg-ment given.
And our lives would be all sun-shine In the sweet-ness of our Lord. A-MEN.

51 I Look to Thee in Every Need

O JESU 8. 6. 8. 6. 8. 8.

Samuel Longfellow, 1864 — Melody from the *Hirschberg Gesangbuch*, 1741

1. I look to Thee in ev - ery need,
2. Thy calm - ness bends se - rene a - bove,
3. Em - bos - omed deep in Thy dear love,
And nev - er look in vain; I feel Thy strong and ten - der love,
My rest - less - ness to still; A - round me flows Thy quick - ening life,
Held in Thy law, I stand; Thy hand in all things I be - hold,
And all is well a - gain: The thought of Thee is might - ier far
To nerve my fal - tering will: Thy pres - ence fills my sol - i - tude;
And all things in Thy hand; Thou lead - est me by un - sought ways,
Than sin and pain and sor - row are.
Thy prov - i - dence turns all to good.
And turn'st my mourn - ing in - to praise. A - MEN.

Father, in Thy Mysterious Presence Kneeling 52

HENLEY 11. 10. 11. 10.

Samuel Johnson, 1846
Lowell Mason, 1854
1. Fa - ther, in Thy mys - te - rious pres - ence kneel - ing,
2. Lord, we have wan - dered forth through doubt and sor - row,
3. Now, Fa - ther, now in Thy dear pres - ence kneel - ing,
Fain would our souls feel all Thy kin - dling love;
And Thou hast made each step an on - ward one;
Our spir - its yearn to feel Thy kin - dling love;
For we are weak, and need some deep re - veal - ing
And we will ev - er trust each un - known mor - row;
Now make us strong; we need Thy deep re - veal - ing
Of trust and strength and calm - ness from a - bove.
Thou wilt sus - tain us till its work is done.
Of trust and strength and calm - ness from a - bove.
A-MEN.

53 Still, Still with Thee

CONSOLATION 11. 10. 11. 10.
Harriet Beecher Stowe (1812–1896)
Arr. from Felix Mendelssohn (1809–1847)
1. Still, still with Thee, when pur - ple morn - ing break - eth,
2. A - lone with Thee, a - mid the mys - tic shad - ows,
3. Still, still with Thee! As to each new - born morn - ing
4. So shall it be at last, in that bright morn - ing,
When the bird wak - eth, and the shad - ows flee;
The sol - emn hush of na - ture new - ly born;
A fresh and sol - emn splen - dor still is given,
When the soul wak - eth and life's shad - ows flee;
Fair - er than morn - ing, love - li - er than day - light,
A - lone with Thee in breath - less ad - o - ra - tion,
So does this bless - ed con - scious - ness, a - wak - ing,
O in that hour, fair - er than day - light dawn - ing,
Dawns the sweet con - scious - ness, I am with Thee.
In the calm dew and fresh - ness of the morn.
Breathe each day near - ness un - to Thee and heaven.
Shall rise the glo - rious thought, I am with Thee.
A-MEN.

He Leadeth Me: O Blessed Thought! 54

HE LEADETH ME L. M. D.

Joseph H. Gilmore, 1862
Lines 3, 4 of Refrain Added

William B. Bradbury, 1864

1. He lead-eth me: O bless-ed thought! O words with heaven-ly com-fort fraught!
2. Some-times 'mid scenes of deep-est gloom, Some-times where E-den's bow-ers bloom,
3. Lord, I would clasp Thy hand in mine, Nor ev-er mur-mur nor re-pine;
4. And when my task on earth is done, When, by Thy grace, the vic-tory's won,
What-e'er I do, wher-e'er I be, Still 'tis God's hand that lead-eth me.
By wa-ters calm, o'er trou-bled sea, Still 'tis His hand that lead-eth me.
Con-tent, what-ev-er lot I see, Since 'tis my God that lead-eth me.
E'en death's cold wave I will not flee, Since God through Jor-dan lead-eth me.
REFRAIN
He lead-eth me, He lead-eth me; By His own hand He lead-eth me:
His faith-ful fol-lower I would be, For by His hand He lead-eth me. A-MEN.

55 We Plow the Fields

WIR PFLÜGEN 7. 6. 7. 6. D. with Refrain

Matthias Claudius, 1782
Trans. by Jane M. Campbell, 1861

Johann A. P. Schulz, 1800

1. We plow the fields, and scat - ter The good seed on the land,
2. He on - ly is the Mak - er Of all things near and far;
3. We thank Thee, then, O Fa - ther, For all things bright and good,
But it is fed and wa - tered By God's al - might - y hand;
He paints the way - side flow - er, He lights the eve - ning star;
The seed - time and the har - vest, Our life, our health, our food;
He sends the snow in win - ter, The warmth to swell the grain,
The winds and waves o - bey Him, By Him the birds are fed;
No gifts have we to of - fer, For all Thy love im - parts,
The breez - es and the sun - shine, And soft re - fresh - ing rain.
Much more to us, His chil - dren, He gives our dai - ly bread.
But that which Thou de - sir - est, Our hum - ble, thank - ful hearts.

We Plow the Fields (Concluded)

Refrain
All good gifts a - round us Are sent from heaven a - bove;
Then thank the Lord, O thank the Lord For all His love. A-men.

Lord of All Being, Throned Afar 56

LOUVAN L. M.

Oliver Wendell Holmes, 1848 — Virgil C. Taylor, 1847

1. Lord of all be - ing, throned a - far, Thy glo - ry flames from sun and star;
2. Sun of our life, Thy quick-ening ray Sheds on our path the glow of day;
3. Our mid-night is Thy smile with-drawn; Our noon-tide is Thy gra-cious dawn;
4. Grant us Thy truth to make us free, And kin-dling hearts that burn for Thee;

Cen - ter and Soul of ev - ery sphere, Yet to each lov-ing heart how near!
Star of our hope, Thy soft-ened light Cheers the long watch-es of the night.
Our rain-bow arch, Thy mer-cy's sign; All, save the clouds of sin, are Thine.
Till all Thy liv - ing al - tars claim One ho - ly light, one heaven-ly flame. A-men.

57 The King of Love My Shepherd Is

DOMINUS REGIT ME 8.7.8.7.
Psalm 23
Henry Williams Baker, 1868
John B. Dykes, 1868
1. The King of love my Shep-herd is, Whose good-ness fail-eth nev - er;
2. Where streams of liv - ing wa - ter flow My ran-somed soul He lead - eth,
3. Per - verse and fool - ish oft I strayed, But yet in love He sought me,
4. In death's dark vale I fear no ill With Thee, dear Lord, be - side me;
5. Thou spread'st a ta - ble in my sight; Thy unc - tion grace be - stow - eth;
6. And so through all the length of days Thy good-ness fail - eth nev - er:
I noth-ing lack if I am His And He is mine for - ev - er.
And where the ver-dant pas-tures grow, With food ce - les - tial feed - eth.
And on His shoul-der gen - tly laid, And home, re - joi - cing, brought me.
Thy rod and staff my com - fort still, Thy cross be - fore to guide me.
And O what trans-port of de - light From Thy pure chal - ice flow - eth!
Good Shep-herd, may I sing Thy praise With - in Thy house for - ev - er. A-MEN.
58 God Is Love; His Mercy Brightens
STUTTGART 8.7.8.7.
John Bowring, 1825
Arr. from Psalmodia Sacra, Gotha, 1715
1. God is Love; His mer - cy bright-ens All the path in which we rove;
2. Chance and change are bus - y ev - er; Man de - cays, and a - ges move;
3. E'en the hour that dark - est seem - eth Will His change-less good-ness prove;
4. He with earth - ly cares en - twin - eth Hope and com - fort from a - bove;
Bliss He wakes, and woe He light-ens: God is Wis-dom, God is Love.
But His mer - cy wan - eth nev - er: God is Wis-dom, God is Love.
From the mist His bright-ness stream-eth: God is Wis-dom, God is Love.
Ev - ery-where His glo - ry shin - eth: God is Wis-dom, God is Love. A-MEN.

Music from *The New Hymnal*, 1916. Used by permission of The Church Pension Fund.

Backward We Look, O God of All Our Days

59

GRATITUDE 10. 10. 10. 10.

Robert Freeman (1878-1940)

T. Carl Whitmer, 1929
This Arrangement, 1940

1. Back - ward we look, O God of all our days, . .
2. In - ward we look, and mar - vel at Thy power, . .
3. For - ward we look, nor fear what wait - eth there; . .
4. Up - ward we look, where march the stars and sun; . .
Guard of our youth, and Guide o'er all our ways; . .
Christ of our souls, who sav - est hour by hour; . .
On - ward we move, re - ly - ing on Thy care; . .
Up - ward we reach, whose lives are but be - gun; . . .
For life, for love, for health, for work, for food, . .
For joy - ful hearts, for ev - ery right - eous mood, . .
Know - ing Thy grace o'er us and ours shall brood, . .
Up - ward and wait, Thy mer - cies O how good! . .
Lord of our lives, . . we sing our grat - i - tude.
Lord of our lives, . . we sing our grat - i - tude.
Lord of our lives, . . we sing our grat - i - tude.
Up - ward and sing, . . O Lord, our grat - i - tude. A - MEN.

60 Watchman, Tell Us of the Night

ST. GEORGE'S, WINDSOR 7. 7. 7. 7. D.
John Bowring, 1825
George J. Elvey, 1859
1. Watch-man, tell us of the night, What its signs of prom - ise are:
2. Watch-man, tell us of the night; High - er yet that star as-cends:
3. Watch-man, tell us of the night, For the morn - ing seems to dawn:
Trav - eler, o'er yon moun-tain's height, See that glo - ry - beam - ing star!
Trav - eler, bless - ed - ness and light, Peace and truth, its course por - tends.
Trav - eler, dark - ness takes its flight; Doubt and ter - ror are with - drawn.
Watch - man, doth its beau - teous ray Aught of joy or hope fore - tell?
Watch - man, will its beams a - lone Gild the spot that gave them birth?
Watch - man, let thy wan-derings cease; Hie thee to thy qui - et home.
Trav - eler, yes; it brings the day, Prom-ised day of Is - ra - el!
Trav - eler, a - ges are its own, And it bursts o'er all the earth!
Trav - eler, lo, the Prince of Peace, Lo, the Son of God is come! A-MEN.

Alternative tune, "Aberystwyth," number 151.

Hail to the Lord's Anointed

TOURS 7.6.7.6.D.

From Psalm 72
James Montgomery, 1821

Berthold Tours, 1872

1. Hail to the Lord's A - noint - ed, Great Da - vid's great - er Son!
2. He shall come down like show - ers Up - on the fruit - ful earth;
3. Kings shall fall down be - fore Him, And gold and in - cense bring;
4. O'er ev - ery foe vic - to - rious, He on His throne shall rest,
Hail, in the time ap - point - ed, His reign on earth be - gun!
And love, joy, hope, like flow - ers, Spring in His path to birth;
All na - tions shall a - dore Him, His praise all peo - ple sing;
From age to age more glo - rious, All - bless - ing and all - blest;
He comes to break op - pres - sion, To set the cap - tive free,
Be - fore Him on the moun - tains Shall peace, the her - ald, go;
For Him shall prayer un - ceas - ing And dai - ly vows as - cend;
The tide of time shall nev - er His cov - e - nant re - move;
To take a - way trans - gres - sion, And rule in eq - ui - ty.
And right - eous - ness, in foun - tains, From hill to val - ley flow.
His King - dom still in - creas - ing, A King - dom with - out end.
His Name shall stand for - ev - er— That Name to us is Love.
A - MEN.

62 Come, Thou Long-expected Jesus

HYFRYDOL 8.7.8.7.D.
Charles Wesley, 1744
Rowland Hugh Prichard (1811–1887)
1. Come, Thou long - ex - pect - ed Je - sus, Born to set Thy peo - ple free;
2. Born Thy peo - ple to de - liv - er, Born a child and yet a King,
From our fears and sins re - lease us; Let us find our rest in Thee.
Born to reign in us for - ev - er, Now Thy gra - cious King-dom bring.
Is - rael's Strength and Con - so - la - tion, Hope of all the earth Thou art;
By Thine own e - ter - nal Spir - it Rule in all our hearts a - lone;
Dear De - sire of ev - ery na - tion, Joy of ev - ery long - ing heart.
By Thine all - suf - fi - cient mer - it Raise us to Thy glo - rious throne. A-MEN.

O Come, O Come, Emmanuel

63

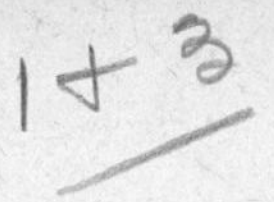
1 & 3

VENI EMMANUEL 8. 8. 8. 8. 8. 8.
From the Latin, Twelfth Century
Stanza 1 Trans. by John Mason Neale, 1851
Stanzas 2, 3 Trans. by Henry S. Coffin, 1916
Ancient Plain Song
Thirteenth Century
Harmonized by J. F. Ohl, 1917
Unison
1. O come, O come, Em - man - u - el, And ran - som cap - tive
2. O come, Thou Wis - dom from on high, And or - der all things
3. O come, De - sire of na - tions, bind All peo - ples in one
Is - ra - el, That mourns in lone - ly ex - ile here
far and nigh; To us the path of knowl - edge show,
heart and mind; Bid en - vy, strife, and quar - rels cease;
Harmony
Un - til the Son of God ap - pear. Re - joice! Re - joice! Em -
And cause us in her ways to go. Re - joice! Re - joice! Em -
Fill the whole world with heav - en's peace. Re - joice! Re - joice! Em -
man - u - el Shall come to thee, O Is - ra - el!
man - u - el Shall come to thee, O Is - ra - el!
man - u - el Shall come to thee, O Is - ra - el! A-MEN.
No amen

64 It Came Upon the Midnight Clear

CAROL C. M. D.
Edmund H. Sears, 1850
Richard S. Willis, 1850
1. It came up-on the mid-night clear, That glo-rious song of old,
2. Still through the clo-ven skies they come, With peace-ful wings un-furled,
3. And ye, be-neath life's crush-ing load, Whose forms are bend-ing low,
4. For, lo, the days are has-tening on, By proph-et bards fore-told,
From an-gels bend-ing near the earth, To touch their harps of gold:
And still their heaven-ly mu-sic floats O'er all the wea-ry world:
Who toil a-long the climb-ing way With pain-ful steps and slow,
When with the ev-er-cir-cling years Comes round the age of gold;
"Peace on the earth, good will to men, From heaven's all-gra-cious King":
A-bove its sad and low-ly plains They bend on hov-ering wing,
Look now! for glad and gold-en hours Come swift-ly on the wing:
When peace shall o-ver all the earth Its an-cient splen-dors fling,
The world in sol-emn still-ness lay, To hear the an-gels sing.
And ev-er o'er its Ba-bel sounds The bless-ed an-gels sing.
O rest be-side the wea-ry road, And hear the an-gels sing!
And the whole world give back the song Which now the an-gels sing.
A-MEN.

Joy to the World!

ANTIOCH C. M.

From Psalm 98
Isaac Watts, 1719

Georg Friedrich Handel, 1742

1. Joy to the world! the Lord is come: Let earth re -
2. Joy to the earth! the Sav - iour reigns: Let men their
3. No more let sins and sor - rows grow, Nor thorns in -
4. He rules the world with truth and grace, And makes the

ceive her King; Let ev - ery heart pre - pare Him room,
songs em - ploy; While fields and floods, rocks, hills, and plains
fest the ground; He comes to make His bless - ings flow
na - tions prove The glo - ries of His right - eous - ness,

And heaven and na - ture sing, And heaven and na - ture
Re - peat the sound - ing joy, Re - peat the sound - ing
Far as the curse is found, Far as the curse is
And won - ders of His love, And won - ders of His

And heaven and na - ture sing, ...
Re - peat the sound - ing joy, ...
Far as the curse is found, ...
And won - ders of His love, ...

And
Re -
Far
And

sing, And heaven, and heaven and na - ture sing.
joy, Re - peat, re - peat the sound - ing joy.
found, Far as, far as the curse is found.
love, And won - ders, won - ders of His love. A-MEN.

heaven and na - ture sing,
peat the sound - ing joy,
as the curse is found,
won - ders of His love,

66 O Little Town of Bethlehem

ST. LOUIS 8. 6. 8. 6. 7. 6. 8. 6.
Phillips Brooks, 1868
Lewis H. Redner, 1868
1. O lit - tle town of Beth - le - hem, How still we see thee lie!
2. For Christ is born of Ma - ry; And gath - ered all a - bove,
3. How si - lent - ly, how si - lent - ly The won - drous gift is given!
4. O ho - ly Child of Beth - le - hem, De - scend to us, we pray!
A - bove thy deep and dream-less sleep The si - lent stars go by.
While mor - tals sleep, the an - gels keep Their watch of won-dering love.
So God im - parts to hu - man hearts The bless - ings of His heaven.
Cast out our sin, and en - ter in, Be born in us to - day.
Yet in thy dark streets shin - eth The ev - er - last - ing Light;
O morn - ing stars, to - geth - er Pro - claim the ho - ly birth;
No ear may hear His com - ing, But in this world of sin,
We hear the Christ - mas an - gels The great glad ti - dings tell;
The hopes and fears of all the years Are met in thee to-night.
And prais - es sing to God the King, And peace to men on earth.
Where meek souls will re - ceive Him still, The dear Christ en - ters in.
O come to us, a - bide with us, Our Lord Em - man - u - el! A - MEN.

While Shepherds Watched Their Flocks by Night 67

CHRISTMAS C. M.
Nahum Tate, 1702
Georg Friedrich Handel, 1728
1. While shep - herds watched their flocks by night,
2. "Fear not," said he — for might - y dread
3. "To you, in Da - vid's town this day,
4. "The heaven - ly Babe you there shall find
All seat - ed on the ground, The an - gel of the Lord came down,
Had seized their trou - bled mind— "Glad ti - dings of great joy I bring
Is born of Da - vid's line, A Sav - iour, who is Christ the Lord,
To hu - man view dis - played, All mean-ly wrapped in swath-ing bands,
And glo - ry shone a - round, And glo - ry shone a - round.
To you and all man - kind, To you and all man - kind.
And this shall be the sign: And this shall be the sign:
And in a man - ger laid, And in a man - ger laid." A-MEN.

5. Thus spake the seraph, and forthwith
   Appeared a shining throng
   Of angels praising God, and thus
   Addressed their joyful song:

6. "All glory be to God on high,
   And to the earth be peace:
   Good will henceforth, from heaven to men,
   Begin and never cease!"

68 Hark! the Herald Angels Sing

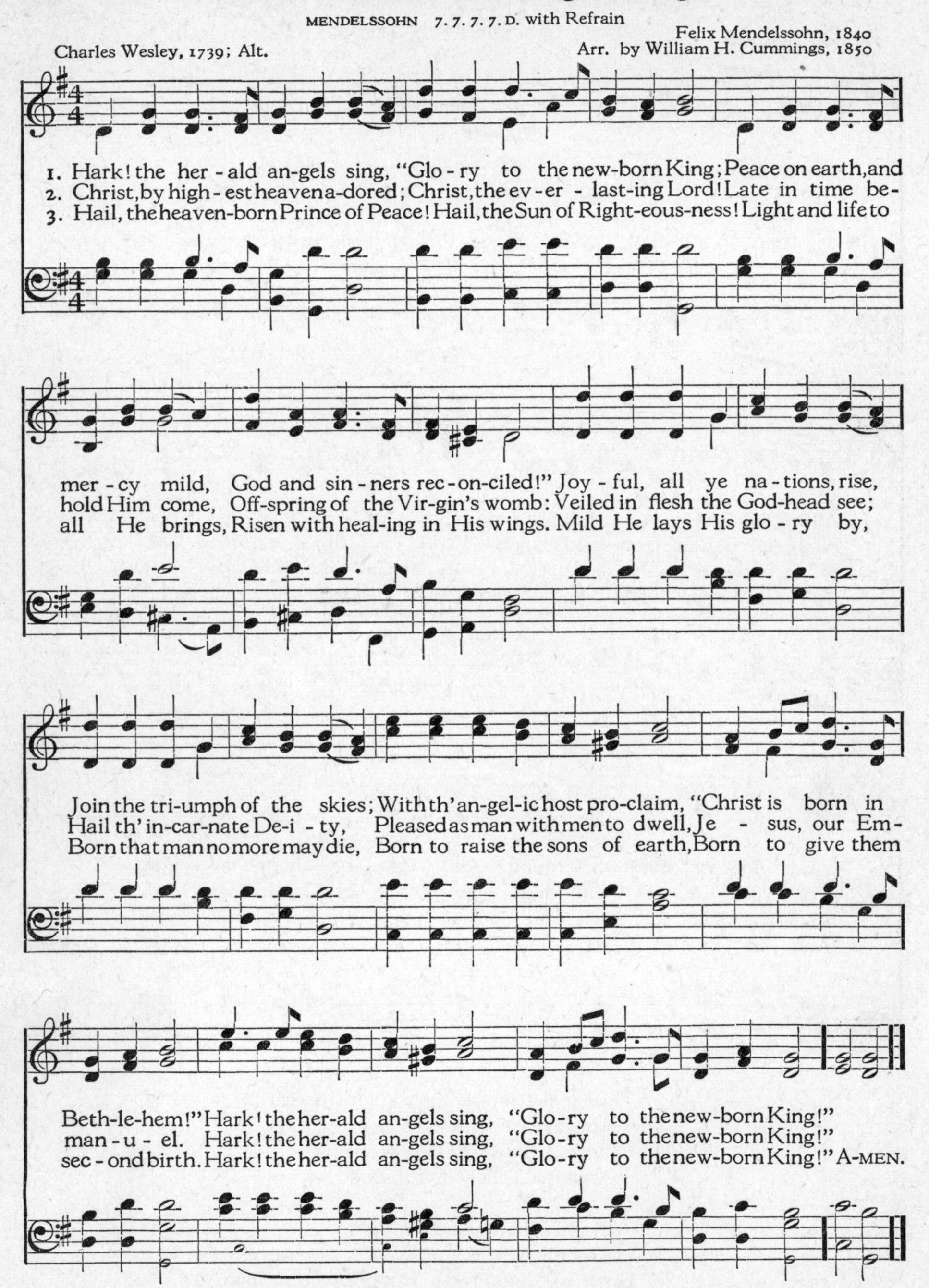
MENDELSSOHN 7.7.7.7.D. with Refrain
Felix Mendelssohn, 1840
Charles Wesley, 1739; Alt.
Arr. by William H. Cummings, 1850
1. Hark! the her - ald an-gels sing, "Glo - ry to the new-born King; Peace on earth, and
2. Christ, by high - est heaven a-dored; Christ, the ev - er - last-ing Lord! Late in time be-
3. Hail, the heaven-born Prince of Peace! Hail, the Sun of Right-eous-ness! Light and life to
mer - cy mild, God and sin - ners rec-on-ciled!" Joy - ful, all ye na - tions, rise,
hold Him come, Off-spring of the Vir-gin's womb: Veiled in flesh the God-head see;
all He brings, Risen with heal-ing in His wings. Mild He lays His glo - ry by,
Join the tri-umph of the skies; With th' an-gel-ic host pro-claim, "Christ is born in
Hail th' in-car-nate De-i - ty, Pleased as man with men to dwell, Je - sus, our Em-
Born that man no more may die, Born to raise the sons of earth, Born to give them
Beth-le-hem!" Hark! the her-ald an-gels sing, "Glo-ry to the new-born King!"
man - u - el. Hark! the her-ald an-gels sing, "Glo-ry to the new-born King!"
sec - ond birth. Hark! the her-ald an-gels sing, "Glo-ry to the new-born King!" A-MEN.

Angels, from the Realms of Glory

REGENT SQUARE 8. 7. 8. 7. with Refrain

James Montgomery, 1816, 1825 — Henry Smart, 1867

1. An - gels, from the realms of glo - ry, Wing your flight o'er
2. Shep - herds, in the fields a - bid - ing, Watch - ing o'er your
3. Sa - ges, leave your con - tem - pla - tions, Bright - er vi - sions
4. Saints, be - fore the al - tar bend - ing, Watch - ing long in

all the earth; Ye who sang cre - a - tion's sto - ry,
flocks by night, God with man is now re - sid - ing,
beam a - far; Seek the great De - sire of na - tions;
hope and fear, Sud - den - ly the Lord, de - scend - ing,

Now pro - claim Mes - si - ah's birth:
Yon - der shines the in - fant Light:
Ye have seen His na - tal star:
In His tem - ple shall ap - pear:

REFRAIN

Come and wor - ship,
Come and wor - ship, Wor - ship Christ, the new - born King! A-MEN.

70 The First Nowell the Angel Did Say

THE FIRST NOWELL Irregular, with Refrain

Old English Carol

Traditional Melody in W. Sandys' *Christmas Carols*, 1833
Descant by Kathryn Reese O'Boyle, 1940

Descant
1. The first Now-ell the an-gel did say, Was to cer-tain poor shep-herds, in fields as they lay, In fields where they lay a-keep-ing their sheep, On a cold win-ter's night that was so deep.
2. They look-ed up and saw a star Shin-ing in the east be-yond them far, And to the earth it gave great light, And so it con-tin-ued both day and night.
3. And by the light of that same star, Three Wise Men came from a coun-try a-far, To seek for a king was their in-tent, And to fol-low the star wher-ev-er it went.
4. This star drew nigh to the north-west, O'er Beth-le-hem then it took its rest, And there it did both stop and stay, Right o-ver the place where Je-sus lay.

The First Nowell the Angel Did Say (Concluded)

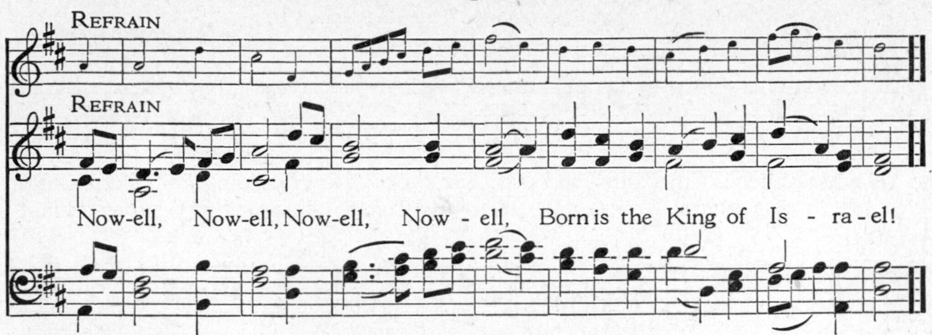
REFRAIN
REFRAIN
Now-ell, Now-ell, Now-ell, Now - ell, Born is the King of Is - ra - el!

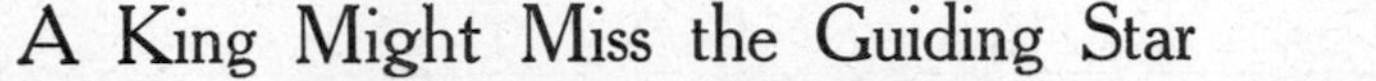

A King Might Miss the Guiding Star 71

BETHLEHEM ROAD 8. 7. 8. 7. 8. 7. Iambic

Louis F. Benson, 1921 | Calvin W. Laufer, 1925

1. A king might miss the guid - ing star, A Wise Man's foot might stum - ble;
2. Some pil-grims seek a hal-lowed shrine; Some sol - diers march to dan - ger;
3. There is no pal - ace in that place, Nor an - y seat of learn - ing,
4. But he who gets to Beth - le - hem Shall hear the ox - en low - ing;
For Beth - le - hem is ver - y far From all ex - cept the hum - ble.
Some trav - elers seek an inn— its sign, "The Ba - by in a Man - ger."
No hill - top vi - sion of God's face, No al - tar can - dles burn - ing.
And, if he hum - bly kneel with them, May catch far trum - pets blow - ing:
'Tis Christ - mas Day! 'Tis Christ - mas Day! And Christ - mas hearts are hum - ble.
When Christ was born on Christ - mas morn, They laid Him in a man - ger.
O come and see our Christ - mas tree And Christ - mas can - dles burn - ing.
From far a - way, on Christ - mas Day, May hear God's trum - pets blow - ing. A - MEN.

72 What Child Is This, Who, Laid to Rest

GREENSLEEVES 8. 7. 8. 7. with Refrain
William C. Dix (1837-1898)
Old English Melody
Unison
1. What Child is this, who, laid to rest, On Ma-ry's lap is sleep-ing?
2. So bring Him in-cense, gold, and myrrh; Come, peas-ant, king, to own Him;
Whom an-gels greet with an-thems sweet, While shep-herds watch are keep-ing?
The King of kings sal-va-tion brings: Let lov-ing hearts en-throne Him.
Refrain Unison or Harmony
This, this is Christ the King, Whom shep-herds guard and an-gels sing:
Haste, haste to bring Him laud, The Babe, the Son of Ma-ry. A-men.

Silent Night! Holy Night! 73

STILLE NACHT Irregular
Joseph Mohr, 1818
Translation from Several Sources
Franz Grüber, 1818
1. Si - lent night! ho - ly night! All is dark, save the light Yon - der, where they sweet vig - il keep O'er the Babe, who in si - lent sleep Rests in heav - en - ly peace, Rests in heav - en - ly peace.
2. Si - lent night! ho - ly night! Dark - ness flies, all is light; Shep - herds hear the an - gels sing: "Al - le - lu - ia! hail the King! Christ the Sav - iour is born! Christ the Sav - iour is born!"
3. Si - lent night! ho - ly night! Son of God, love's pure light Ra - diant beams from Thy ho - ly face, With the dawn of re - deem - ing grace, Je - sus, Lord, at Thy birth, Je - sus, Lord, at Thy birth.
4. Si - lent night! ho - ly night! Won - drous star, lend thy light! With the an - gels let us sing Al - le - lu - ia to our King; Christ the Sav - iour is born, Christ the Sav - iour is born!
A - MEN.

74 O Come, All Ye Faithful

ADESTE FIDELES Irregular
From the Latin, Eighteenth Century
Trans. by Frederick Oakeley, 1841; Alt.
J. F. Wade's
Cantus Diversi, 1751
Descant by Lawrence Curry, 1940
Descant
1. O come, all ye faith - ful, Joy - ful and tri - um - phant,
2. O sing, choirs of an - gels; Sing in ex - ul - ta - tion,
3. All hail! Lord, we greet Thee, Born this hap - py morn - ing:
O come ye, O come ye to Beth - le - hem; Come and be - hold Him,
O sing, all ye cit - i - zens of heav - en a - bove; Glo - ry to God, all
O Je - sus, to Thee be all glo - ry given; Word of the Fa - ther,
O come. . . . . a - dore. . . .
REFRAIN
Born the King of an - gels; O come, let us a - dore Him, O come, let us a -
Glo - ry in the high - est;
Now in flesh ap - pear - ing;

O Come, All Ye Faithful (Concluded)

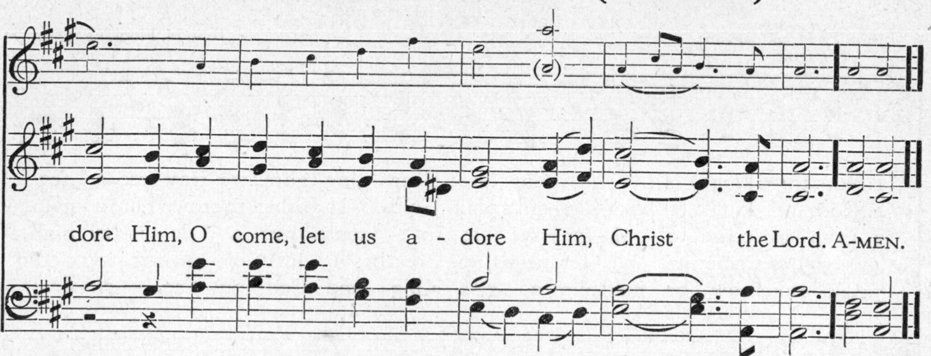
dore Him, O come, let us a - dore Him, Christ the Lord. A-MEN.

Away in a Manger 75

MUELLER 11. 11. 11. 11.

Martin Luther, 1530

Carl Mueller

1. A - way in a man - ger, no crib for His bed, The lit - tle Lord
2. The cat - tle are low - ing, the poor Ba - by wakes, But lit - tle Lord
Je - sus laid down His sweet head. The stars in the sky looked
Je - sus, no cry - ing He makes. I love Thee,Lord Je - sus, look
down where He lay, The lit - tle Lord Je - sus, a - sleep on the hay.
down from the sky, And stay by my side un - til morn-ing is nigh. A-MEN.

76 We Three Kings of Orient Are

KINGS OF ORIENT 8. 8. 8. 6. with Refrain

John H. Hopkins, 1862 — John H. Hopkins, 1862

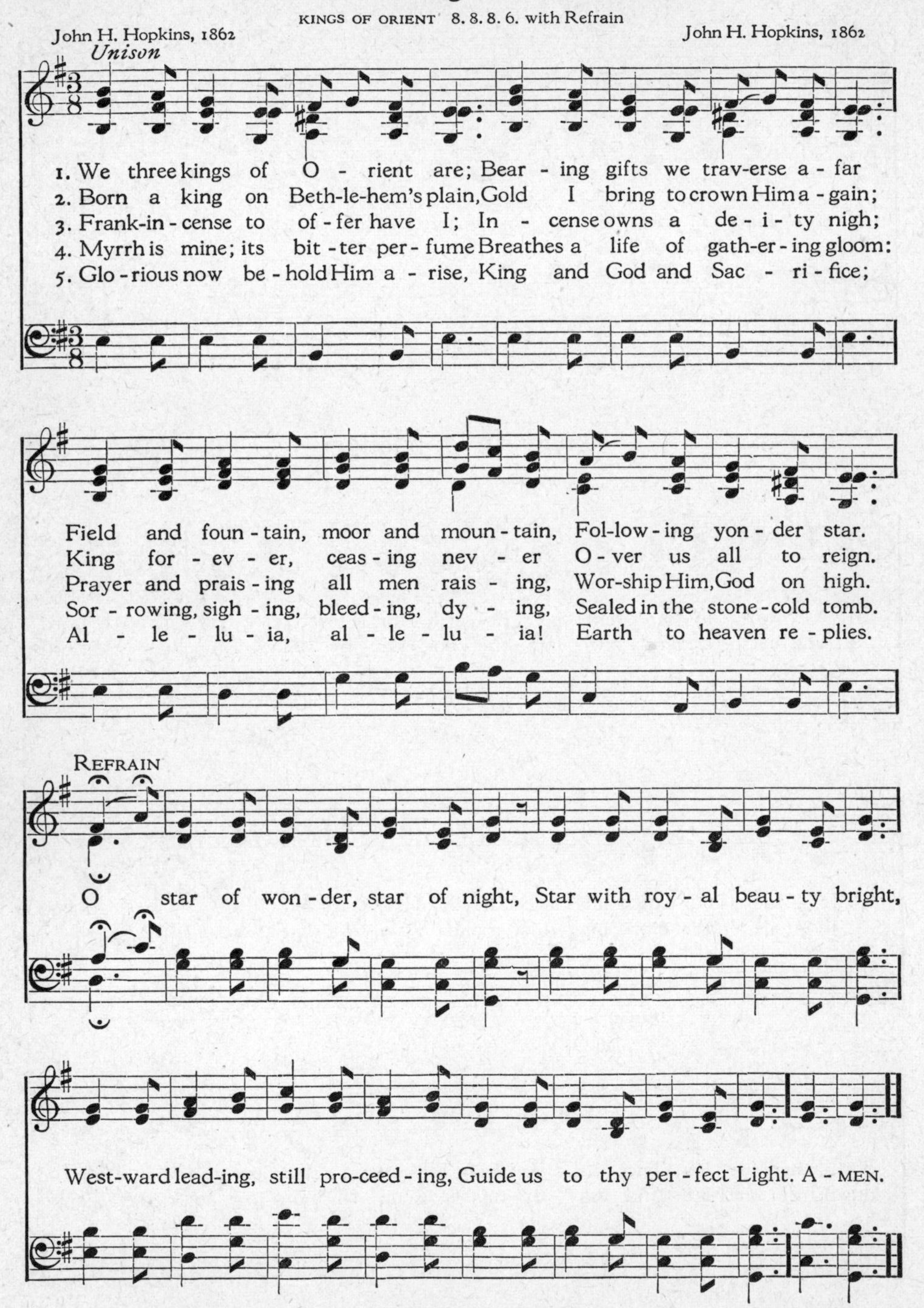
Unison
1. We three kings of O - rient are; Bear - ing gifts we trav-erse a - far
2. Born a king on Beth-le-hem's plain, Gold I bring to crown Him a - gain;
3. Frank-in - cense to of - fer have I; In - cense owns a de - i - ty nigh;
4. Myrrh is mine; its bit - ter per - fume Breathes a life of gath-er - ing gloom:
5. Glo - rious now be - hold Him a - rise, King and God and Sac - ri - fice;
Field and foun - tain, moor and moun - tain, Fol-low - ing yon - der star.
King for - ev - er, ceas - ing nev - er O - ver us all to reign.
Prayer and prais - ing all men rais - ing, Wor-ship Him, God on high.
Sor - rowing, sigh - ing, bleed - ing, dy - ing, Sealed in the stone - cold tomb.
Al - le - lu - ia, al - le - lu - ia! Earth to heaven re - plies.
REFRAIN
O star of won - der, star of night, Star with roy - al beau - ty bright,
West-ward lead-ing, still pro-ceed - ing, Guide us to thy per - fect Light. A - MEN.

As with Gladness Men of Old

DIX 7.7.7.7.7.7.
William C. Dix, 1861
Arr. from Conrad Kocher, 1838
1. As with glad - ness men of old Did the guid - ing
2. As with joy - ful steps they sped To that low - ly
3. As they of - fered gifts most rare At that man - ger
4. Ho - ly Je - sus, ev - ery day Keep us in the
star be - hold; As with joy they hailed its light,
man - ger bed, There to bend the knee be - fore
rude and bare; So may we with ho - ly joy,
nar - row way; And, when earth - ly things are past,
Lead - ing on - ward, beam - ing bright; So, most gra - cious
Him whom heaven and earth a - dore; So may we with
Pure, and free from sin's al - loy, All our cost - liest
Bring our ran - somed souls at last Where they need no
God, may we Ev - er - more be led by Thee.
will - ing feet Ev - er seek Thy mer - cy seat.
treas - ures bring, Christ, to Thee, our heaven - ly King.
star to guide, Where no clouds Thy glo - ry hide.
A-MEN.

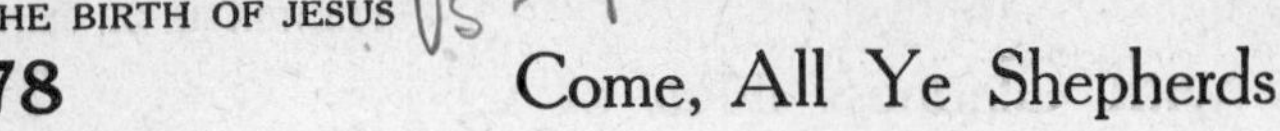

78 Come, All Ye Shepherds

KOMMET IHR HIRTEN 10. 10. 10. 10. 4.

Trans. by Mari Ruef Hofer, 1912

Bohemian Folk Song

1. Come, all ye shep - herds, ye chil - dren of earth,
2. Has - ten then, has - ten to Beth - le - hem's stall,
3. An - gels and shep - herds to - geth - er we go,
Come, come,
Haste to
So to-
Come ye, bring greet - ings to yon heaven - ly birth.
There to dis - cov - er the heav - en - ly call.
Seek - ing this Sav - iour from all earth - ly woe;
Come, greet
Seek the
Saved from
For Christ the Lord un - to us is giv - en, Whom God for Sav - iour
With ho - ly feel - ing there hum - bly kneel - ing We will a - dore Him,
While an - gels wing - ing, His prais - es sing - ing, Heaven's ech - oes ring - ing,
sent down from heav - en: Fear ye Him not!
bow down be - fore Him, Wor - ship the King.
peace on earth bring - ing, Good will to men.
A - MEN.
No amen

There's a Song in the Air

CHRISTMAS SONG 6. 6. 6. 6. 12. 12.

Josiah G. Holland, 1872 — Karl P. Harrington, 1904

1. There's a song in the air! There's a star in the sky! There's a moth - er's deep prayer And a ba - by's low cry! And the star rains its fire while the beau - ti - ful sing, For the man - ger of Beth - le - hem cra - dles a King.
2. There's a tu - mult of joy O'er the won - der - ful birth! For the Vir - gin's sweet Boy Is the Lord of the earth. Aye! the star rains its fire and the beau - ti - ful sing, For the man - ger of Beth - le - hem cra - dles a King.
3. In the light of that star Lie the a - ges im - pearled; And that song from a - far Has swept o - ver the world. Ev - ery hearth is a - flame, and the beau - ti - ful sing In the homes of the na - tions that Je - sus is King.
4. We re - joice in the light, And we ech - o the song That comes down through the night From the heav - en - ly throng; Aye! we shout to the love - ly e - van - gel they bring, And we greet in His cra - dle our Sav - iour and King.
A - MEN.

80 Good Christian Men, Rejoice

IN DULCI JUBILO 6. 6. 7. 9. 7. 8. 5. 5.
From the Latin, Medieval
Trans. by John Mason Neale, 1853
Fourteenth Century German Melody
Harmonized by John Stainer, 1867
1. Good Chris-tian men, re - joice . . With heart, and soul, and voice; . .
2. Good Chris-tian men, re - joice . . With heart, and soul, and voice; . .
3. Good Chris-tian men, re - joice . . With heart, and soul, and voice; . .
Give ye heed to what we say: News! news! Je - sus Christ is born to-day:
Now ye hear of end - less bliss: Joy! joy! Je - sus Christ was born for this!
Now ye need not fear the grave: Peace! peace! Je - sus Christ was born to save!
Ox and ass be - fore Him bow, And He is in the man - ger now.
He has oped the heaven-ly door, And man is bless - ed ev - er - more.
Calls you one and calls you all, To gain His ev - er - last - ing hall.
Christ is born to - day! . . Christ is born to - day!
Christ was born for this! . . Christ was born for this!
Christ was born to save! . . Christ was born to save!
A-MEN.

Shepherds! Shake Off Your Drowsy Sleep

BESANÇON CAROL 8. 7. 9. 8. with Refrain
From the French
Harmonized by Lawrence Curry, 1940
1. Shep-herds! shake off your drow-sy sleep, Rise and leave your sil-ly sheep; An-gels from heaven a-round loud sing-ing, Ti-dings of great joy are bring-ing.
2. Hark! e-ven now the bells ring round, Lis-ten to their mer-ry sound; Hark! how the birds new songs are mak-ing, As if win-ter's chains were break-ing.
3. Com-eth at length the age of peace, Strife and sor-row now shall cease; Proph-ets fore-told the won-drous sto-ry Of this heaven-born Prince of Glo-ry.
4. Shep-herds! then up and quick a-way, Seek the Babe ere break of day; He is the Hope of ev-ery na-tion, All in Him shall find sal-va-tion.
REFRAIN
Shep-herds! the cho-rus come and swell! Sing Now-ell, O sing Now-ell!
Shep-herds, the cho-rus come and swell,
Sing Now-ell,

82 While by My Sheep

JÜNGST Irregular
Seventeenth Century Carol
From the German
Arr. by Hugo Jüngst (1853–1923); Alt.
1. While by my sheep I watched at night, Glad ti - dings brought an an - gel bright. How great my joy! Great my joy! Joy, joy, joy! Joy, joy, joy! Praise we the Lord in heaven on high! Praise we the Lord in heaven on high!
2. There shall be born, so he did say, In Beth - le - hem a Child to - day; How great my joy! Great my joy! Joy, joy, joy! Joy, joy, joy! Praise we the Lord in heaven on high! Praise we the Lord in heaven on high!
3. There shall the Child lie in a stall, This Child who shall re - deem us all. How great our joy! Great our joy! Joy, joy, joy! Joy, joy, joy! Praise we the Lord in heaven on high! Praise we the Lord in heaven on high!
4. This gift of God we'll cher - ish well, That ev - er joy our hearts shall fill. How great our joy! Great our joy! Joy, joy, joy! Joy, joy, joy! Praise we the Lord in heaven on high! Praise we the Lord in heaven on high!
f
p echo
f
p echo
f
p echo

The Hidden Years at Nazareth! 83

BETHLEHEM C. M. D.
Allen Eastman Cross, 1926
Gottfried W. Fink, 1842
1. The hid - den years at Naz - a - reth! How deep and still they seem,
2. The hid - den years at Naz - a - reth! How clear and true they lie,
3. The hid - den years at Naz - a - reth! How ra - di - ant they rise,
Like riv - ers flow - ing in the dark Or wa - ters in a dream!
As o - pen to the smile of God As to the Syr - ian sky!
With life and death in bal - ance laid Be - fore a Lad's clear eyes!
Like wa - ters un - der Syr - ian stars Re - flect - ing lights a - bove,
As o - pen to the heart of man As to the gen - ial sun,
O soul of youth, for - ev - er choose, For - get - ting fate or fear,
Re - peat - ing in their si - lent depths The won - der of God's love!
With dreams of vast ad - ven - tur - ing, And deeds of kind - ness done!
To live for truth or die with God, Who stands be - side thee here! A-MEN.

84 We Would See Jesus

CUSHMAN 11. 10. 11. 10.

J. Edgar Park, 1913 — Herbert B. Turner, 1905; Alt.

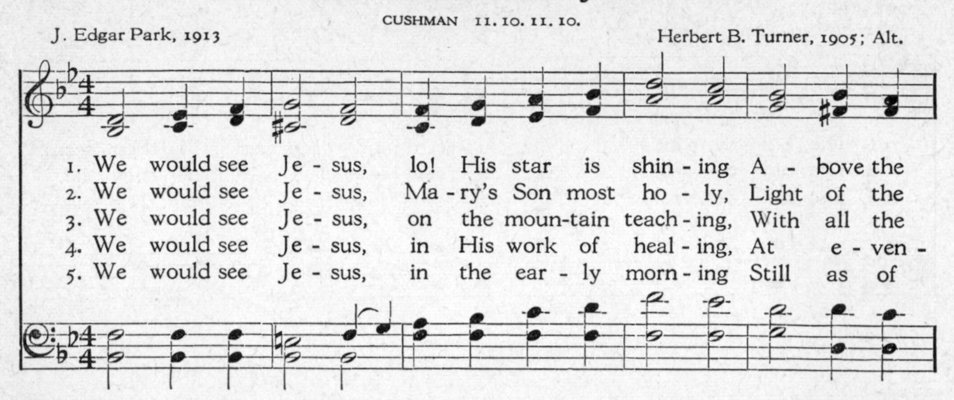
1. We would see Je - sus, lo! His star is shin - ing A - bove the
2. We would see Je - sus, Ma - ry's Son most ho - ly, Light of the
3. We would see Je - sus, on the moun-tain teach - ing, With all the
4. We would see Je - sus, in His work of heal - ing, At e - ven -
5. We would see Je - sus, in the ear - ly morn - ing Still as of

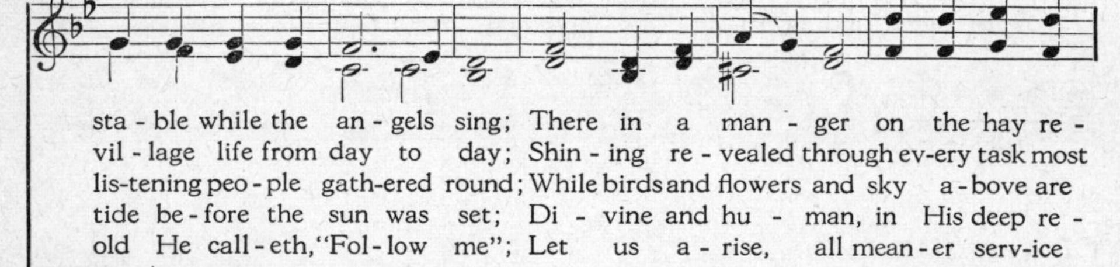
sta - ble while the an - gels sing; There in a man - ger on the hay re -
vil - lage life from day to day; Shin - ing re - vealed through ev-ery task most
lis-tening peo - ple gath-ered round; While birds and flowers and sky a - bove are
tide be - fore the sun was set; Di - vine and hu - man, in His deep re -
old He call - eth, "Fol - low me"; Let us a - rise, all mean - er serv-ice

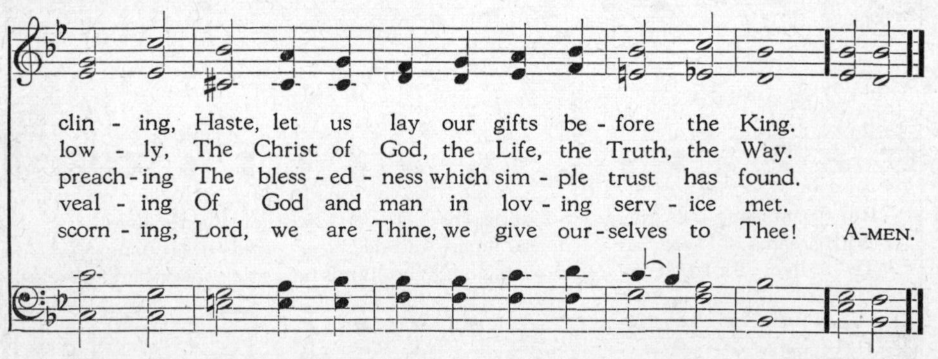
clin - ing, Haste, let us lay our gifts be - fore the King.
low - ly, The Christ of God, the Life, the Truth, the Way.
preach - ing The bless - ed - ness which sim - ple trust has found.
veal - ing Of God and man in lov - ing serv - ice met.
scorn - ing, Lord, we are Thine, we give our - selves to Thee! A-MEN.

O Master Workman of the Race

AMESBURY C. M. D.

Jay T. Stocking, 1912 — Uzziah C. Burnap, 1895

1. O Mas - ter Work-man of the race, Thou Man of Gal - i - lee,
2. O Car - pen - ter of Naz - a - reth, Build - er of life di - vine,
3. O Thou who dost the vi - sion send And giv - est each his task,
Who with the eyes of ear - ly youth E - ter - nal things didst see,
Who shap - est man to God's own law, Thy - self the fair de - sign,
And with the task suf - fi - cient strength, Show us Thy will, we ask;
We thank Thee for Thy boy - hood faith That shone Thy whole life through:
Build us a tower of Christ - like height, That we the land may view,
Give us a con-science bold and good, Give us a pur - pose true,
"Did ye not know it is my work, My Fa-ther's work to do?"
And see, like Thee, our no - blest work, Our Fa-ther's work to do.
That it may be our high - est joy Our Fa-ther's work to do.
A-MEN.

86 When the Golden Evening Gathered

STOCKWELL, NEW 8. 7. 11. 8. 7. 11.
William J. Dawson (1854–1928)
Calvin W. Laufer, 1928
1. When the gold - en eve - ning gath - ered On the shore of Gal - i - lee,
2. Not in robes of pur - ple splen - dor, Not in silk - en soft - ness shod,
3. For He healed their sick at e - ven, And He cured the lep - er's sore,
4. Not in robes of pur - ple splen - dor, But in lives that do His will,
When the fish - ing boats lay qui - et by the sea,
But in rai - ment worn with trav - el came their God;
So that sin - ful men and wom - en sinned no more;
And in pa - tient acts of kind - ness He comes still;
Long a - go the peo - ple won - dered, Though no sign was in the sky,
And the peo - ple knew His pres - ence By the heart that ceased to sigh
And the world grew mirth - ful - heart - ed, And for - got its mis - er - y
And the peo - ple cry with won - der, Though no sign is in the sky,
For the glo - ry of the Lord was pass - ing by.
When the glo - ry of the Lord was pass - ing by.
When the glo - ry of the Lord was pass - ing by.
That the glo - ry of the Lord is pass - ing by. A - MEN.

My Master Was So Very Poor 87

MY MASTER [Day] L. M.

Harry Lee (1875-) George Henry Day, 1929

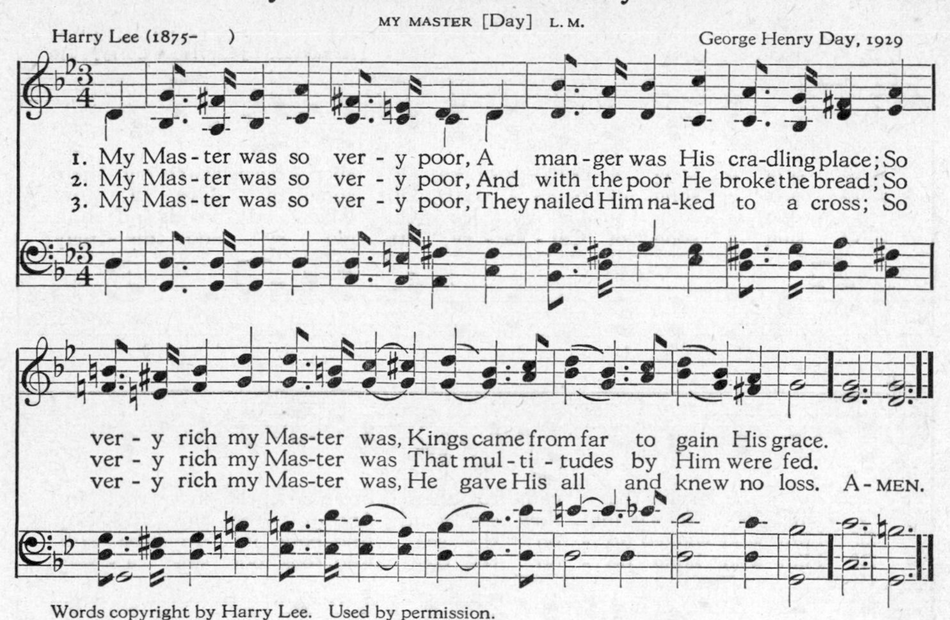
1. My Mas-ter was so ver-y poor, A man-ger was His cra-dling place; So
2. My Mas-ter was so ver-y poor, And with the poor He broke the bread; So
3. My Mas-ter was so ver-y poor, They nailed Him na-ked to a cross; So
ver-y rich my Mas-ter was, Kings came from far to gain His grace.
ver-y rich my Mas-ter was That mul-ti-tudes by Him were fed.
ver-y rich my Mas-ter was, He gave His all and knew no loss. A-MEN.

By Roads That Wound Uphill and Down 88

QUEBEC L. M.

Louis F. Benson, 1927 Henry Baker, 1862

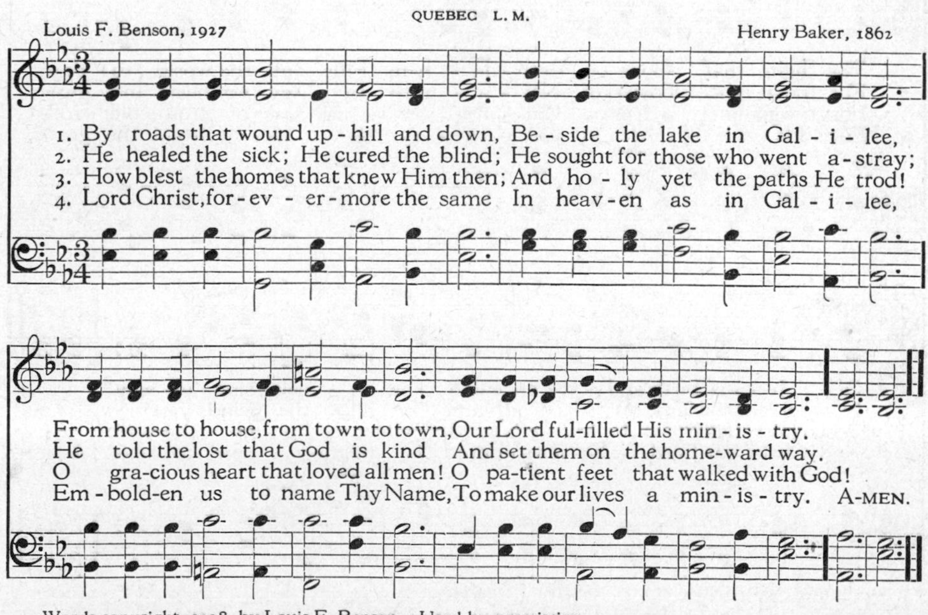
1. By roads that wound up-hill and down, Be-side the lake in Gal-i-lee,
2. He healed the sick; He cured the blind; He sought for those who went a-stray;
3. How blest the homes that knew Him then; And ho-ly yet the paths He trod!
4. Lord Christ, for-ev-er-more the same In heav-en as in Gal-i-lee,
From house to house, from town to town, Our Lord ful-filled His min-is-try.
He told the lost that God is kind And set them on the home-ward way.
O gra-cious heart that loved all men! O pa-tient feet that walked with God!
Em-bold-en us to name Thy Name, To make our lives a min-is-try. A-MEN.

89 O Sing a Song of Bethlehem

KINGSFOLD C. M. D.

Louis F. Benson (1855-1930)

English Traditional Melody
Harmonized by Lawrence Curry, 1940

1. O sing a song of Beth-le-hem, Of shep-herds watch-ing there,
And of the news that came to them From an-gels in the air:
The light that shone on Beth-le-hem Fills all the world to-day;
Of Je-sus' birth and peace on earth The an-gels sing al-way.
2. O sing a song of Naz-a-reth, Of sun-ny days of joy,
O sing of fra-grant flow-ers' breath, And of the sin-less Boy:
For now the flowers of Naz-a-reth In ev-ery heart may grow;
Now spreads the fame of His dear Name On all the winds that blow.
3. O sing a song of Gal-i-lee, Of lake and woods and hill,
Of Him who walked up-on the sea And bade its waves be still:
For though, like waves on Gal-i-lee, Dark seas of trou-ble roll,
When faith has heard the Mas-ter's word, Falls peace up-on the soul.
4. O sing a song of Cal-va-ry, Its glo-ry and dis-may;
Of Him who hung up-on the tree, And took our sins a-way:
For He who died on Cal-va-ry Is ris-en from the grave,
And Christ, our Lord, by heaven a-dored, Is might-y now to save. A-MEN.

All Glory, Laud, and Honor

ST. THEODULPH 7. 6. 7. 6. D.
Theodulph of Orleans, c. 820
Trans. by John M. Neale, 1854; Alt.
Melchior Teschner, c. 1615
1. All glo - ry, laud, and hon - or To Thee, Re - deem - er, King,
2. The com - pa - ny of an - gels Are prais - ing Thee on high,
3. To Thee, be - fore Thy Pas - sion, They sang their hymns of praise;
To whom the lips of chil - dren Made sweet ho - san - nas ring.
And mor - tal men, and all things Cre - a - ted, make re - ply.
To Thee, now high ex - alt - ed, Our mel - o - dy we raise.
Thou art the King of Is - ra - el, Thou Da - vid's roy - al Son,
The peo - ple of the He - brews With palms be - fore Thee went;
Thou didst ac - cept their prais - es; Ac - cept the praise we bring,
Who in the Lord's Name com - est, The King and Bless - ed One.
Our praise and prayer and an - thems Be - fore Thee we pre - sent.
Who in all good de - light - est, Thou good and gra - cious King. A - MEN.

91 When, His Salvation Bringing

TOURS 7. 6. 7. 6. D.

John King, 1830 — Berthold Tours, 1872

1. When, His sal - va - tion bring - ing, To Zi - on Je - sus came,
2. And since the Lord re - tain - eth His love for chil - dren still,
3. For should we fail pro - claim - ing Our great Re - deem - er's praise,
The chil - dren all stood sing - ing Ho - san - na to His Name:
Though now as King He reign - eth On Zi - on's heaven - ly hill,
The stones, our si - lence sham - ing, Would their ho - san - nas raise.
Nor did their zeal of - fend Him, But, as He rode a - long,
We'll flock a - round His ban - ner Who sits up - on His throne,
But shall we on - ly ren - der The trib - ute of our words?
He let them still at - tend Him, And smiled to hear their song.
And cry a - loud, "Ho - san - na To Da - vid's roy - al Son!"
No; while our hearts are ten - der, They too shall be the Lord's. A-MEN.

Lift Up Your Heads, Ye Mighty Gates

TRURO L. M.

Georg Weissel, 1642
Trans. by Catherine Winkworth, 1855; Alt.

T. Williams' *Psalmodia Evangelica*, 1789

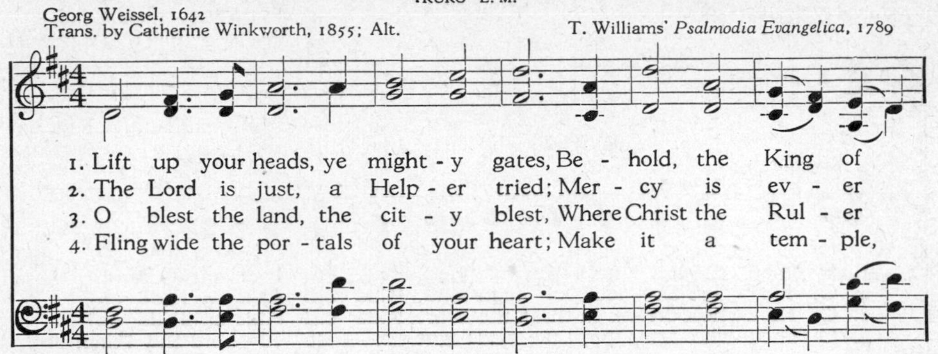
1. Lift up your heads, ye might - y gates, Be - hold, the King of
2. The Lord is just, a Help - er tried; Mer - cy is ev - er
3. O blest the land, the cit - y blest, Where Christ the Rul - er
4. Fling wide the por - tals of your heart; Make it a tem - ple,

glo - ry waits; The King of kings is draw - ing near;
at His side; His king ly crown is ho - li - ness,
is con - fessed! O hap - py hearts and hap - py homes
set a - part From earth - ly use for Heaven's em - ploy,

The Sav - iour of the world is here!
His scep - ter pit - y in dis - tress.
To whom this King in tri - umph comes!
A - dorned with prayer, and love, and joy. A - MEN.

5. Redeemer, come! I open wide
My heart to Thee; here, Lord, abide.
Let me Thy inner presence feel;
Thy grace and love in me reveal.

6. So come, my Sovereign; enter in,
Let new and nobler life begin;
Thy Holy Spirit guide us on
Until our glorious goal is won.

93 O Thou Eternal Christ of God

PERCIVAL SMITH C. M. D.
Calvin W. Laufer, 1933
Calvin W. Laufer, 1934
Arr. by Lawrence Curry, 1940
Descant
2. O Ho - ly Sav - iour of man-kind, Ride on! Ride on!
4. O Thou who art the Life and Light, Ex - alt - ed Lord
Unison
1. O Thou E - ter - nal Christ of God, Ride on! Ride on! Ride on!
2. O Ho - ly Sav - iour of man-kind, Ride on! Ride on! Ride on!
3. O Thou whose dreams en-thrall the heart, Ride on! Ride on! Ride on!
4. O Thou who art the Life and Light, Ex - alt - ed Lord and King,
Ride on! We bear with Thee the cross, Thy will be done.
and King, We hail Thy maj - es - ty, ho - san - na sing.
Es - tab - lish Thou for - ev - er - more The tri - umph now be - gun.
We bear with Thee the scourge and cross If so Thy will be done.
Ride on till tyr - an - ny and greed Are ev - er - more un - done.
We hail Thine au - gust maj - es - ty And loud ho - san - na sing,
Ride on! Ride on, O Christ!
Ride on! Ride on, O Christ!
A might - y host, by Thee re-deemed, Is march-ing in Thy train:
And be the road up - hill or down, Un - bro - ken or well - trod,
In mart and court and par - lia - ment The com-mon good in - crease,
Un - til in ev - ery land and clime Thine ends of love are won:

O Thou Eternal Christ of God (Concluded)

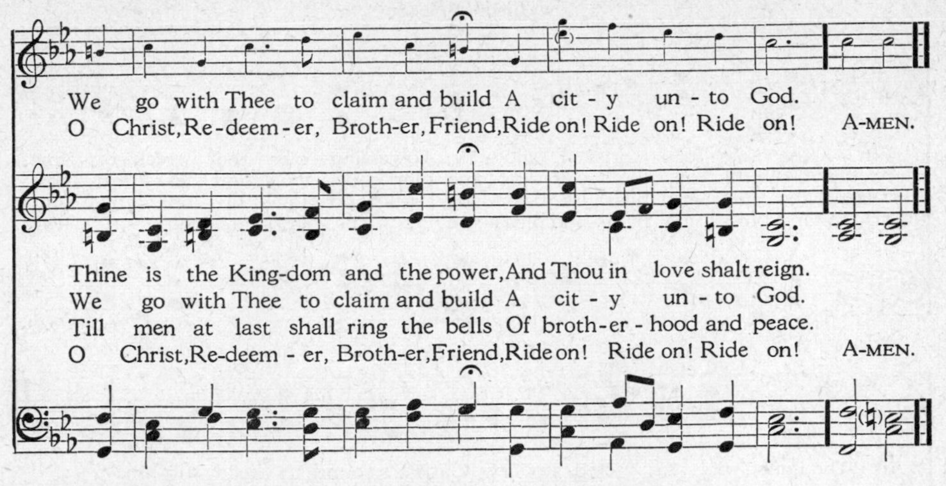
We go with Thee to claim and build A cit - y un - to God.
O Christ, Re-deem - er, Broth-er, Friend, Ride on! Ride on! Ride on! A-MEN.
Thine is the King-dom and the power, And Thou in love shalt reign.
We go with Thee to claim and build A cit - y un - to God.
Till men at last shall ring the bells Of broth-er - hood and peace.
O Christ, Re-deem - er, Broth-er, Friend, Ride on! Ride on! Ride on! A-MEN.

Ride On! Ride On in Majesty! 94

ST. DROSTANE L. M.

Henry H. Milman, 1827
Stanza 1 Alt.

John B. Dykes, 1862

1. Ride on! Ride on in maj - es - ty! Hark! all the tribes ho - san - na cry;
2. Ride on! Ride on in maj - es - ty! In low - ly pomp ride on to die:
3. Ride on! Ride on in maj - es - ty! Thy last and fier - cest strife is nigh;
4. Ride on! Ride on in maj - es - ty! In low - ly pomp ride on to die;

O Sav-iour meek, pur-sue Thy road With palms and scat-tered gar-ments strowed.
O Christ, Thy tri-umphs now be-gin O'er cap - tive death and con-quered sin.
The Fa-ther on His sap-phire throne Ex - pects His own a-noint-ed Son.
Bow Thy meek head to mor - tal pain, Then take, O God, Thy power, and reign. A-MEN.

95 In the Cross of Christ I Glory

RATHBUN 8. 7. 8. 7.

John Bowring, 1825 — Ithamar Conkey, 1851

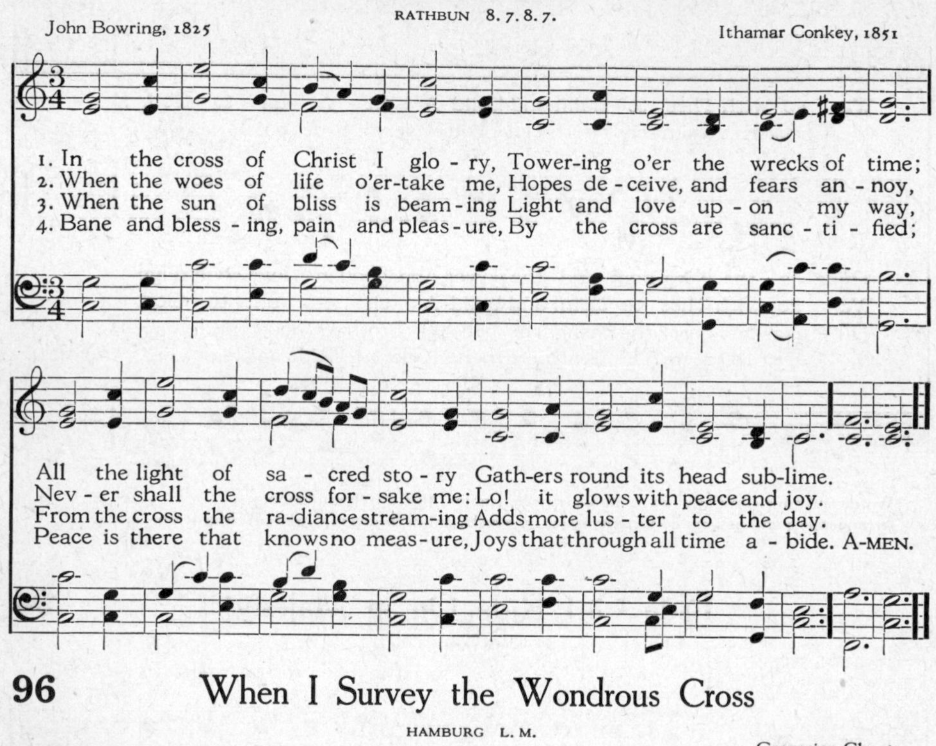
1. In the cross of Christ I glo - ry, Tower-ing o'er the wrecks of time;
2. When the woes of life o'er-take me, Hopes de - ceive, and fears an - noy,
3. When the sun of bliss is beam - ing Light and love up - on my way,
4. Bane and bless - ing, pain and pleas - ure, By the cross are sanc - ti - fied;
All the light of sa - cred sto - ry Gath-ers round its head sub-lime.
Nev - er shall the cross for - sake me: Lo! it glows with peace and joy.
From the cross the ra-diance stream-ing Adds more lus - ter to the day.
Peace is there that knows no meas - ure, Joys that through all time a - bide. A-MEN.

96 When I Survey the Wondrous Cross

HAMBURG L. M.

Isaac Watts, 1707 — Gregorian Chant, Arr. by Lowell Mason, 1824

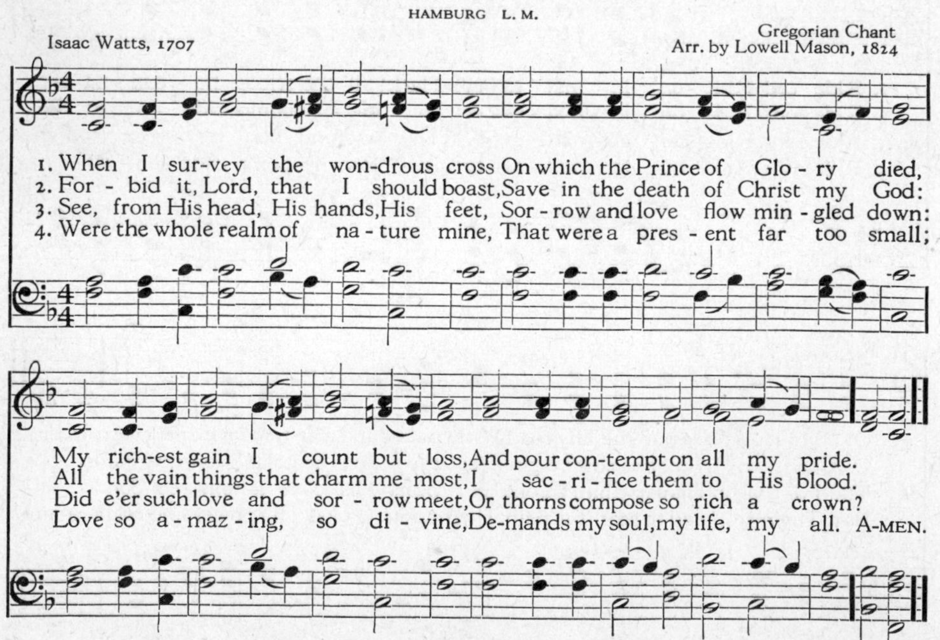
1. When I sur-vey the won-drous cross On which the Prince of Glo - ry died,
2. For - bid it, Lord, that I should boast, Save in the death of Christ my God:
3. See, from His head, His hands, His feet, Sor - row and love flow min - gled down:
4. Were the whole realm of na - ture mine, That were a pres - ent far too small;
My rich-est gain I count but loss, And pour con-tempt on all my pride.
All the vain things that charm me most, I sac - ri - fice them to His blood.
Did e'er such love and sor - row meet, Or thorns compose so rich a crown?
Love so a - maz - ing, so di - vine, De-mands my soul, my life, my all. A-MEN.

There Is a Green Hill Far Away 97

MEDITATION C. M.

Cecil Frances Alexander, 1848 — John H. Gower, 1890

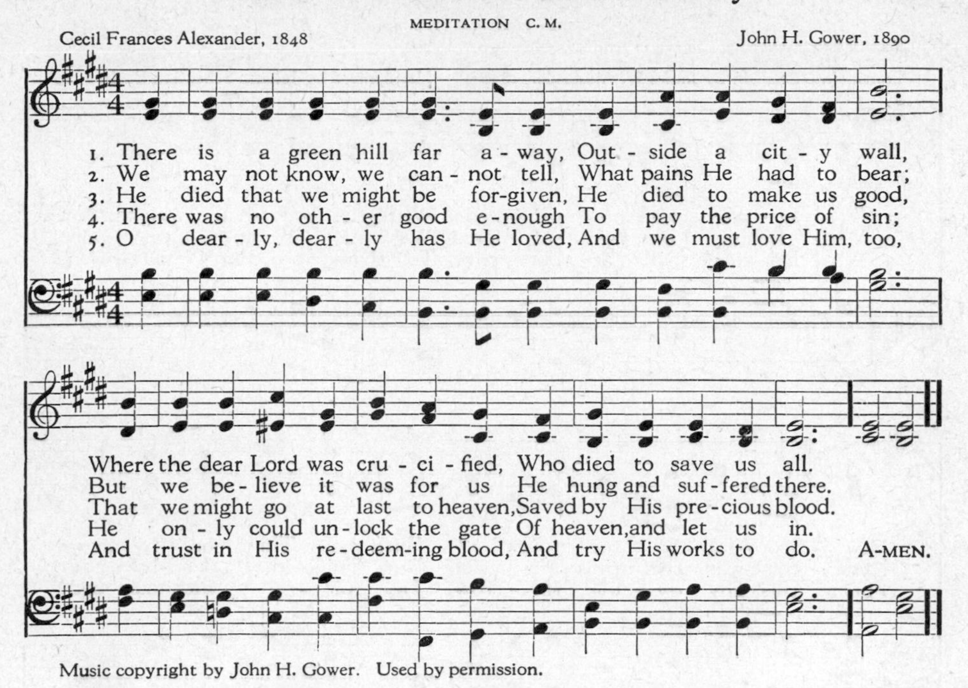
1. There is a green hill far a-way, Out-side a cit-y wall,
2. We may not know, we can-not tell, What pains He had to bear;
3. He died that we might be for-given, He died to make us good,
4. There was no oth-er good e-nough To pay the price of sin;
5. O dear-ly, dear-ly has He loved, And we must love Him, too,
Where the dear Lord was cru-ci-fied, Who died to save us all.
But we be-lieve it was for us He hung and suf-fered there.
That we might go at last to heaven, Saved by His pre-cious blood.
He on-ly could un-lock the gate Of heaven, and let us in.
And trust in His re-deem-ing blood, And try His works to do.
A-MEN.

'Tis Midnight; and on Olive's Brow 98

OLIVE'S BROW L. M.

William B. Tappan, 1822 — William B. Bradbury, 1853

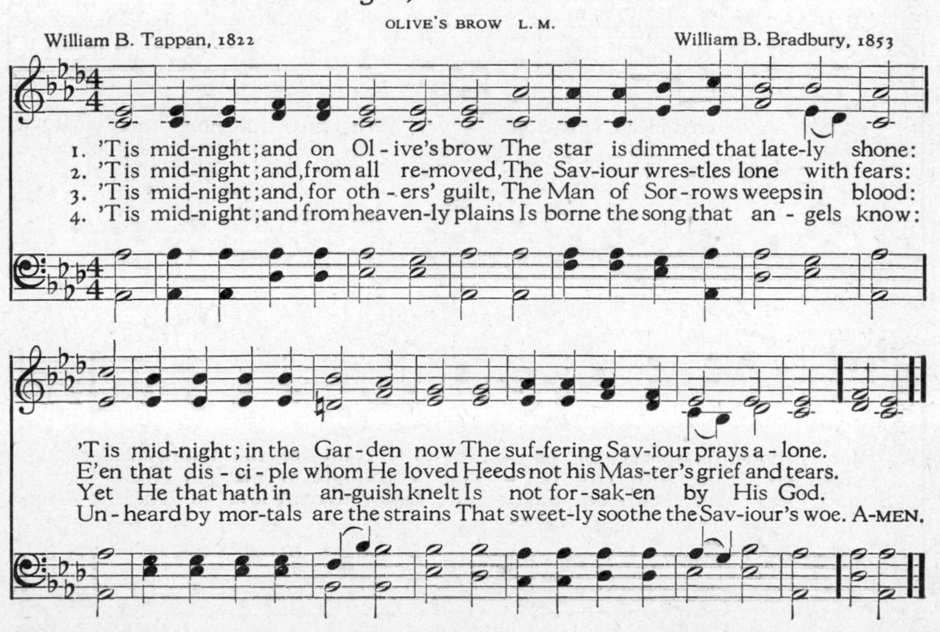
1. 'Tis mid-night; and on Ol-ive's brow The star is dimmed that late-ly shone:
2. 'Tis mid-night; and, from all re-moved, The Sav-iour wres-tles lone with fears:
3. 'Tis mid-night; and, for oth-ers' guilt, The Man of Sor-rows weeps in blood:
4. 'Tis mid-night; and from heaven-ly plains Is borne the song that an-gels know:
'Tis mid-night; in the Gar-den now The suf-fering Sav-iour prays a-lone.
E'en that dis-ci-ple whom He loved Heeds not his Mas-ter's grief and tears.
Yet He that hath in an-guish knelt Is not for-sak-en by His God.
Un-heard by mor-tals are the strains That sweet-ly soothe the Sav-iour's woe.
A-MEN.

99 O Sacred Head, Now Wounded

PASSION CHORALE 7. 6. 7. 6. D.
Ascribed to Bernard of Clairvaux (1091–1153)
Trans. (Into German) by Paul Gerhardt, 1656
Trans. (Into English) by James W. Alexander, 1830
Hans Leo Hassler, 1601
Harmonized by Johann Sebastian Bach, 1729
1. O sa - cred Head, now wound-ed, With grief and shame weighed down;
2. What Thou, my Lord, hast suf - fered Was all for sin - ners' gain:
3. What lan - guage shall I bor - row To thank Thee, dear - est Friend,
Now scorn-ful - ly sur - round - ed With thorns, Thine on - ly crown;
Mine, mine was the trans - gres - sion, But Thine the dead - ly pain.
For this Thy dy - ing sor - row, Thy pit - y with - out end?
O sa - cred Head, what glo - ry, What bliss till now was Thine!
Lo, here I fall, my Sav - iour! 'T is I de - serve Thy place;
O make me Thine for - ev - er; And should I faint - ing be,
Yet, though de - spised and go - ry, I joy to call Thee mine.
Look on me with Thy fa - vor, Vouch-safe to me Thy grace.
Lord, let me nev - er, nev - er Out - live my love to Thee.
A-MEN.

Into the Woods My Master Went

100

LANIER Irregular

Sidney Lanier, 1880

Peter C. Lutkin, 1905

1. In - to the woods my Mas - ter went, Clean for - spent, for - spent;
2. Out of the woods my Mas - ter went, And He was well con - tent;
In - to the woods my Mas - ter came, For-spent with love and shame. But the
Out of the woods my Mas - ter came, Con - tent with death and shame. When
ol - ives they were not blind to Him, The lit - tle gray leaves were kind to Him,
death and shame would woo Him last, From un - der the trees they drew Him last,
The thorn tree had a mind to Him, When in - to the woods He came.
'T was on a tree they slew Him last, When out of the woods He came. A-MEN.

101 Were You There?

WERE YOU THERE Irregular

Negro Spiritual
Harmonized by Lawrence Curry, 1940

1. Were you there when they cru - ci - fied my Lord? (Were you there?) Were you there when they cru - ci - fied my Lord? (my Lord) Oh! . . . . Some-times it caus - es me to trem-ble, trem-ble, trem - ble; Were you there when they cru - ci - fied my Lord?
2. Were you there when they nailed Him to the tree? (Were you there?) Were you there when they nailed Him to the tree? (the tree) Oh! . . . . Some-times it caus - es me to trem-ble, trem-ble, trem - ble; Were you there when they nailed Him to the tree?
3. Were you there when they pierced Him in the side? (Were you there?) Were you there when they pierced Him in the side? (the side) Oh! . . . . Some-times it caus - es me to trem-ble, trem-ble, trem - ble; Were you there when they pierced Him in the side?
4. Were you there when they laid Him in the tomb? (Were you there?) Were you there when they laid Him in the tomb? (the tomb) Oh! . . . . Some-times it caus - es me to trem-ble, trem-ble, trem - ble; Were you there when they laid Him in the tomb?

The Day of Resurrection!

LANCASHIRE 7. 6. 7. 6. D.
John of Damascus, Eighth Century
Trans. by John Mason Neale, 1862; Alt.
Henry Smart, 1836
1. The day of res - ur - rec - tion! Earth, tell it out a - broad:
2. Our hearts be pure from e - vil, That we may see a - right
3. Now let the heavens be joy - ful, Let earth her song be - gin;
The Pass - o - ver of glad - ness, The Pass - o - ver of God.
The Lord in rays e - ter - nal Of res - ur - rec - tion light;
Let the round world keep tri - umph, And all that is there - in;
From death to life e - ter - nal, From this world to the sky,
And, lis - tening to His ac - cents, May hear, so calm and plain,
Let all things seen and un - seen Their notes of glad - ness blend,
Our Christ hath brought us o - ver With hymns of vic - to - ry.
His own "All hail!" and, hear - ing, May raise the vic - tor strain.
For Christ the Lord hath ris - en, Our Joy that hath no end.
A-MEN.

103 Jesus Christ Is Risen Today

EASTER HYMN 7. 7. 7. 7. with Alleluias
From the Latin, Fourteenth Century
Stanza 4, Charles Wesley, 1740
Lyra Davidica, 1708
1. Jesus Christ is risen today, Alleluia!
Our triumphant holy day, Alleluia!
Who did once, upon the cross, Alleluia!
Suffer to redeem our loss. Alleluia!
2. Hymns of praise then let us sing, Alleluia!
Unto Christ our heavenly King, Alleluia!
Who endured the cross and grave, Alleluia!
Sinners to redeem and save. Alleluia!
3. But the pains which He endured, Alleluia!
Our salvation have procured; Alleluia!
Now above the sky He's King, Alleluia!
Where the angels ever sing. Alleluia!
4. Sing we to our God above, Alleluia!
Praise eternal as His love; Alleluia!
Praise Him, all ye heavenly host, Alleluia!
Father, Son, and Holy Ghost. Alleluia! A-MEN.

Alternative tune, "Llanfair," number 104.

Christ the Lord Is Risen Today

LLANFAIR 7. 7. 7. 7. with Alleluias
Robert Williams, 1817
Harmonized by Lawrence Curry, 1940
Charles Wesley (1707–1788)
1. "Christ the Lord is risen to - day," Al - le - lu - ia!
2. Vain the stone, the watch, the seal; Al - le - lu - ia!
3. Lives a - gain our glo - rious King; Al - le - lu - ia!
4. Soar we now where Christ has led, Al - le - lu - ia!
5. Hail, the Lord of earth and heaven! Al - le - lu - ia!
Sons of men and an - gels say; Al - le - lu - ia!
Christ has burst the gates of hell: Al - le - lu - ia!
Where, O death, is now thy sting? Al - le - lu - ia!
Fol - lowing our ex - alt - ed Head; Al - le - lu - ia!
Praise to Thee by both be given; Al - le - lu - ia!
Raise your joys and tri - umphs high; Al - le - lu - ia!
Death in vain for - bids His rise; Al - le - lu - ia!
Once He died, our souls to save; Al - le - lu - ia!
Made like Him, like Him we rise; Al - le - lu - ia!
Thee we greet tri - um - phant now; Al - le - lu - ia!
Sing, ye heavens, and earth, re - ply; Al - le - lu - ia!
Christ has o - pened par - a - dise. Al - le - lu - ia!
Where thy vic - to - ry, O grave? Al - le - lu - ia!
Ours the cross, the grave, the skies. Al - le - lu - ia!
Hail, the Res - ur - rec - tion Thou! Al - le - lu - ia! A-MEN.

Alternative tune, "Easter Hymn," number 103.

105 The Strife Is O'er, the Battle Done

PALESTRINA 8. 8. 8. 4. with Alleluias
From the Latin
Trans. by Francis Pott, 1861
Giovanni P. da Palestrina, 1591
Adapted by William Henry Monk (1823-1889)
Al - le - lu - ia! Al - le - lu - ia! Al - le - lu - ia!
Org.
1. The strife is o'er, the battle done;
2. The powers of death have done their worst,
3. The three sad days have quick - ly sped;
4. He closed the yawn - ing gates of hell;
5. Lord, by the stripes which wound - ed Thee,
The vic - to - ry of life is won; The song of
But Christ their le - gions hath dis - persed: Let shouts of
He ris - es glo - rious from the dead: All glo - ry
The bars from heaven's high por - tals fell: Let hymns of
From death's dread sting Thy serv - ants free, That we may
tri - umph has be - gun. Al - le - lu - ia!
ho - ly joy out - burst. Al - le - lu - ia!
to our ris - en Head! Al - le - lu - ia!
praise His tri - umphs tell. Al - le - lu - ia!
live and sing to Thee. Al - le - lu - ia! A - MEN.
D.S.

Thine Is the Glory

HANDEL 10.11.11.11.
E. Budry, 1884
Trans. by R. Birch Hoyle, 1923
Georg Friedrich Handel (1685-1759)
1. Thine is the glo - ry, Ris - en, con - quering Son,
2. Lo! Je - sus meets thee, Ris - en from the tomb;
3. No more we doubt Thee, Glo - rious Prince of Life!
Ref. Thine is the glo - ry, Ris - en, con - quering Son,
Fine
End - less is the vic - tory Thou o'er death hast won.
Lov - ing - ly He greets thee, Scat - ters fear and gloom;
Life is nought with - out Thee; Aid us in our strife;
End - less is the vic - tory Thou o'er death hast won.
An - gels in bright rai - ment Rolled the stone a - way,
Let His Church with glad - ness Hymns of tri - umph sing,
Make us more than con - querors Through Thy death - less love.
D.C. al Fine
Kept the fold - ed grave-clothes Where Thy bod - y lay.
For her Lord now liv - eth; Death hath lost its sting.
Bring us safe through Jor - dan To Thy home a - bove. A-men.

107 O Sons and Daughters

O FILII ET FILIAE 8. 8. 8. with Alleluias

Jean Tisserand, d. 1494
Trans. by John Mason Neale, 1852

French, Fifteenth Century

Al - le - lu - ia! Al - le - lu - ia! Al - le - lu - ia! Al - le - lu - ia!
1. O sons and daugh - ters, let us sing!
2. That Eas - ter morn, at break of day,
3. An an - gel clad in white they see,
4. How blest are they who have not seen,
5. On this most ho - ly day of days,
The King of heaven, the glo - rious King, O'er death to - day rose tri - umph - ing.
The faith - ful wom - en went their way To seek the tomb where Je - sus lay.
Who sat, and spake un - to the three, "Your Lord doth go to Gal - i - lee."
And yet whose faith hath con - stant been; For they e - ter - nal life shall win.
Our hearts and voi - ces, Lord, we raise To Thee, in ju - bi - lee and praise.
Al - le - lu - ia! Al - le - lu - ia!
D.S.
A - MEN.

Come, Ye Faithful, Raise the Strain

ST. KEVIN 7. 6. 7. 6. D.
John of Damascus, Eighth Century
Trans. by John Mason Neale, 1859
Arthur S. Sullivan, 1872
1. Come, ye faith - ful, raise the strain Of tri - um - phant glad - ness:
2. 'T is the spring of souls to - day: Christ hath burst His pris - on,
God hath brought His peo - ple forth In - to joy from sad - ness.
And from three days' sleep in death As a sun hath ris - en;
Now re - joice, Je - ru - sa - lem, And with true af - fec - tion
All the win - ter of our sins, Long and dark, is fly - ing
Wel - come in un - wea - ried strains Je - sus' res - ur - rec - tion.
From His light, to whom we give Laud and praise un - dy - ing. A-MEN.

109 Welcome, Happy Morning!

HERMAS 6. 5. 6. 5. D. with Refrain

Venantius Fortunatus (530–609)
Trans. by John Ellerton (1826–1893)

Frances Ridley Havergal (1836–1879)

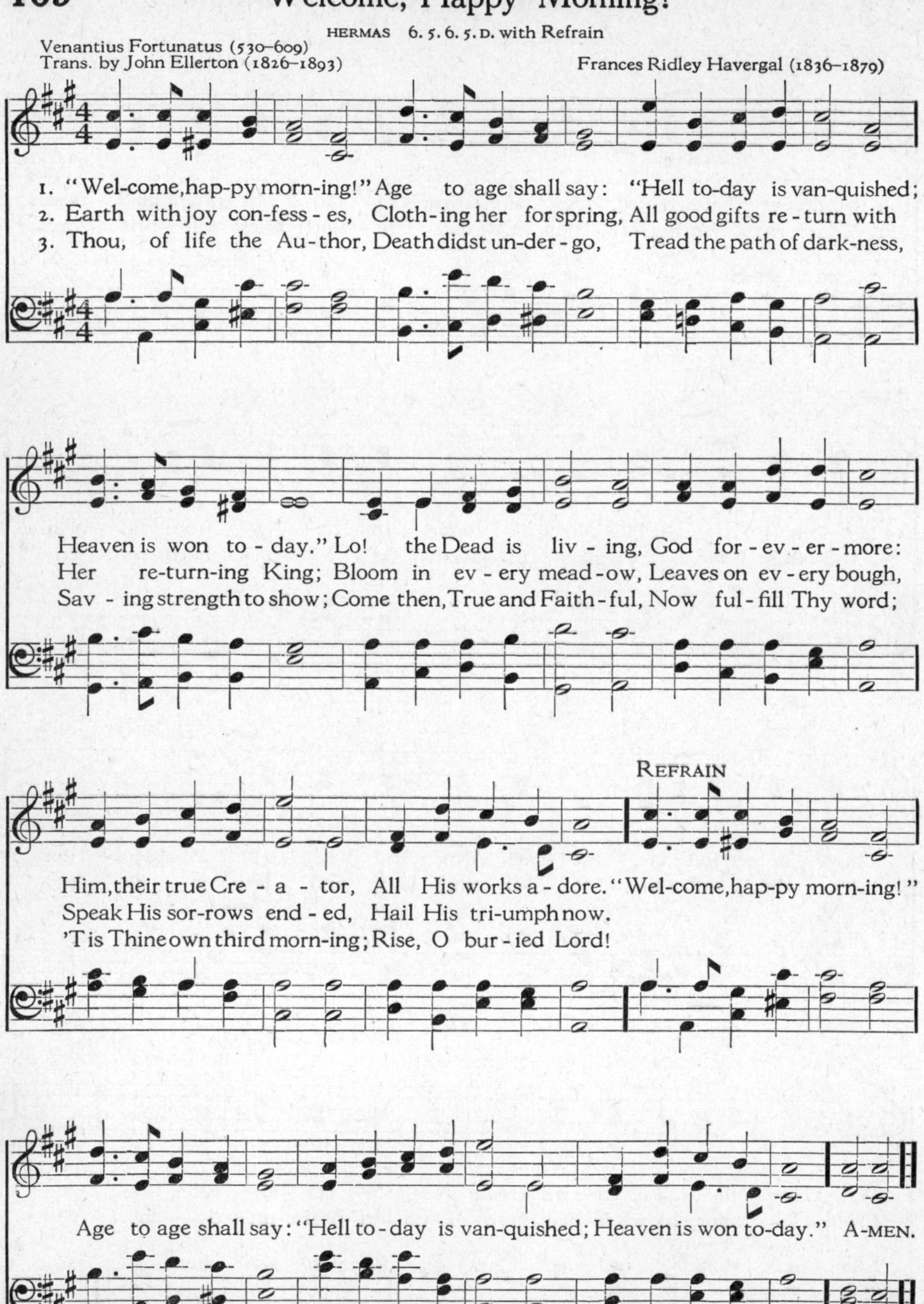
1. "Wel-come, hap-py morn-ing!" Age to age shall say: "Hell to-day is van-quished; Heaven is won to-day." Lo! the Dead is liv-ing, God for-ev-er-more: Him, their true Cre-a-tor, All His works a-dore.
2. Earth with joy con-fess-es, Cloth-ing her for spring, All good gifts re-turn with Her re-turn-ing King; Bloom in ev-ery mead-ow, Leaves on ev-ery bough, Speak His sor-rows end-ed, Hail His tri-umph now.
3. Thou, of life the Au-thor, Death didst un-der-go, Tread the path of dark-ness, Sav-ing strength to show; Come then, True and Faith-ful, Now ful-fill Thy word; 'T is Thine own third morn-ing; Rise, O bur-ied Lord!
REFRAIN
"Wel-come, hap-py morn-ing!" Age to age shall say: "Hell to-day is van-quished; Heaven is won to-day." A-MEN.

O Thou, in All Thy Might So Far 110

SERENITY C. M.

Frederick L. Hosmer, 1876 — Arr. from William V. Wallace, 1856

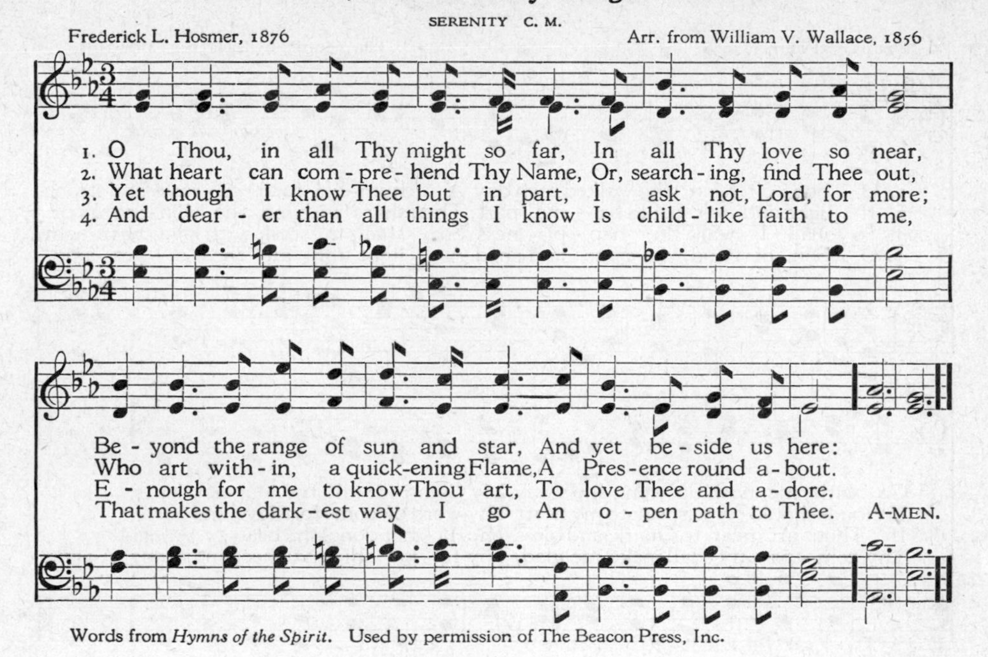
1. O Thou, in all Thy might so far, In all Thy love so near,
2. What heart can com-pre-hend Thy Name, Or, search-ing, find Thee out,
3. Yet though I know Thee but in part, I ask not, Lord, for more;
4. And dear-er than all things I know Is child-like faith to me,
Be-yond the range of sun and star, And yet be-side us here:
Who art with-in, a quick-ening Flame, A Pres-ence round a-bout.
E-nough for me to know Thou art, To love Thee and a-dore.
That makes the dark-est way I go An o-pen path to Thee. A-MEN.

Words from *Hymns of the Spirit*. Used by permission of The Beacon Press, Inc.

We Bear the Strain of Earthly Care 111

AZMON C. M.

Ozora Stearns Davis, 1909 — Carl G. Gläser (1784–1829), Arr. by Lowell Mason (1792–1872)

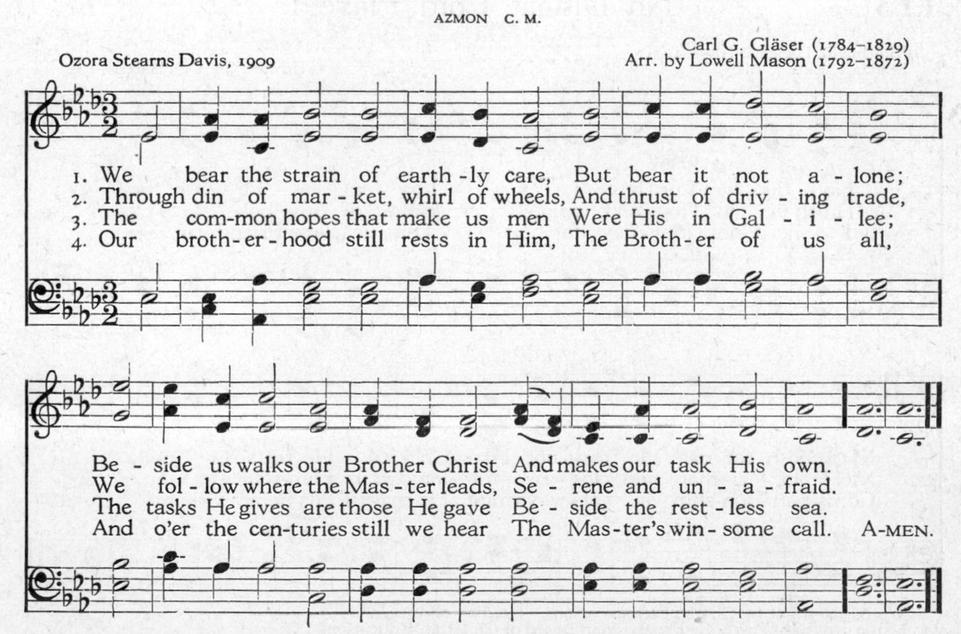
1. We bear the strain of earth-ly care, But bear it not a-lone;
2. Through din of mar-ket, whirl of wheels, And thrust of driv-ing trade,
3. The com-mon hopes that make us men Were His in Gal-i-lee;
4. Our broth-er-hood still rests in Him, The Broth-er of us all,
Be-side us walks our Brother Christ And makes our task His own.
We fol-low where the Mas-ter leads, Se-rene and un-a-fraid.
The tasks He gives are those He gave Be-side the rest-less sea.
And o'er the cen-turies still we hear The Mas-ter's win-some call. A-MEN.

112 O Son of Man, Who Walked Each Day

SOLDAU L. M.

Nancy Byrd Turner, 1928

Wittenberg Gesangbuch, 1524
Harmonized by Lawrence Curry, 1940

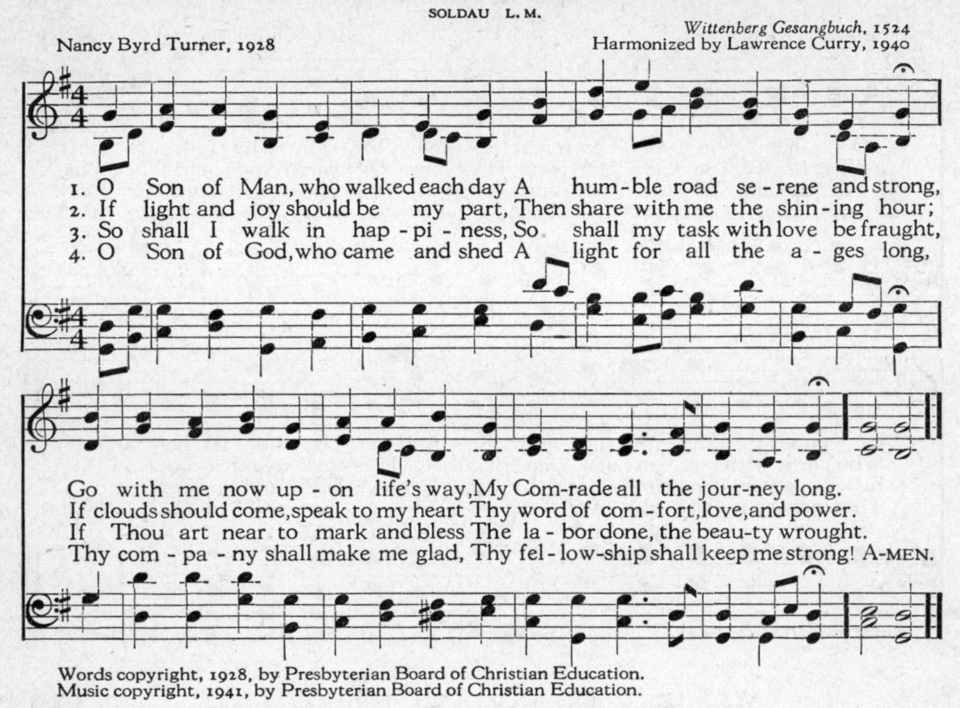
1. O Son of Man, who walked each day A hum-ble road se-rene and strong,
2. If light and joy should be my part, Then share with me the shin-ing hour;
3. So shall I walk in hap-pi-ness, So shall my task with love be fraught,
4. O Son of God, who came and shed A light for all the a-ges long,
Go with me now up-on life's way, My Com-rade all the jour-ney long.
If clouds should come, speak to my heart Thy word of com-fort, love, and power.
If Thou art near to mark and bless The la-bor done, the beau-ty wrought.
Thy com-pa-ny shall make me glad, Thy fel-low-ship shall keep me strong! A-MEN.

113 No Distant Lord Have I

LLUELYN S. M.

Maltbie D. Babcock (1858–1901)
Stanza 2, Line 3, Alt.

Edward Shippen Barnes, 1927

1. No dis-tant Lord have I, Lov-ing a-far to be;
2. Broth-er in joy and pain, Bone of my bone was He;
3. I need not jour-ney far This dear-est Friend to see;
Made flesh for me, He can-not rest Un-til He rests in me.
More in-ti-mate and clos-er still—He dwells Him-self in me.
Com-pan-ion-ship is al-ways mine: He makes His home with me. A-MEN.

O Son of Man, Our Hero Strong and Tender 114

CHARTERHOUSE 11.10.11.10.
Frank Fletcher, 1921
David Evans, 1927
Unison
1. O Son of Man, our He - ro strong and ten - der, Whose serv-ants are the brave in all the earth, Our liv - ing sac - ri - fice to Thee we ren - der, Who shar-est all our sor-rows, all our mirth.
2. O feet so strong to climb the path of du - ty, O lips di - vine that taught the words of truth, Kind eyes that marked the lil - ies in their beau - ty, And heart that kin-dled at the zeal of youth;
3. Lov - er of chil - dren, boy-hood's in - spi - ra - tion, Of all man - kind the Serv - ant and the King; O Lord of joy and hope and con-so - la - tion, To Thee our fears and joys and hopes we bring.
4. Not in our fail - ures on - ly and our sad - ness We seek Thy pres - ence, Com - fort - er and Friend; O rich man's Guest, be with us in our glad - ness, O poor man's Mate, our low-li-est tasks at - tend. A-MEN.
Harmony

115 Be Thou My Vision

SLANE 10. 10. 10. 10.

Ancient Irish
Trans. by Mary Byrne; Versified by Eleanor Hull, 1927

Ancient Irish Traditional Melody
Harmonized by David Evans, 1927

Unison

1. Be Thou my Vi - sion, O Lord of my heart;
2. Be Thou my Wis - dom, and Thou my true Word;
3. Rich - es I heed not, nor man's emp - ty praise,
4. High King of heav - en, my vic - to - ry won,

Nought be all else to me, save that Thou art—
I ev - er with Thee and Thou with me, Lord;
Thou mine in - her - it - ance, now and al - ways:
May I reach heav - en's joys, O bright heaven's Sun!

Thou my best thought, by day or by night, . . .
Thou my great Fa - ther, I Thy true son; . . . .
Thou and Thou on - ly, first in my heart, . . .
Heart of my own heart, what - ev - er be - fall, ...

Wak - ing or sleep - ing, Thy pres - ence my light.
Thou in me dwell - ing, and I with Thee one.
High King of heav - en, my Treas - ure Thou art.
Still be my Vi - sion, O Rul - er of all. A - MEN.

Hark, What a Sound

WELWYN 11. 10. 11. 10.
Frederick William Henry Myers (1843-1901)
Alfred Scott-Gatty (1847-1918)
1. Hark, what a sound, and too di - vine for hear - ing,
2. Sure - ly He com - eth, and a thou - sand voi - ces
3. So ev - en I, and with a pang more thrill - ing,
4. Yea, through life, death, through sor - row and through sin - ning
Stirs on the earth and trem - bles in the air!
Shout to the saints and to the deaf are dumb;
So ev - en I, and with a hope more sweet,
He shall suf - fice me, for He hath suf - ficed;
Is it the thun - der of the Lord's ap - pear - ing?
Sure - ly He com - eth, and the earth re - joi - ces,
Yearn for the sign, O Christ, of Thy ful - fill - ing,
Christ is the end, for Christ was the be - gin - ning,
Is it the mu - sic of His peo - ple's prayer?
Glad in His com - ing who hath sworn, "I come."
Faint for the flam - ing of Thine ad - vent feet.
Christ the be - gin - ning, for the end is Christ. A - MEN.

117 Wake, Awake, for Night Is Flying

WACHET AUF Irregular

Philip Nicolai, 1599
Trans. by Catherine Winkworth, 1858

Melody by Philip Nicolai, 1599
Harmonized by Johann Sebastian Bach (1685–1750)

1. Wake, a - wake, for night is fly - ing, The watch - men on the
2. Zi - on hears the watch - men sing - ing, And all her heart with
3. Now let all the heavens a - dore Thee, And men and an - gels

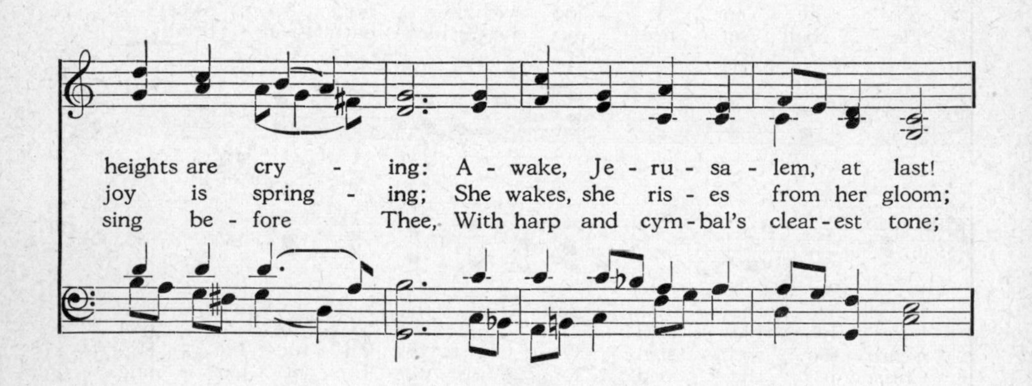
heights are cry - ing: A - wake, Je - ru - sa - lem, at last!
joy is spring - ing; She wakes, she ris - es from her gloom;
sing be - fore Thee, With harp and cym - bal's clear - est tone;

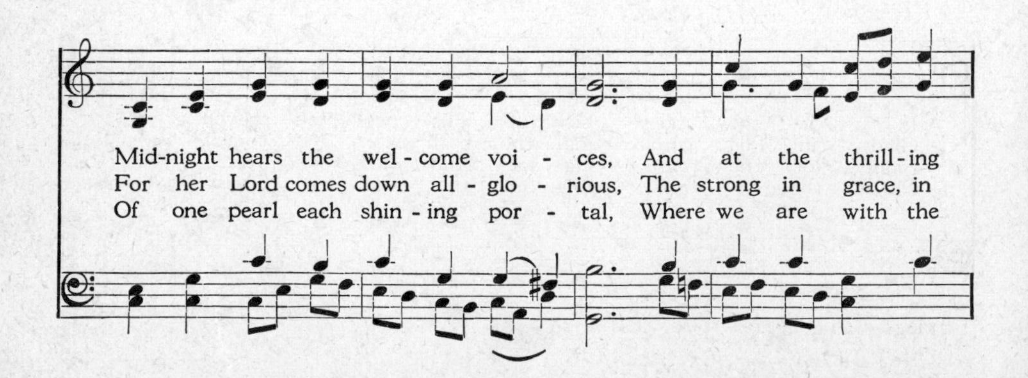
Mid-night hears the wel - come voi - ces, And at the thrill - ing
For her Lord comes down all - glo - rious, The strong in grace, in
Of one pearl each shin - ing por - tal, Where we are with the

Wake, Awake, for Night Is Flying (Concluded)

cry re - joi - ces; Come forth, ye vir - gins, night is past! The
truth vic - to - rious, Her Star is risen, her Light is come! Ah,
choir im - mor - tal Of an - gels round Thy daz - zling throne; Nor

Bride-groom comes; a - wake, Your lamps with glad - ness take; Hal - le - lu - jah! And
come, Thou bless-ed Lord, O Je - sus, Son of God! Hal - le - lu - jah! We
eye hath seen, nor ear Hath yet at - tained to hear What there is ours; But

for His mar-riage feast pre-pare, For ye must go to meet Him there.
fol - low till the halls we see Where Thou hast bid us sup with Thee.
we re-joice and sing to Thee Our hymns of joy e - ter - nal - ly. A-MEN.

118 There's a Light Upon the Mountains

MOUNT HOLYOKE 8. 7. 8. 7. D.
Henry Burton, 1910; Alt.
M. L. Wostenholm, 1910
1. There's a light up-on the moun-tains, And the day is at the spring,
When our eyes shall see the beau-ty And the glo-ry of the King;
Wea-ry was our heart with wait-ing, And the night watch seemed so long,
But His tri-umph day is break-ing, And we hail it with a song.
2. In the fad-ing of the star-light We may see the com-ing morn;
And the lights of men are pal-ing In the splen-dors of the dawn;
For the east-ern skies are glow-ing As with light of hid-den fire,
And the hearts of men are stir-ring With the throbs of deep de-sire.
3. He is break-ing down the bar-riers; He is cast-ing up the way;
He is call-ing for His an-gels To build up the gates of day:
But His an-gels here are hu-man, Not the shin-ing hosts a-bove;
For the drum-beats of His ar-my Are the heart-beats of our love.
4. Hark! we hear a dis-tant mu-sic, And it comes with full-er swell;
'Tis the tri-umph song of Je-sus, Of our King, Em-man-u-el!
Go ye forth with joy to meet Him! And, my soul, be swift to bring
All thy sweet-est and thy dear-est For the tri-umph of our King!
A-MEN.

Fairest Lord Jesus

SCHÖNSTER HERR JESU 5. 6. 8. 5. 5. 8.

From the German, Seventeenth Century

Silesian Folk Song
From *Schlesische Volkslieder*, Leipzig, 1842
Descant by W. Frederic Miller, 1940

Descant
2. Fair are the wood-lands,
3. Fair is the moon-light,
(*Descant to third stanza ad lib.*)
1. Fair-est Lord Je-sus, Rul-er of all na-ture, O Thou of
2. Fair are the mead-ows, Fair-er still the wood-lands, Robed in the
3. Fair is the sun-shine, Fair-er still the moon-light, And all the
Robed in the bloom-ing garb of spring: Je-sus is fair-er, Je-sus is
And all the twin-kling star-ry host: Je-sus shines bright-er, Je-sus shines
God and man the Son, Thee will I cher-ish, Thee will I
bloom-ing garb of spring: Je-sus is fair-er, Je-sus is
twin-kling, star-ry host: Je-sus shines bright-er, Je-sus shines
pur-er, Who makes the woe-ful heart to sing.
pur-er, Than all the an-gels heaven can boast. A-MEN.
hon-or, Thou, my soul's Glo-ry, Joy, and Crown.
pur-er, Who makes the woe-ful heart to sing.
pur-er, Than all the an-gels heaven can boast. A-MEN.

120 Crown Him with Many Crowns

DIADEMATA S. M. D.
Matthew Bridges, 1851
George J. Elvey, 1868
Descant by Donald D. Kettring, 1940
Descant (with 4th stanza only)
4. Crown Him Lord, The Po - ten - tate of time;
1. Crown Him with man - y crowns, The Lamb up - on His throne;
2. Crown Him the Lord of love: Be - hold His hands and side,
3. Crown Him the Lord of peace; Whose power a scep - ter sways
4. Crown Him the Lord of years, The Po - ten - tate of time;
Crown Him Lord, In - ef - fa - bly sub - lime:
Hark! how the heaven-ly an - them drowns All mu - sic but its own:
Rich wounds, yet vis - i - ble a - bove, In beau - ty glo - ri - fied:
From pole to pole, that wars may cease, Ab-sorbed in prayer and praise:
Cre - a - tor of the roll - ing spheres, In - ef - fa - bly sub - lime:
Crown Him Lord! Crown Him Lord!
A - wake, my soul, and sing Of Him who died for thee,
No an - gel in the sky Can ful - ly bear that sight,
His reign shall know no end; And round His pier - ced feet
All hail, Re - deem - er, hail! For Thou hast died for me:

Crown Him with Many Crowns (Concluded)
Crown Him Lord E - ter - nal - ly! A - MEN.
And hail Him as thy match-less King Through all e - ter - ni - ty.
But down-ward bends his burn-ing eye At mys - ter - ies so bright.
Fair flowers of par - a - dise ex - tend Their fra - grance ev - er sweet.
Thy praise shall nev - er, nev - er fail Through-out e - ter - ni - ty. A - MEN.
Descant copyright, 1941, by Presbyterian Board of Christian Education.
Shepherd of Tender Youth
121
KIRBY BEDON 6. 6. 4. 6. 6. 6. 4.
Clement of Alexandria, 220
Trans. by Henry M. Dexter, 1846
Edward Bunnett, 1887
1. Shep - herd of ten - der youth, Guid - ing in love and truth,
2. Thou art our ho - ly Lord, The all - sub - du - ing Word,
3. Ev - er be Thou our Guide, Our Shep-herd, and our Pride,
4. So now, and till we die, Sound we Thy prais - es high,
Through de - vious ways; Christ, our tri - um-phant King, We come Thy Name to
Heal - er of strife; Thou didst Thy-self a - base, That from sin's deep dis-
Our Staff and Song; Je - sus, Thou Christ of God, By Thy per - en - nial
And joy - ful sing; Let all the ho - ly throng Who to Thy Church be-
sing; Hith - er our chil - dren bring To sound Thy praise.
grace Thou might-est save our race, And give us life.
word, Lead us where Thou hast trod, Make our faith strong.
long, U - nite and swell the song To Christ, our King. A-MEN.

122 All Hail the Power of Jesus' Name!

CORONATION C.M.
(FIRST TUNE)
Edward Perronet, 1779, 1780
Stanza 1, Line 4, Alt.; Stanza 3 Recast
Stanza 4 Added by John Rippon, 1787
Oliver Holden, 1793
Descant by Lawrence Curry, 1940
1. All hail the power of Je - sus' Name! Let an - gels pros - trate fall;
2. Sin - ners, whose love can ne'er for - get The worm-wood and the gall,
3. Let ev - ery kin - dred, ev - ery tribe, On this ter - res - trial ball,
4. O that with yon - der sa - cred throng We at His feet may fall!
Descant
Bring forth the roy - al di - a - dem, And crown Him Lord of all;
Go, spread your tro - phies at His feet, And crown Him Lord of all;
To Him all maj - es - ty as - cribe, And crown Him Lord of all;
We'll join the ev - er - last - ing song, And crown Him Lord of all;
Bring forth the roy - al di - a - dem, And crown Him Lord of all.
Go, spread your tro - phies at His feet, And crown Him Lord of all.
To Him all maj - es - ty as - cribe, And crown Him Lord of all.
We'll join the ev - er - last - ing song, And crown Him Lord of all. A - MEN.

All Hail the Power of Jesus' Name! 122

MILES LANE C. M.
(SECOND TUNE)
Edward Perronet, 1779, 1780
Stanza 1, Line 4, Alt.; Stanza 3 Recast
Stanza 4 Added by John Rippon, 1787
William Shrubsole, 1779; Alt.
Descant by Lawrence Curry, 1940
1. All hail the power of Je - sus' Name! Let an - gels pros - trate fall;
2. Sin - ners, whose love can ne'er for - get The worm - wood and the gall,
3. Let ev - ery kin - dred, ev - ery tribe, On this ter - res - trial ball,
4. O that with yon - der sa - cred throng We at His feet may fall!
Descant
And crown Him Lord,
Bring forth the roy - al di - a - dem, And crown Him,
Go, spread your tro - phies at His feet, And crown Him,
To Him all maj - es - ty as - cribe, And crown Him,
We'll join the ev - er - last - ing song, And crown Him,
crown Him Lord, crown Him, crown Him Lord of all. A-MEN.
crown Him, crown Him, crown Him Lord of all.
crown Him, crown Him, crown Him Lord of all.
crown Him, crown Him, crown Him Lord of all.
crown Him, crown Him, crown Him Lord of all. A - MEN.

123 Rejoice, the Lord Is King

DARWALL'S 148TH 6. 6. 6. 6. 8. 8.

Charles Wesley, 1746
Stanza 1, Line 3, Alt.

John Darwall, 1770

1. Re - joice, the Lord is King: Your Lord and King a - dore!
2. His King-dom can - not fail, He rules o'er earth and heaven;
3. He sits at God's right hand Till all His foes sub - mit,
Re - joice, give thanks, and sing, And tri - umph
The keys of death and hell Are to our
And bow to His com - mand, And fall be -
ev - er - more: Lift up your heart, lift up your voice!
Je - sus given: Lift up your heart, lift up your voice!
neath His feet: Lift up your heart, lift up your voice!
Re - joice, a - gain I say, re - joice!
Re - joice, a - gain I say, re - joice!
Re - joice, a - gain I say, re - joice! A - MEN.

Rejoice, Ye Pure in Heart

MARION S. M. with Refrain

Edward H. Plumptre, 1865 — Arthur H. Messiter, 1885

1. Re - joice, ye pure in heart, Re - joice, give thanks, and sing:
2. Bright youth and snow-crowned age, Strong men and maid - ens meek,
3. With all the an - gel choirs, With all the saints on earth,
Your fes - tal ban - ner wave on high, The cross of Christ your King.
Raise high your free, ex - ult - ing song, God's won-drous prais - es speak.
Pour out the strains of joy and bliss, True rap - ture, no - blest mirth!
REFRAIN
Re - joice, re - joice, Re - joice, give thanks, and sing! A-MEN.
Re - joice, re - joice,

4. Still lift your standard high,
   Still march in firm array;
As warriors through the darkness toil
   Till dawns the golden day.

5. Then on, ye pure in heart,
   Rejoice, give thanks, and sing;
Your festal banner wave on high,
   The cross of Christ your King.

125 Ye Servants of God, Your Master Proclaim

LYONS 10. 10. 11. 11.

Charles Wesley, 1744
Stanza 3, Line 3, Alt.

Arr. from J. Michael Haydn (1737–1806)

1. Ye serv - ants of God, your Mas - ter pro - claim,
2. God rul - eth on high, al - might - y to save;
3. Sal - va - tion to God who sits on the throne!
4. Then let us a - dore, and give Him His right,
And pub - lish a - broad His won - der - ful Name;
And still He is nigh— His pres - ence we have:
Let all cry a - loud and hon - or the Son:
All glo - ry and power, and wis - dom and might,
The Name, all - vic - to - rious, of Je - sus ex - tol;
The great con - gre - ga - tion His tri - umph shall sing,
The prais - es of Je - sus the an - gels pro - claim,
All hon - or and bless - ing, with an - gels a - bove,
His King - dom is glo - rious, and rules o - ver all.
As - crib - ing sal - va - tion to Je - sus, our King.
Fall down on their fa - ces and wor - ship the Lamb.
And thanks nev - er ceas - ing, and in - fi - nite love. A - MEN.

More About Jesus

MORE ABOUT JESUS L. M. with Refrain

E. E. Hewitt

John R. Sweney (1837-1899)

1. More a-bout Je-sus would I know, More of His grace to oth-ers show;
2. More a-bout Je-sus let me learn, More of His ho-ly will dis-cern;
3. More a-bout Je-sus; in His Word, Hold-ing com-mun-ion with my Lord;
4. More a-bout Je-sus on His throne, Rich-es in glo-ry all His own;
More of His sav-ing full-ness see, More of His love who died for me.
Spir-it of God, my Teach-er be, Show-ing the things of Christ to me.
Hear-ing His voice in ev-ery line, Mak-ing each faith-ful say-ing mine.
More of His King-dom's sure in-crease; More of His com-ing, Prince of Peace.
REFRAIN
More, more a-bout Je-sus, More, more a-bout Je-sus;
More of His sav-ing full-ness see, More of His love who died for me. A-MEN.

127 Spirit of God, Descend Upon My Heart

MORECAMBE 10. 10. 10. 10.
George Croly, 1854
Frederick C. Atkinson, c. 1870
1. Spir - it of God, de - scend up - on my heart; Wean it from earth; through all its puls - es move; Stoop to my weak - ness, might - y as Thou art, And make me love Thee as I ought to love.
2. I ask no dream, no proph - et ec - sta - sies, No sud - den rend - ing of the veil of clay, No an - gel vis - it - ant, no o-pening skies; But take the dim - ness of my soul a - way.
3. Teach me to feel that Thou art al - ways nigh; Teach me the strug - gles of the soul to bear, To check the ris - ing doubt, the reb - el sigh; Teach me the pa - tience of un - an - swered prayer.
4. Teach me to love Thee as Thine an - gels love, One ho - ly pas - sion fill - ing all my frame; The bap - tism of the heaven - de - scend-ed Dove, My heart an al - tar, and Thy love the flame.
A-MEN.

128 Holy Spirit, Truth Divine

MERCY 7. 7. 7. 7.

Samuel Longfellow, 1864

Arr. from Louis M. Gottschalk, 1867

1. Ho - ly Spir - it, Truth di - vine, Dawn up - on this soul of mine;
2. Ho - ly Spir - it, Love di - vine, Glow with - in this heart of mine;
3. Ho - ly Spir - it, Power di - vine, Fill and nerve this will of mine;
4. Ho - ly Spir - it, Right di - vine, King with - in my con - science reign;

Holy Spirit, Truth Divine (Concluded)

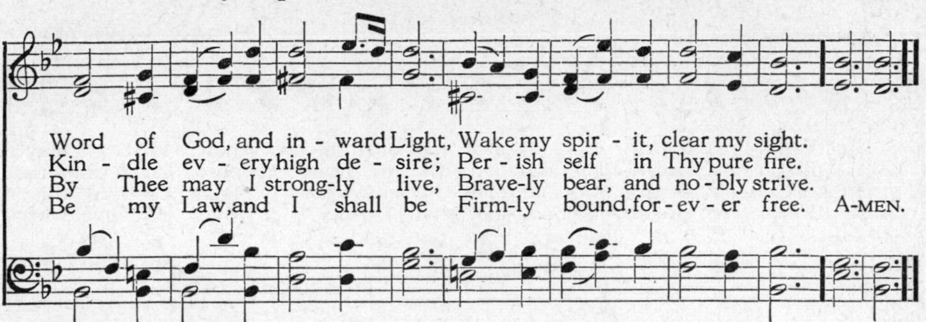

Word of God, and in - ward Light, Wake my spir - it, clear my sight.
Kin - dle ev - ery high de - sire; Per - ish self in Thy pure fire.
By Thee may I strong-ly live, Brave-ly bear, and no - bly strive.
Be my Law, and I shall be Firm-ly bound, for - ev - er free. A-MEN.

Come, Holy Ghost 129

EMPAYTAZ L. M.

From the Latin, c. Ninth Century
Trans. by John Cosin, 1627; Alt.

Collection of H. L. Empaytaz, 1817

1. Come, Ho - ly Ghost, our souls in - spire, And light - en with ce - les - tial fire; Thou the a - noint - ing Spir - it art, Who dost Thy seven - fold gifts im - part.
2. Thy bless - ed unc - tion from a - bove Is com - fort, life, and fire of love; En - a - ble with per - pet - ual light The dull - ness of our blind - ed sight.
3. A - noint our hearts and cheer our face With the a - bun-dance of Thy grace; Keep far our foes; give peace at home; Where Thou art Guide, no ill can come.
4. Teach us to know the Fa - ther, Son, And Thee, of both, to be but One; That through the a - ges all a - long Thy praise may be our end - less song. A - MEN.

130 Breathe on Me, Breath of God

TRENTHAM S. M.

Edwin Hatch, 1886 — Robert Jackson, 1894

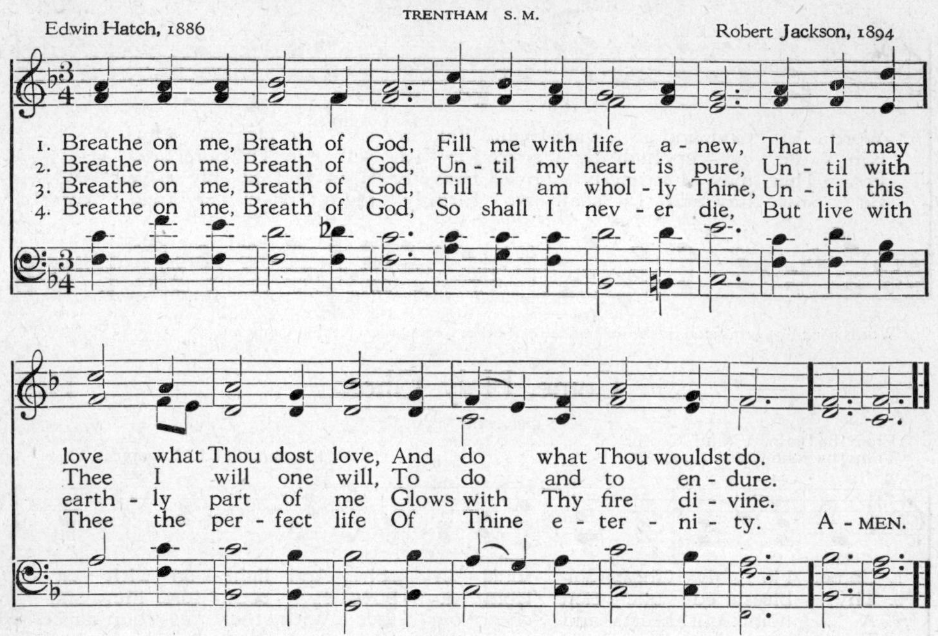
1. Breathe on me, Breath of God, Fill me with life a - new, That I may love what Thou dost love, And do what Thou wouldst do.
2. Breathe on me, Breath of God, Un - til my heart is pure, Un - til with Thee I will one will, To do and to en - dure.
3. Breathe on me, Breath of God, Till I am whol - ly Thine, Un - til this earth - ly part of me Glows with Thy fire di - vine.
4. Breathe on me, Breath of God, So shall I nev - er die, But live with Thee the per - fect life Of Thine e - ter - ni - ty. A - MEN.

Music used by permission of Mrs. Ethel Taylor.

131 Thy Home Is with the Humble, Lord

NAOMI C. M.

Frederick W. Faber, 1849 — Hans G. Nägeli (1768-1836), Arr. by Lowell Mason, 1836

1. Thy home is with the hum - ble, Lord; The sim - plest are the best; Thy lod - ging is in child-like hearts; Thou mak - est there Thy rest.
2. Dear Com - fort - er, e - ter - nal Love, If Thou wilt stay with me, Of low - ly thoughts and sim - ple ways I'll build a house for Thee.
3. Who made this beat - ing heart of mine But Thou, my heaven - ly Guest? Let no one have it, then, but Thee, And let it be Thy rest. A - MEN.

O Word of God Incarnate

MUNICH 7.6.7.6. D.

William Walsham How, 1867

Neuvermehrtes Meiningisches Gesangbuch, 1693

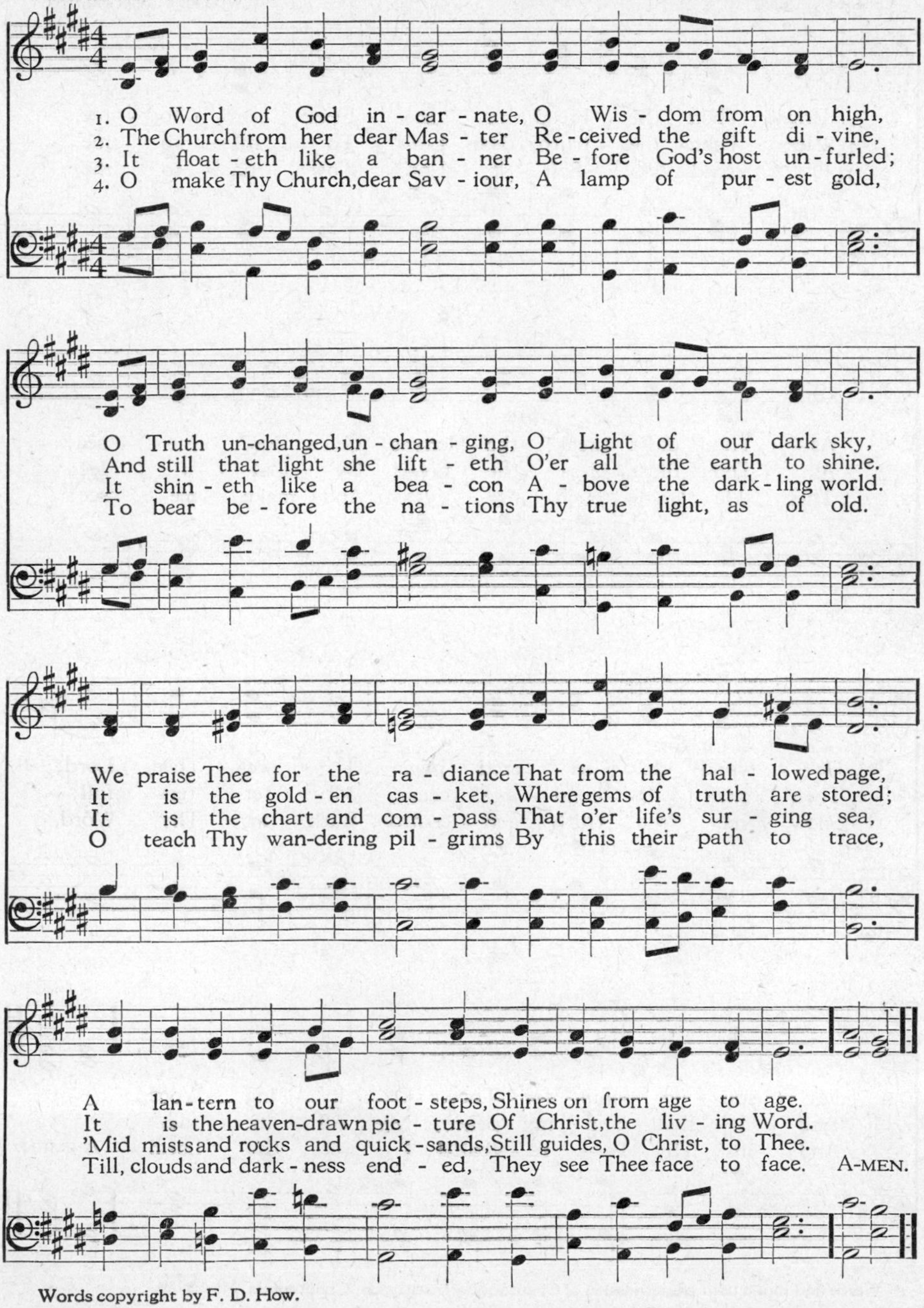

1. O Word of God in - car - nate, O Wis - dom from on high,
2. The Church from her dear Mas - ter Re - ceived the gift di - vine,
3. It float - eth like a ban - ner Be - fore God's host un - furled;
4. O make Thy Church, dear Sav - iour, A lamp of pur - est gold,

O Truth un-changed, un - chan - ging, O Light of our dark sky,
And still that light she lift - eth O'er all the earth to shine.
It shin - eth like a bea - con A - bove the dark - ling world.
To bear be - fore the na - tions Thy true light, as of old.

We praise Thee for the ra - diance That from the hal - lowed page,
It is the gold - en cas - ket, Where gems of truth are stored;
It is the chart and com - pass That o'er life's sur - ging sea,
O teach Thy wan-dering pil - grims By this their path to trace,

A lan - tern to our foot - steps, Shines on from age to age.
It is the heaven-drawn pic - ture Of Christ, the liv - ing Word.
'Mid mists and rocks and quick - sands, Still guides, O Christ, to Thee.
Till, clouds and dark - ness end - ed, They see Thee face to face. A-MEN.

133 Break Thou the Bread of Life

BREAD OF LIFE 6. 4. 6. 4. D.

Mary Ann Lathbury, 1877
Stanza 3 Added

William F. Sherwin, 1877

1. Break Thou the bread of life, Dear Lord, to me,
2. Bless Thou the truth, dear Lord, To me— to me,
3. O send Thy Spir - it, Lord, Now un - to me,
As Thou didst break the loaves Be - side the sea;
As Thou didst bless the bread By Gal - i - lee;
That He may touch my eyes, And make me see:
Be - yond the sa - cred page I seek Thee, Lord;
Then shall all bond - age cease, All fet - ters fall;
Show me the truth con - cealed With - in Thy Word,
My spir - it pants for Thee, O liv - ing Word.
And I shall find my peace, My All in all.
And in Thy Book re - vealed I see the Lord.
A - MEN.

The Heavens Declare Thy Glory, Lord — 134

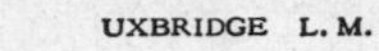
UXBRIDGE L. M.

Psalm 19
Isaac Watts, 1719

Lowell Mason, 1830

1. The heavens de-clare Thy glo - ry, Lord; In ev - ery star Thy wis - dom shines;
2. The roll-ing sun, the chan-ging light, And nights and days, Thy power con-fess;
3. Nor shall Thy spread-ing gos-pel rest Till through the world Thy truth has run;
4. Thy no-blest won-ders here we view In souls re-newed, and sins for - given:

But when our eyes be-hold Thy Word, We read Thy Name in fair-er lines.
But the blest Vol-ume Thou hast writ Re-veals Thy jus-tice and Thy grace.
Till Christ has all the na-tions blest That see the light, or feel the sun.
Lord, cleanse my sins, my soul re-new, And make Thy Word my guide to heaven. A-MEN.

Father of Mercies, in Thy Word — 135

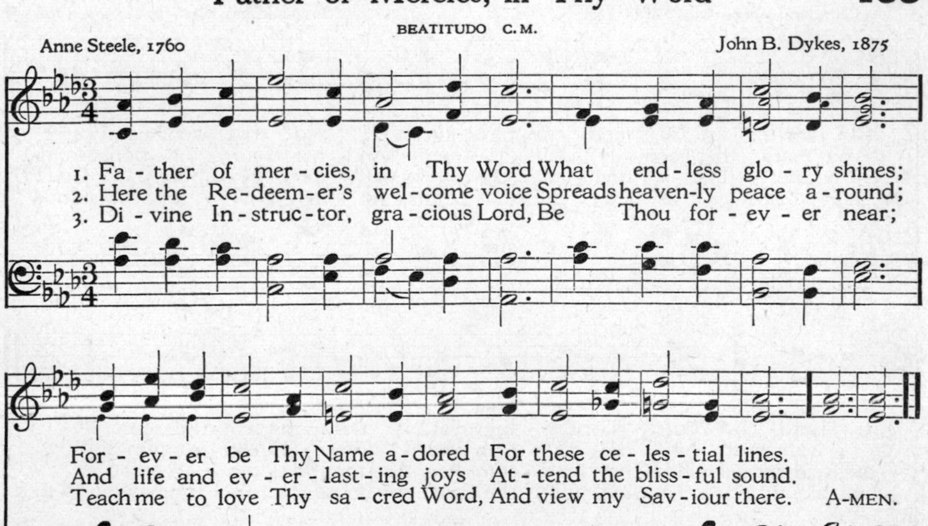
BEATITUDO C.M.
Anne Steele, 1760
John B. Dykes, 1875
1. Fa - ther of mer - cies, in Thy Word What end - less glo - ry shines;
2. Here the Re-deem-er's wel-come voice Spreads heaven-ly peace a - round;
3. Di - vine In - struc - tor, gra - cious Lord, Be Thou for - ev - er near;
For - ev - er be Thy Name a - dored For these ce - les - tial lines.
And life and ev - er - last - ing joys At - tend the bliss - ful sound.
Teach me to love Thy sa - cred Word, And view my Sav - iour there. A-MEN.

136 The Spirit Breathes Upon the Word

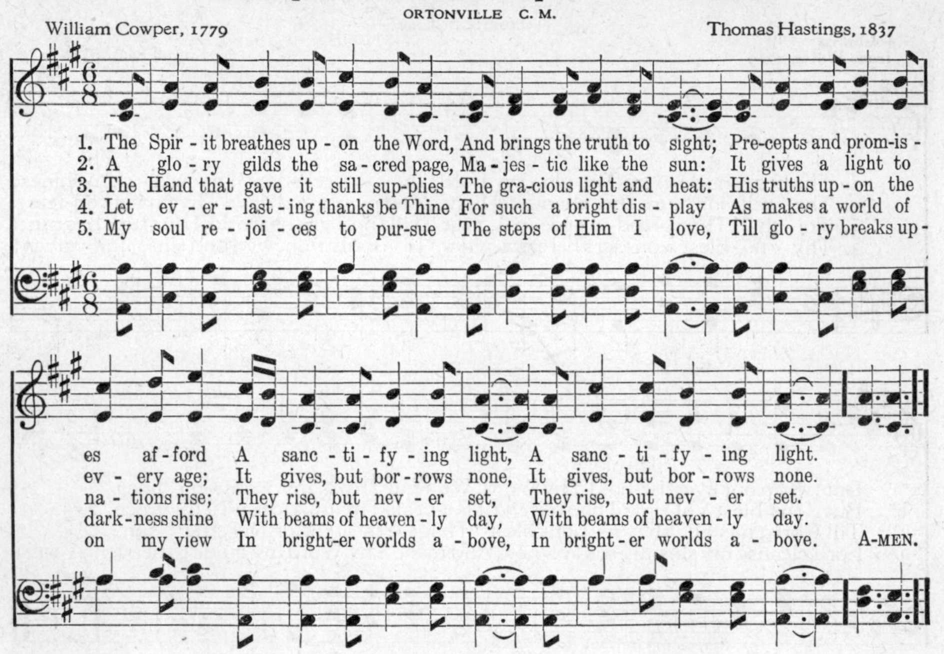
ORTONVILLE C. M.
William Cowper, 1779
Thomas Hastings, 1837
1. The Spir - it breathes up - on the Word, And brings the truth to sight; Pre-cepts and prom-is - es af - ford A sanc - ti - fy - ing light, A sanc - ti - fy - ing light.
2. A glo - ry gilds the sa - cred page, Ma - jes - tic like the sun: It gives a light to ev - ery age; It gives, but bor - rows none, It gives, but bor - rows none.
3. The Hand that gave it still sup-plies The gra-cious light and heat: His truths up - on the na - tions rise; They rise, but nev - er set, They rise, but nev - er set.
4. Let ev - er - last - ing thanks be Thine For such a bright dis - play As makes a world of dark - ness shine With beams of heaven - ly day, With beams of heaven - ly day.
5. My soul re - joi - ces to pur-sue The steps of Him I love, Till glo - ry breaks up - on my view In bright-er worlds a - bove, In bright - er worlds a - bove.
A-MEN.

137 O Where Are Kings and Empires Now

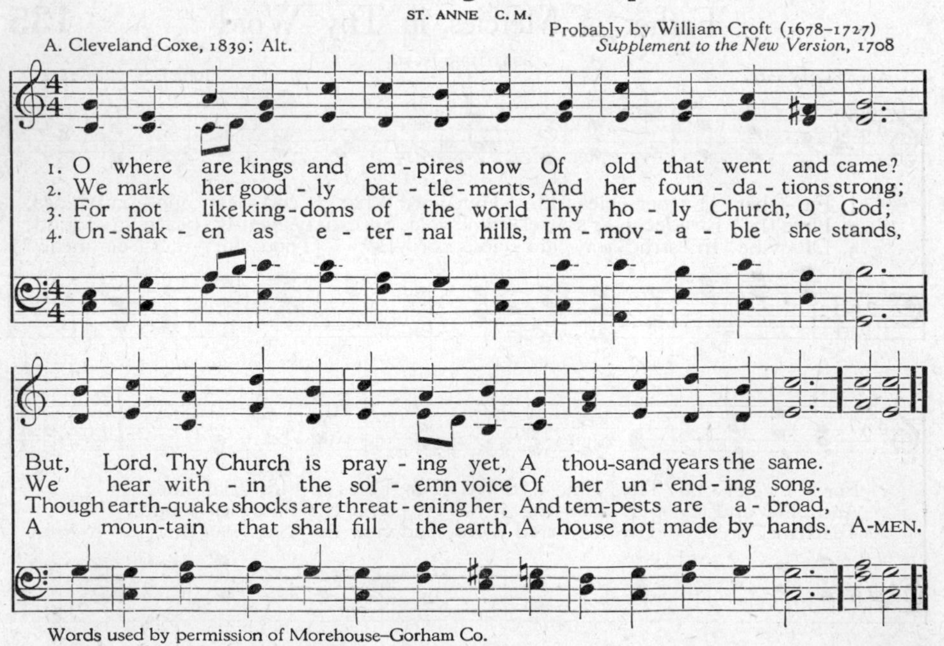
ST. ANNE C. M.
Probably by William Croft (1678–1727)
A. Cleveland Coxe, 1839; Alt.
Supplement to the New Version, 1708
1. O where are kings and em - pires now Of old that went and came? But, Lord, Thy Church is pray - ing yet, A thou-sand years the same.
2. We mark her good - ly bat - tle-ments, And her foun - da - tions strong; We hear with - in the sol - emn voice Of her un - end - ing song.
3. For not like king - doms of the world Thy ho - ly Church, O God; Though earth-quake shocks are threat - ening her, And tem-pests are a - broad,
4. Un - shak - en as e - ter - nal hills, Im - mov - a - ble she stands, A moun-tain that shall fill the earth, A house not made by hands.
A-MEN.

The Church's One Foundation

AURELIA 7. 6. 7. 6. D.

Samuel J. Stone, 1866 — Samuel S. Wesley, 1864

1. The Church's one Foun-da - tion Is Je - sus Christ her Lord;
2. E - lect from ev - ery na - tion, Yet one o'er all the earth,
3. Though with a scorn - ful won - der Men see her sore op-pressed,
4. 'Mid toil and trib - u - la - tion, And tu - mult of her war,
5. Yet she on earth hath un - ion With God the Three in One,
She is His new cre - a - tion By wa - ter and the word:
Her char - ter of sal - va - tion One Lord, one faith, one birth;
By schisms rent a - sun - der, By her - e - sies dis-tressed,
She waits the con - sum - ma - tion Of peace for - ev - er - more;
And mys - tic sweet com-mun - ion With those whose rest is won:
From heaven He came and sought her To be His ho - ly Bride;
One ho - ly Name she bless - es, Par - takes one ho - ly food,
Yet saints their watch are keep - ing, Their cry goes up, "How long?"
Till with the vi - sion glo - rious Her long - ing eyes are blest,
O hap - py ones and ho - ly! Lord, give us grace that we,
With His own blood He bought her, And for her life He died.
And to one hope she press - es, With ev - ery grace en-dued.
And soon the night of weep - ing Shall be the morn of song.
And the great Church vic - to - rious Shall be the Church at rest.
Like them, the meek and low - ly, On high may dwell with Thee. A-MEN.

139 Glorious Things of Thee Are Spoken

AUSTRIAN HYMN 8. 7. 8. 7. D.
John Newton, 1779
Franz Joseph Haydn, 1797
1. Glo - rious things of thee are spo - ken, Zi - on, cit - y of our God;
2. See, the streams of liv - ing wa - ters, Spring-ing from e - ter - nal Love,
3. Round each hab - i - ta - tion hov-ering, See the cloud and fire ap - pear
4. Sav - iour, if of Zi - on's cit - y I, through grace, a mem - ber am,
He whose word can - not be bro - ken Formed thee for His own a - bode:
Well sup - ply thy sons and daugh-ters, And all fear of want re - move:
For a glo - ry and a cov-ering, Show-ing that the Lord is near:
Let the world de - ride or pit - y, I will glo - ry in Thy Name:
On the Rock of A - ges found-ed, What can shake thy sure re - pose?
Who can faint, while such a riv - er Ev - er flows their thirst to as-suage;
Thus de - riv - ing from their ban - ner Light by night and shade by day,
Fad - ing is the world-ling's pleas-ure, All his boast - ed pomp and show;
With sal - va - tion's walls sur - round-ed, Thou mayst smile at all thy foes.
Grace, which, like the Lord the Giv - er, Nev - er fails from age to age?
Safe they feed up - on the man - na Which He gives them when they pray.
Sol - id joys and last - ing treas-ure None but Zi - on's chil-dren know. A-MEN.

I Love Thy Kingdom, Lord 140

ST. THOMAS S. M.

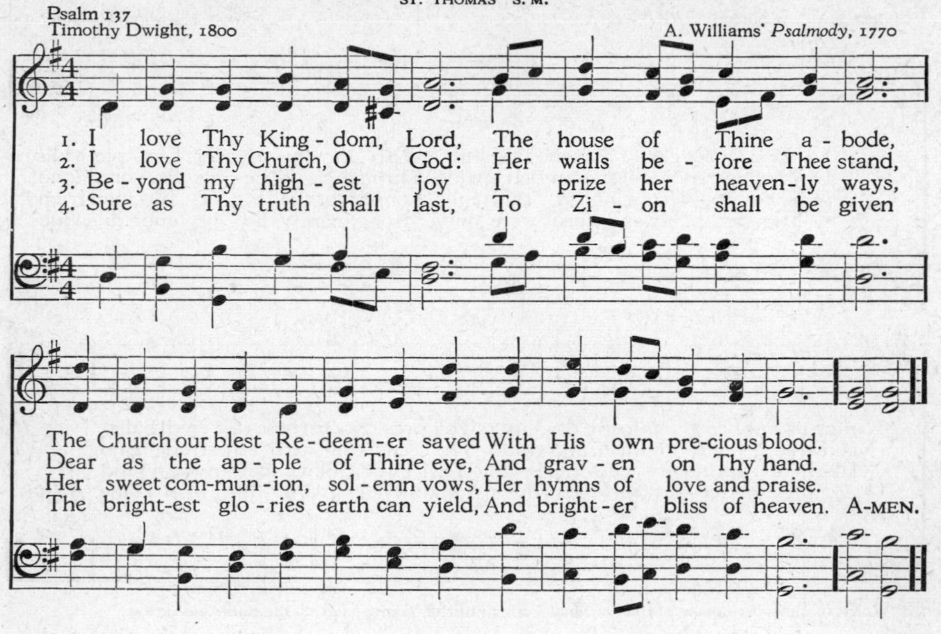
Psalm 137
Timothy Dwight, 1800
A. Williams' *Psalmody*, 1770
1. I love Thy King-dom, Lord, The house of Thine a-bode,
2. I love Thy Church, O God: Her walls be-fore Thee stand,
3. Be-yond my high-est joy I prize her heaven-ly ways,
4. Sure as Thy truth shall last, To Zi-on shall be given
The Church our blest Re-deem-er saved With His own pre-cious blood.
Dear as the ap-ple of Thine eye, And grav-en on Thy hand.
Her sweet com-mun-ion, sol-emn vows, Her hymns of love and praise.
The bright-est glo-ries earth can yield, And bright-er bliss of heaven. A-MEN.

Blest Be the Tie That Binds 141

DENNIS S. M.

John Fawcett, 1782
Stanza 4 Alt.
Hans G. Nägeli (1768–1836)
Arr. by Lowell Mason, 1845
1. Blest be the tie that binds Our hearts in Chris-tian love:
2. Be-fore our Fa-ther's throne We pour our ar-dent prayers;
3. We share our mu-tual woes, Our mu-tual bur-dens bear,
4. When we are called to part From those we hold in love,
5. From sor-row, toil, and pain, And sin, we shall be free;
The fel-low-ship of kin-dred minds Is like to that a-bove.
Our fears, our hopes, our aims, are one, Our com-forts and our cares.
And of-ten for each oth-er flows The sym-pa-thiz-ing tear.
We shall be with them still in heart, And hope to meet a-bove.
And per-fect love and friend-ship reign Through all e-ter-ni-ty. A-MEN.

142 O Thou Whose Glory Shone Like Fire

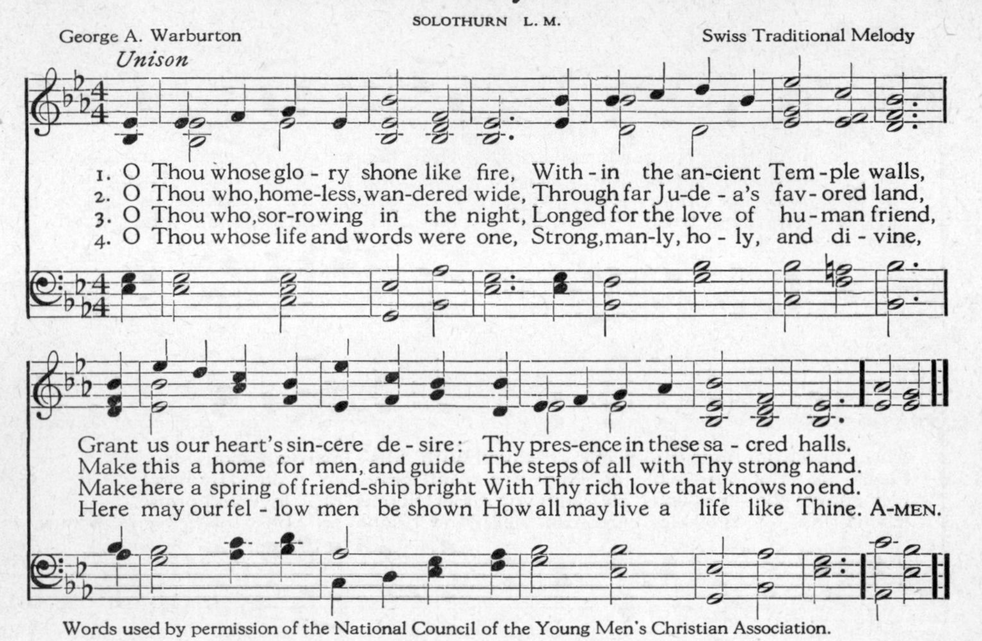
SOLOTHURN L. M.
George A. Warburton
Swiss Traditional Melody
Unison
1. O Thou whose glo - ry shone like fire, With - in the an-cient Tem - ple walls,
2. O Thou who, home-less, wan-dered wide, Through far Ju-de - a's fav - ored land,
3. O Thou who, sor-rowing in the night, Longed for the love of hu - man friend,
4. O Thou whose life and words were one, Strong, man-ly, ho - ly, and di - vine,
Grant us our heart's sin-cere de - sire: Thy pres-ence in these sa - cred halls.
Make this a home for men, and guide The steps of all with Thy strong hand.
Make here a spring of friend-ship bright With Thy rich love that knows no end.
Here may our fel - low men be shown How all may live a life like Thine. A-MEN.

Words used by permission of the National Council of the Young Men's Christian Association.

143 O Light, from Age to Age the Same

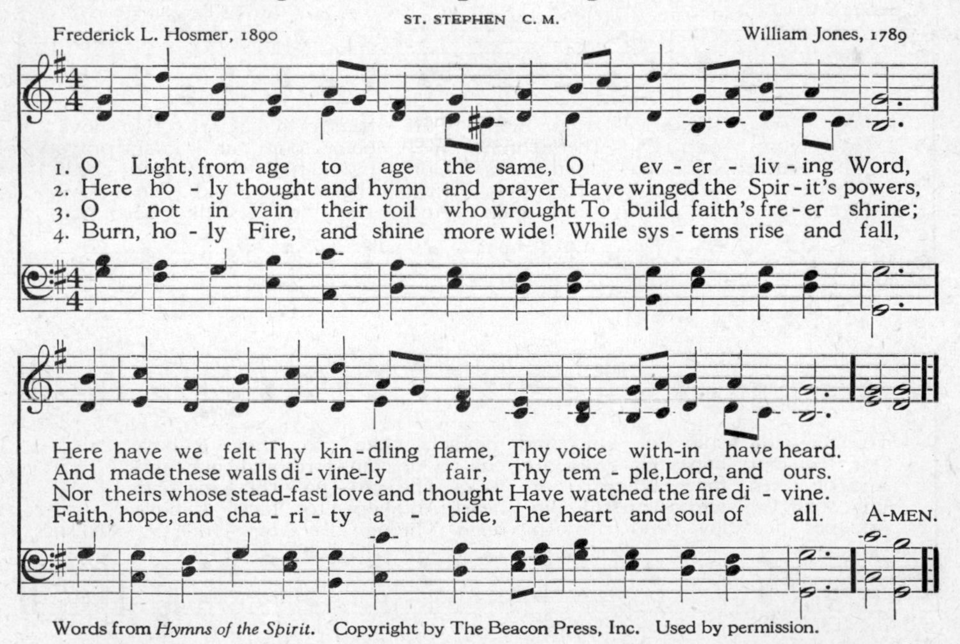
ST. STEPHEN C. M.
Frederick L. Hosmer, 1890
William Jones, 1789
1. O Light, from age to age the same, O ev - er - liv - ing Word,
2. Here ho - ly thought and hymn and prayer Have winged the Spir - it's powers,
3. O not in vain their toil who wrought To build faith's fre - er shrine;
4. Burn, ho - ly Fire, and shine more wide! While sys - tems rise and fall,
Here have we felt Thy kin - dling flame, Thy voice with-in have heard.
And made these walls di - vine-ly fair, Thy tem - ple, Lord, and ours.
Nor theirs whose stead-fast love and thought Have watched the fire di - vine.
Faith, hope, and cha - ri - ty a - bide, The heart and soul of all. A-MEN.

I Think When I Read That Sweet Story of Old 144

SWEET STORY Irregular
Greek Folk Song
Jemima Luke, 1841
Arr. by William B. Bradbury, 1859
1. I think when I read that sweet sto - ry of old,
2. I wish that His hands had been placed on my head,
3. Yet still to His foot - stool in prayer I may go,
4. In that beau - ti - ful place He is gone to pre - pare
5. I long for the joy of that glo - ri - ous time,
When Je - sus was here a - mong men,
That His arm had been thrown a - round me,
And ask for a share in His love;
For all who are washed and for - given;
The sweet - est and bright - est and best,
How He called lit - tle chil - dren as lambs to His fold,
And that I might have seen His kind look when He said,
And if I now ear - nest - ly seek Him be - low,
And man - y dear chil - dren are gath - er - ing there,
When the dear lit - tle chil - dren of ev - er - y clime
I should like to have been with them then.
"Let the lit - tle ones come un - to Me."
I shall see Him and hear Him a - bove.
For of such is the King - dom of heaven.
All shall crowd to His arms and be blest.
A-MEN.

 One stanza omitted.

145 For the Bread, Which Thou Hast Broken

AGAPE 8. 7. 8. 7.

Louis F. Benson, 1924 C. J. Dickinson (1822-1883)

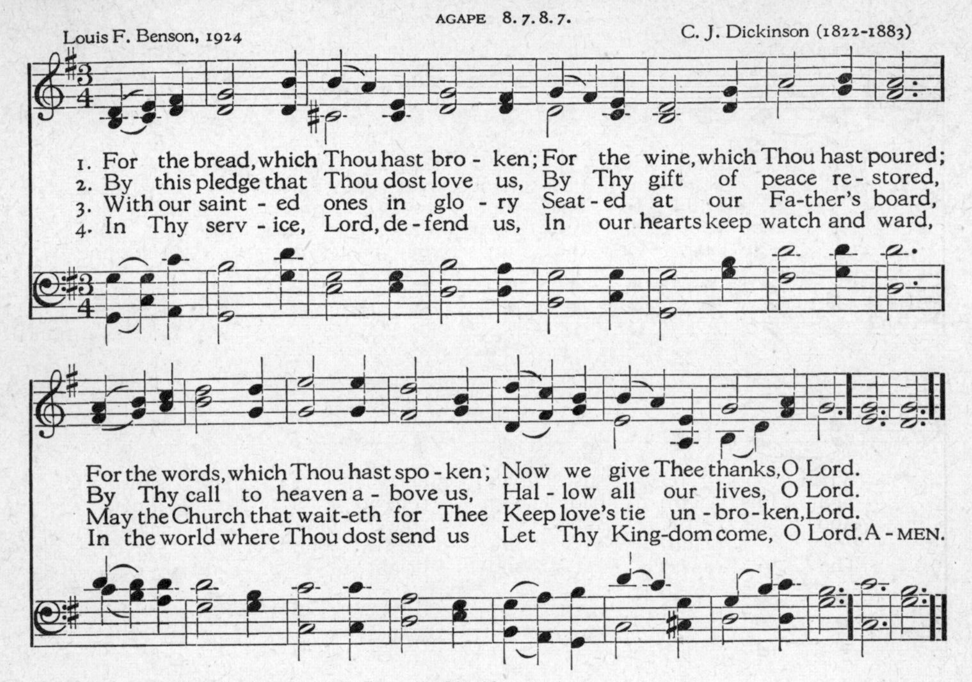
1. For the bread, which Thou hast bro - ken; For the wine, which Thou hast poured;
2. By this pledge that Thou dost love us, By Thy gift of peace re - stored,
3. With our saint - ed ones in glo - ry Seat - ed at our Fa-ther's board,
4. In Thy serv - ice, Lord, de - fend us, In our hearts keep watch and ward,
For the words, which Thou hast spo - ken; Now we give Thee thanks, O Lord.
By Thy call to heaven a - bove us, Hal - low all our lives, O Lord.
May the Church that wait-eth for Thee Keep love's tie un - bro - ken, Lord.
In the world where Thou dost send us Let Thy King-dom come, O Lord. A - MEN.

146 Bread of the World in Mercy Broken

EUCHARISTIC HYMN 9. 8. 9. 8.

Reginald Heber, 1827 John S. B. Hodges, 1869

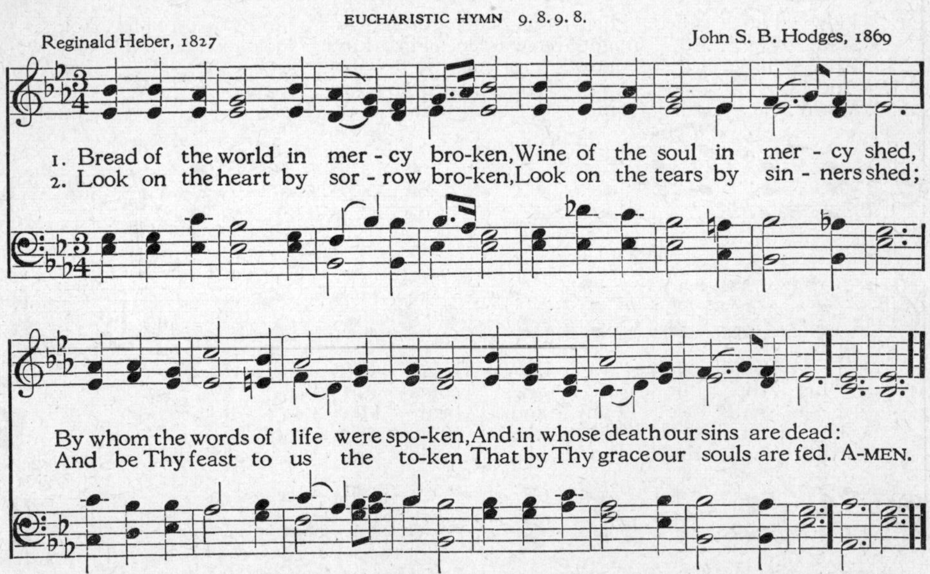
1. Bread of the world in mer - cy bro-ken, Wine of the soul in mer - cy shed,
2. Look on the heart by sor - row bro-ken, Look on the tears by sin - ners shed;
By whom the words of life were spo-ken, And in whose death our sins are dead:
And be Thy feast to us the to-ken That by Thy grace our souls are fed. A-MEN.

Jesus, Thou Joy of Loving Hearts 147

QUEBEC L. M.

From the Latin, Eleventh Century
Arr. and Trans. by Ray Palmer, 1858

Henry Baker, 1862

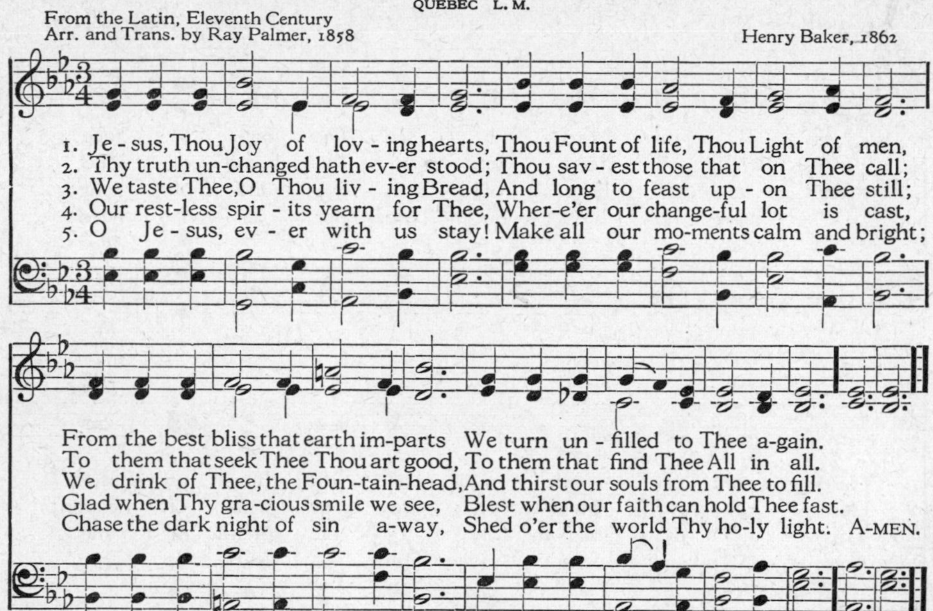
1. Je - sus, Thou Joy of lov - ing hearts, Thou Fount of life, Thou Light of men,
2. Thy truth un-changed hath ev-er stood; Thou sav - est those that on Thee call;
3. We taste Thee, O Thou liv - ing Bread, And long to feast up - on Thee still;
4. Our rest-less spir - its yearn for Thee, Wher-e'er our change-ful lot is cast,
5. O Je - sus, ev - er with us stay! Make all our mo-ments calm and bright;
From the best bliss that earth im-parts We turn un - filled to Thee a-gain.
To them that seek Thee Thou art good, To them that find Thee All in all.
We drink of Thee, the Foun-tain-head, And thirst our souls from Thee to fill.
Glad when Thy gra-cious smile we see, Blest when our faith can hold Thee fast.
Chase the dark night of sin a-way, Shed o'er the world Thy ho-ly light. A-MEN.

Music used by permission of M. Morley Horder.

The Lord's My Shepherd 148

EVAN C. M.

Psalm 23, *Scottish Psalter*, 1650
Based on Francis Rous and Others

William H. Havergal, 1846

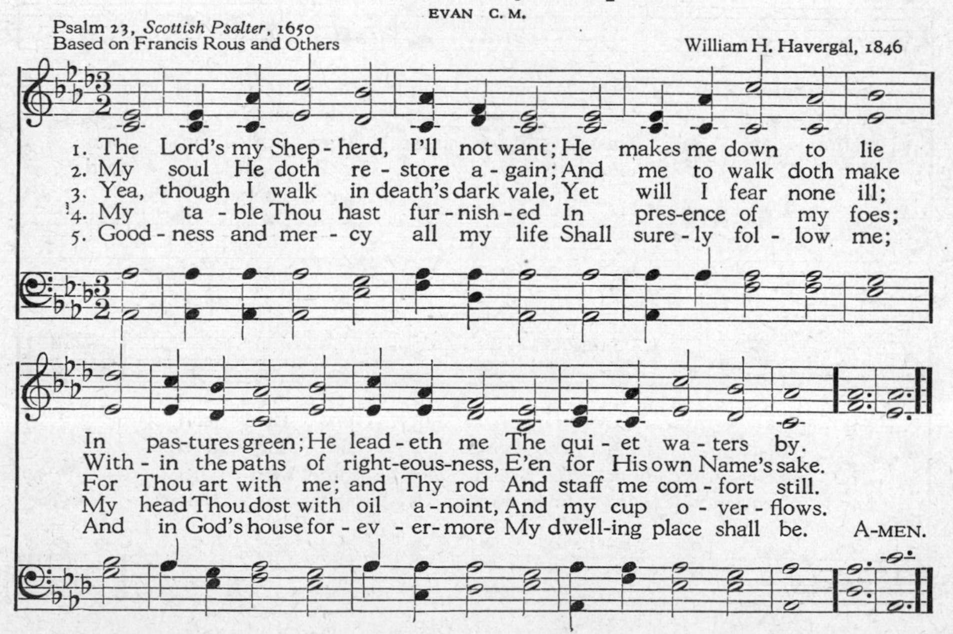
1. The Lord's my Shep - herd, I'll not want; He makes me down to lie
2. My soul He doth re - store a - gain; And me to walk doth make
3. Yea, though I walk in death's dark vale, Yet will I fear none ill;
4. My ta - ble Thou hast fur - nish - ed In pres-ence of my foes;
5. Good - ness and mer - cy all my life Shall sure - ly fol - low me;
In pas-tures green; He lead - eth me The qui - et wa - ters by.
With - in the paths of right-eous-ness, E'en for His own Name's sake.
For Thou art with me; and Thy rod And staff me com - fort still.
My head Thou dost with oil a - noint, And my cup o - ver - flows.
And in God's house for - ev - er-more My dwell-ing place shall be. A-MEN.

149 Here, O My Lord, I See Thee Face to Face

MORECAMBE 10. 10. 10. 10.
Horatius Bonar, 1855
Frederick C. Atkinson, 1870
1. Here, O my Lord, I see Thee face to face;
2. Here would I feed up - on the bread of God,
3. This is the hour of ban - quet and of song;
4. I have no help but Thine, nor do I need
Here would I touch and han - dle things un - seen,
Here drink with Thee the roy - al wine of heaven;
This is the heaven - ly ta - ble spread for me:
An - oth - er arm save Thine to lean up - on:
Here grasp with firm - er hand e - ter - nal grace,
Here would I lay a - side each earth - ly load,
Here let me feast, and, feast - ing, still pro - long
It is e - nough, my Lord, e - nough in - deed;
And all my wea - ri - ness up - on Thee lean.
Here taste a - fresh the calm of sin for - given.
The brief, bright hour of fel - low - ship with Thee.
My strength is in Thy might, Thy might a - lone.
A-MEN.

Dear Lord and Father of Mankind

REST 8. 6. 8. 8. 6.

John Greenleaf Whittier, 1872 | Frederick C. Maker, 1887

1. Dear Lord and Fa - ther of man - kind, For - give our fool - ish ways;
2. In sim - ple trust like theirs who heard, Be - side the Syr - ian sea,
3. O Sab - bath rest by Gal - i - lee! O calm of hills a - bove,
4. Drop Thy still dews of qui - et - ness, Till all our striv - ings cease;
5. Breathe through the heats of our de - sire Thy cool - ness and Thy balm;

Re - clothe us in our right - ful mind, In pur - er lives Thy
The gra - cious call - ing of the Lord, Let us, like them, with -
Where Je - sus knelt to share with Thee The si - lence of e -
Take from our souls the strain and stress, And let our or - dered
Let sense be dumb, let flesh re - tire; Speak through the earth-quake,

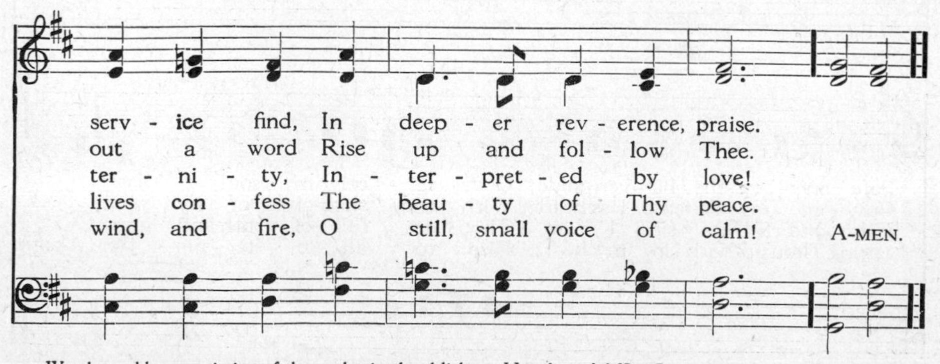
serv - ice find, In deep - er rev - erence, praise.
out a word Rise up and fol - low Thee.
ter - ni - ty, In - ter - pret - ed by love!
lives con - fess The beau - ty of Thy peace.
wind, and fire, O still, small voice of calm!
A-MEN.

151 Jesus, Lover of My Soul

ABERYSTWYTH 7.7.7.7. D.
(FIRST TUNE)

Charles Wesley, 1740 | Joseph Parry, 1879

1. Je - sus. Lov - er of my soul, Let me to Thy bos - om fly,
2. Oth - er ref - uge have I none; Hangs my help - less soul on Thee;
3. Thou, O Christ, art all I want; More than all in Thee I find:
4. Plen - teous grace with Thee is found, Grace to cov - er all my sin;
While the near - er wa - ters roll, While the tem - pest still is high:
Leave, ah! leave me not a - lone, Still sup - port and com - fort me.
Raise the fall - en, cheer the faint, Heal the sick, and lead the blind.
Let the heal - ing streams a - bound; Make and keep me pure with - in.
Hide me, O my Sav - iour, hide, Till the storm of life is past;
All my trust on Thee is stayed, All my help from Thee I bring;
Just and ho - ly is Thy Name; I am all un - right - eous-ness;
Thou of life the Foun - tain art, Free - ly let me take of Thee;
Safe in - to the ha - ven guide; O re - ceive my soul at last!
Cov - er my de-fense - less head With the shad - ow of Thy wing.
False and full of sin I am, Thou art full of truth and grace.
Spring Thou up with - in my heart, Rise to all e - ter - ni - ty. A-MEN.

Music used by permission of Hughes and Son, publishers, Wrexham, Great Britain.

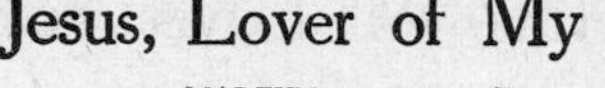

Jesus, Lover of My Soul 151

MARTYN 7. 7. 7. 7. D.
(SECOND TUNE)

Charles Wesley, 1740 — Simeon B. Marsh, 1834

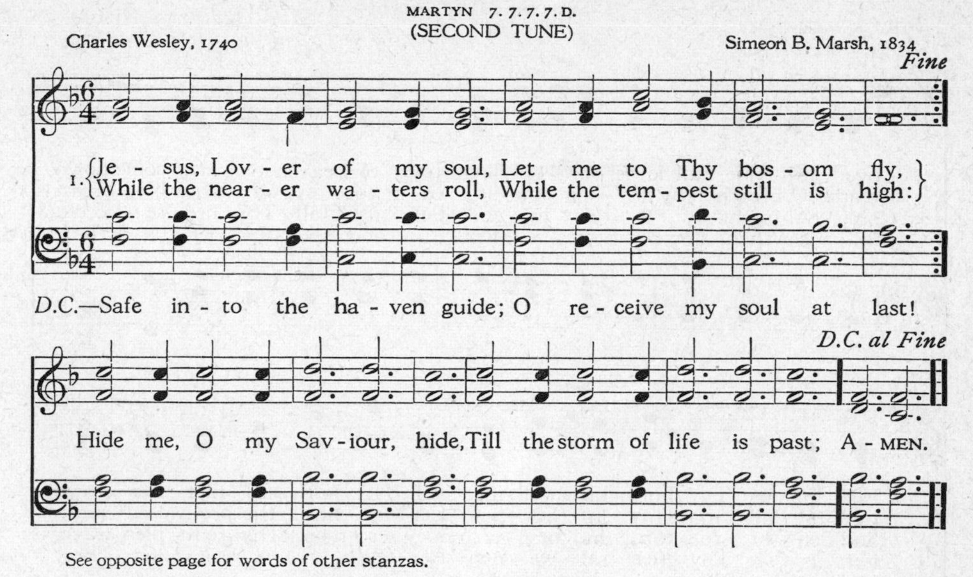
Fine
1. {Je - sus, Lov - er of my soul, Let me to Thy bos - om fly,
While the near - er wa - ters roll, While the tem - pest still is high:}
D.C.—Safe in - to the ha - ven guide; O re - ceive my soul at last!
D.C. al Fine
Hide me, O my Sav - iour, hide, Till the storm of life is past; A - MEN.

See opposite page for words of other stanzas.

I Name Thy Hallowed Name 152

SWABIA S. M.

Louis F. Benson, 1926 — Johann M. Spiess, 1745

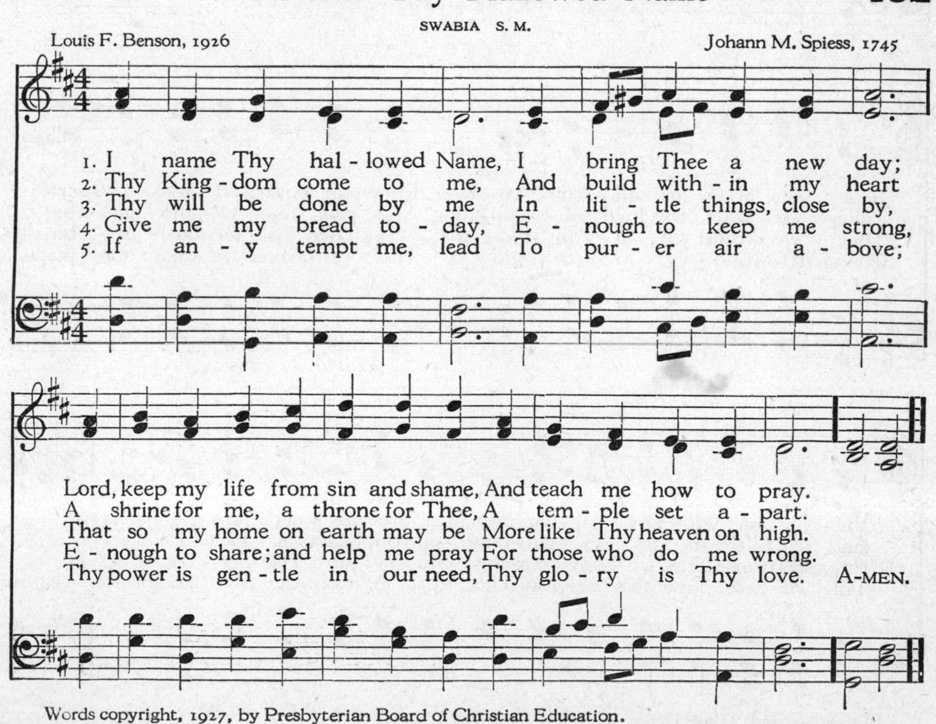
1. I name Thy hal - lowed Name, I bring Thee a new day;
2. Thy King - dom come to me, And build with - in my heart
3. Thy will be done by me In lit - tle things, close by,
4. Give me my bread to - day, E - nough to keep me strong,
5. If an - y tempt me, lead To pur - er air a - bove;
Lord, keep my life from sin and shame, And teach me how to pray.
A shrine for me, a throne for Thee, A tem - ple set a - part.
That so my home on earth may be More like Thy heaven on high.
E - nough to share; and help me pray For those who do me wrong.
Thy power is gen - tle in our need, Thy glo - ry is Thy love. A-MEN.

153 Love Divine, All Loves Excelling

BEECHER 8.7.8.7.D.
Charles Wesley, 1747
Stanza 2 Alt.
John Zundel, 1870
1. Love di - vine, all loves ex - cel - ling, Joy of heaven, to earth come down,
2. Breathe, O breathe Thy lov - ing Spir - it In - to ev - ery trou - bled breast!
3. Come, Al-might - y to de - liv - er, Let us all Thy life re - ceive;
4. Fin - ish, then, Thy new cre - a - tion; Pure and spot - less let us be;
Fix in us Thy hum - ble dwell - ing, All Thy faith - ful mer - cies crown!
Let us all in Thee in - her - it, Let us find the prom - ised rest;
Sud-den - ly re - turn, and nev - er, Nev - er more Thy tem - ples leave.
Let us see Thy great sal - va - tion Per - fect - ly re - stored in Thee;
Je - sus, Thou art all com - pas - sion, Pure, un - bound - ed love Thou art;
Take a - way the love of sin - ning; Al - pha and O - me - ga be;
Thee we would be al - ways bless - ing, Serve Thee as Thy hosts a - bove;
Changed from glo - ry in - to glo - ry, Till in heaven we take our place,
Vis - it us with Thy sal - va - tion, En - ter ev - ery trem - bling heart.
End of faith, as its Be - gin - ning, Set our hearts at lib - er - ty.
Pray, and praise Thee with - out ceas - ing, Glo - ry in Thy per - fect love.
Till we cast our crowns be - fore Thee, Lost in won - der, love, and praise. A-MEN.

Alternative tune, "Love Divine [Le Jeune]," number 200.

Rock of Ages, Cleft for Me

TOPLADY 7.7.7.7.7.7.
Augustus M. Toplady, 1776
Stanza 4, Line 2, Alt. by
Thomas Cotterill, 1815
Thomas Hastings, 1830
1. Rock of A - ges, cleft for me, Let me hide my - self in Thee; Let the wa - ter and the blood, From Thy riv - en side which flowed, Be of sin the dou - ble cure, Cleanse me from its guilt and power.
2. Not the la - bors of my hands Can ful - fill Thy law's de - mands; Could my zeal no res - pite know, Could my tears for - ev - er flow, All for sin could not a - tone; Thou must save, and Thou a - lone.
3. Noth - ing in my hand I bring, Sim - ply to Thy cross I cling; Na - ked, come to Thee for dress, Help - less, look to Thee for grace; Foul, I to the foun - tain fly; Wash me, Sav - iour, or I die.
4. While I draw this fleet - ing breath, When my eye - lids close in death, When I soar to worlds un - known, See Thee on Thy judg - ment throne, Rock of A - ges, cleft for me, Let me hide my - self in Thee.
A-MEN.

155 I Need Thee Every Hour

NEED 6. 4. 6. 4. with Refrain
Annie S. Hawks, 1872
Refrain Added by Robert Lowry
Robert Lowry, 1872
1. I need Thee ev - ery hour, Most gra - cious Lord;
2. I need Thee ev - ery hour; Stay Thou near by;
3. I need Thee ev - ery hour, In joy or pain;
4. I need Thee ev - ery hour; Teach me Thy will,
5. I need Thee ev - ery hour, Most Ho - ly One;
No ten - der voice like Thine Can peace af - ford.
Temp - ta - tions lose their power When Thou art nigh.
Come quick - ly, and a - bide, Or life is vain.
And Thy rich prom - is - es In me ful - fill.
O make me Thine in - deed, Thou bless - ed Son.
REFRAIN
I need Thee, O I need Thee, Ev - ery hour I need Thee!
O bless me now, my Sav - iour— I come to Thee! A - MEN.

Nearer, My God, to Thee

BETHANY 6. 4. 6. 4. 6. 6. 6. 4.
Sarah F. Adams, 1841
Lowell Mason, 1856
1. Near - er, my God, to Thee, Near - er to Thee!
2. Though like the wan - der - er, The sun gone down,
3. There let the way ap - pear Steps un - to heaven:
4. Then, with my wak - ing thoughts Bright with Thy praise,
5. Or if on joy - ful wing Cleav - ing the sky,
E'en though it be a cross That rais - eth me;
Dark - ness be o - ver me, My rest a stone;
All that Thou send - est me In mer - cy given:
Out of my ston - y griefs Beth - el I'll raise;
Sun, moon, and stars for - got, Up - ward I fly,
Still all my song shall be, Near - er, my God, to Thee,
Yet in my dreams I'd be Near - er, my God, to Thee,
An - gels to beck - on me Near - er, my God, to Thee,
So by my woes to be Near - er, my God, to Thee,
Still all my song shall be, Near - er, my God, to Thee,
Near - er, my God, to Thee, Near - er to Thee!
Near - er, my God, to Thee, Near - er to Thee!
Near - er, my God, to Thee, Near - er to Thee!
Near - er, my God, to Thee, Near - er to Thee!
Near - er, my God, to Thee, Near - er to Thee!
A-MEN.

157 Jesus, Saviour, Pilot Me

PILOT 7.7.7.7.7.7.
Edward Hopper, 1871
John E. Gould, 1871
1. Je - sus, Sav - iour, pi - lot me O - ver
2. As a moth - er stills her child, Thou canst
3. When at last I near the shore, And the
life's tem - pes - tuous sea; Un - known waves be - fore me roll,
hush the o - cean wild; Bois - terous waves o - bey Thy will
fear - ful break - ers roar 'Twixt me and the peace - ful rest,
Hid - ing rock and treach - erous shoal; Chart and
When Thou say'st to them, "Be still!" Won - drous
Then, while lean - ing on Thy breast, May I
com - pass came from Thee: Je - sus, Sav - iour, pi - lot me.
Sov - ereign of the sea, Je - sus, Sav - iour, pi - lot me.
hear Thee say to me, "Fear not, I will pi - lot thee." A - MEN.

What a Friend We Have in Jesus

WHAT A FRIEND 8.7.8.7.D.
Joseph Scriven (1820–1886)
C. Crozat Converse, 1868
1. What a Friend we have in Je - sus, All our sins and griefs to bear!
2. Have we tri - als and temp - ta - tions? Is there trou - ble an - y - where?
3. Are we weak and heav - y - la - den, Cum-bered with a load of care?
What a priv - i - lege to car - ry Ev - ery-thing to God in prayer!
We should nev - er be dis - cour - aged: Take it to the Lord in prayer!
Pre - cious Sav - iour, still our Ref - uge— Take it to the Lord in prayer!
O what peace we of - ten for - feit, O what need-less pain we bear,
Can we find a friend so faith - ful, Who will all our sor - rows share?
Do thy friends de - spise, for - sake thee? Take it to the Lord in prayer!
All be-cause we do not car - ry Ev - ery-thing to God in prayer!
Je - sus knows our ev - ery weak - ness— Take it to the Lord in prayer!
In His arms He'll take and shield thee, Thou wilt find a sol - ace there. A-MEN.

159 Now to Heaven Our Prayer Ascending

AR HYD Y NOS 8. 4. 8. 4. 8. 8. 8. 4.
Welsh Traditional Melody
Harmonized by L. O. Emerson, 1906
William E. Hickson (1810-1870)
1. Now to heaven our prayer as-cend-ing, God speed the right!
2. Pa-tient, firm, and per-se-ver-ing, God speed the right!
3. Still our on-ward course pur-su-ing, God speed the right!
In a no-ble cause con-tend-ing, God speed the right!
No e-vent or dan-ger fear-ing, God speed the right!
Ev-ery foe at length sub-du-ing, God speed the right!
May we live our lives be-fore Thee, Like the good and great in sto-ry,
Pains, nor toils, nor tri-als heed-ing, Nev-er from the truth re-ced-ing,
Truth! thy cause, what-e'er de-lay it, There's no power on earth can stay it,
If we fail, we fail with glo-ry— God speed the right!
And in Heaven's own time suc-ceed-ing, God speed the right!
Proud-ly let us then o-bey it, God speed the right! A-MEN.

Dear Lord, Who Sought at Dawn of Day 160

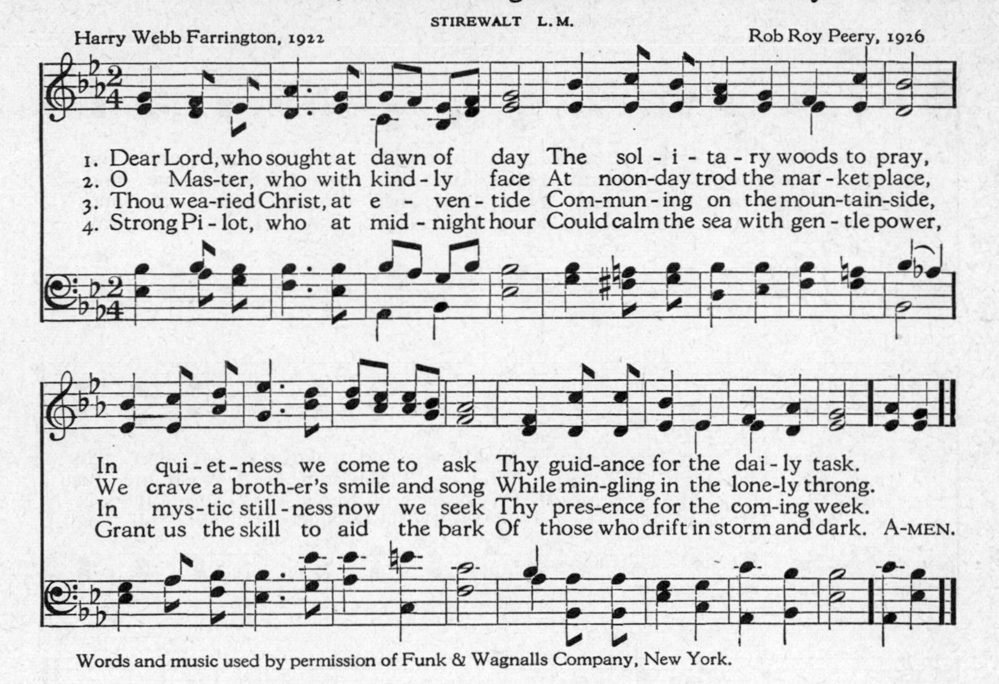
STIREWALT L. M.
Harry Webb Farrington, 1922
Rob Roy Peery, 1926
1. Dear Lord, who sought at dawn of day The sol-i-ta-ry woods to pray,
2. O Mas-ter, who with kind-ly face At noon-day trod the mar-ket place,
3. Thou wea-ried Christ, at e-ven-tide Com-mun-ing on the moun-tain-side,
4. Strong Pi-lot, who at mid-night hour Could calm the sea with gen-tle power,
In qui-et-ness we come to ask Thy guid-ance for the dai-ly task.
We crave a broth-er's smile and song While min-gling in the lone-ly throng.
In mys-tic still-ness now we seek Thy pres-ence for the com-ing week.
Grant us the skill to aid the bark Of those who drift in storm and dark. A-MEN.
Words and music used by permission of Funk & Wagnalls Company, New York.

Prayer Is the Soul's Sincere Desire 161

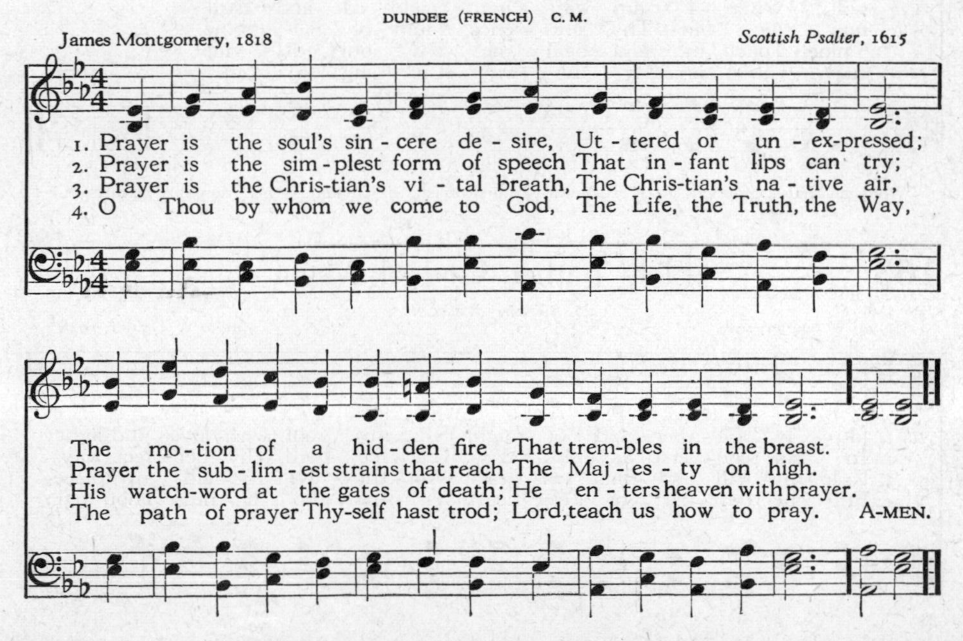
DUNDEE (FRENCH) C. M.
James Montgomery, 1818
Scottish Psalter, 1615
1. Prayer is the soul's sin-cere de-sire, Ut-tered or un-ex-pressed;
2. Prayer is the sim-plest form of speech That in-fant lips can try;
3. Prayer is the Chris-tian's vi-tal breath, The Chris-tian's na-tive air,
4. O Thou by whom we come to God, The Life, the Truth, the Way,
The mo-tion of a hid-den fire That trem-bles in the breast.
Prayer the sub-lim-est strains that reach The Maj-es-ty on high.
His watch-word at the gates of death; He en-ters heaven with prayer.
The path of prayer Thy-self hast trod; Lord, teach us how to pray. A-MEN.

162 Have Thine Own Way, Lord!

HAVE THINE OWN WAY 5.4.5.4.D.

Adelaide A. Pollard, 1906 — George C. Stebbins, 1907

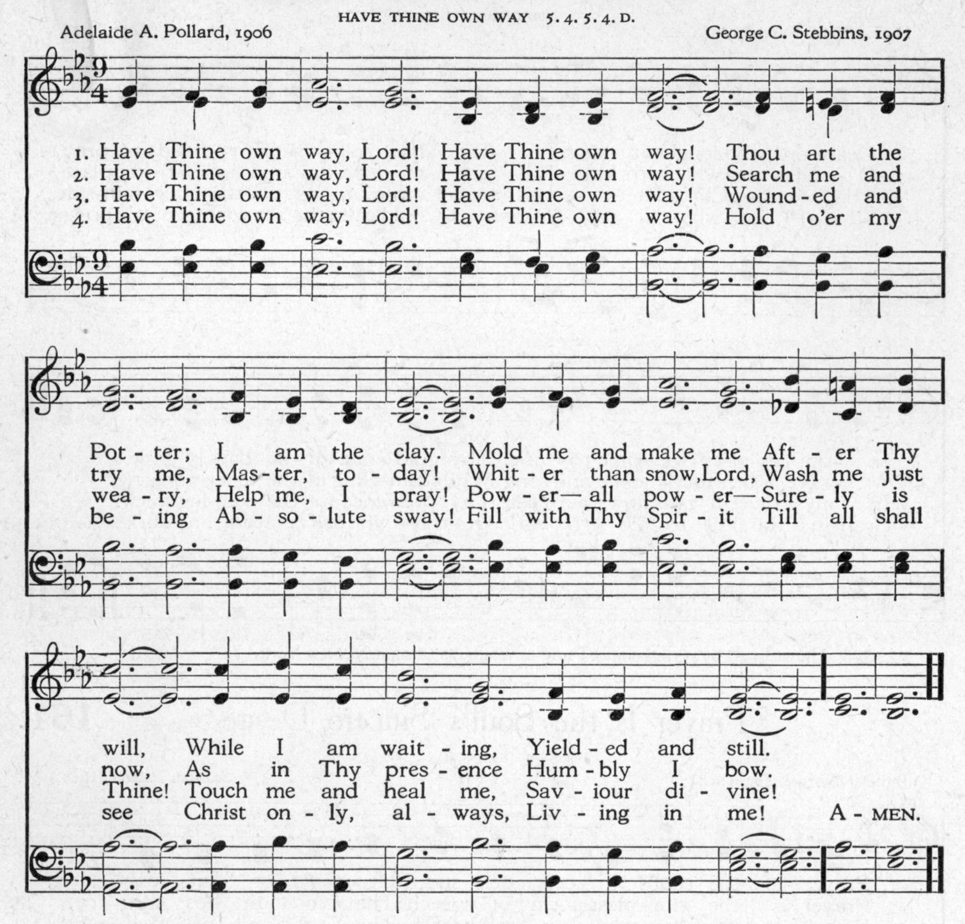
1. Have Thine own way, Lord! Have Thine own way! Thou art the
2. Have Thine own way, Lord! Have Thine own way! Search me and
3. Have Thine own way, Lord! Have Thine own way! Wound-ed and
4. Have Thine own way, Lord! Have Thine own way! Hold o'er my
Pot-ter; I am the clay. Mold me and make me Aft-er Thy
try me, Mas-ter, to-day! Whit-er than snow, Lord, Wash me just
wea-ry, Help me, I pray! Pow-er—all pow-er—Sure-ly is
be-ing Ab-so-lute sway! Fill with Thy Spir-it Till all shall
will, While I am wait-ing, Yield-ed and still.
now, As in Thy pres-ence Hum-bly I bow.
Thine! Touch me and heal me, Sav-iour di-vine!
see Christ on-ly, al-ways, Liv-ing in me! A-MEN.

163 Holy Father, God of Might

HANNA 7.7.7.5.

Calvin W. Laufer, 1928 — Calvin W. Laufer, 1928

1. Ho-ly Fa-ther, God of might, Fill my soul with love and light;
2. In our con-verse day by day Teach me, Lord, Thy per-fect way;
3. Rule my will and grant me grace Wor-thi-ly to fill my place;
4. Fill the tem-ple of my heart With the ho-li-ness Thou art;

Holy Father, God of Might (Concluded)

Though un - wor - thy in Thy sight, Come and dwell with me.
Be my con - stant Joy and Stay As I walk with Thee.
May the love that lights Thy face Guide and heart - en me.
Nev - er - more from me de - part: Make my heart Thy home. A-MEN.

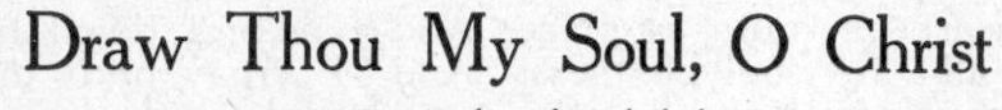

Draw Thou My Soul, O Christ 164

ST. EDMUND 6. 4. 6. 4. 6. 6. 6. 4.

Lucy Larcom, 1892 — Arthur S. Sullivan, 1872

1. Draw Thou my soul, O Christ, Clos - er to Thine; Breathe in - to
2. Lead forth my soul, O Christ, One with Thine own, Joy - ful to
3. Not for my - self a - lone May my prayer be; Lift Thou Thy
ev - ery wish Thy will di - vine: Raised my low self a - bove, Won by Thy
fol - low Thee Through paths un-known: In Thee my strength re - new; Give me Thy
world, O Christ, Clos - er to Thee: Cleanse it from guilt and wrong, Teach it sal -
death-less love, Ev - er, O Christ, through mine Let Thy life shine.
work to do: Through me Thy truth be shown, Thy love made known.
va - tion's song, Till earth, as heaven, ful - fill God's ho - ly will. A-MEN.

PRAYER AND HOPE

165 'Mid All the Traffic of the Ways

ST. AGNES C. M.

John Oxenham, 1917 — John B. Dykes, 1866

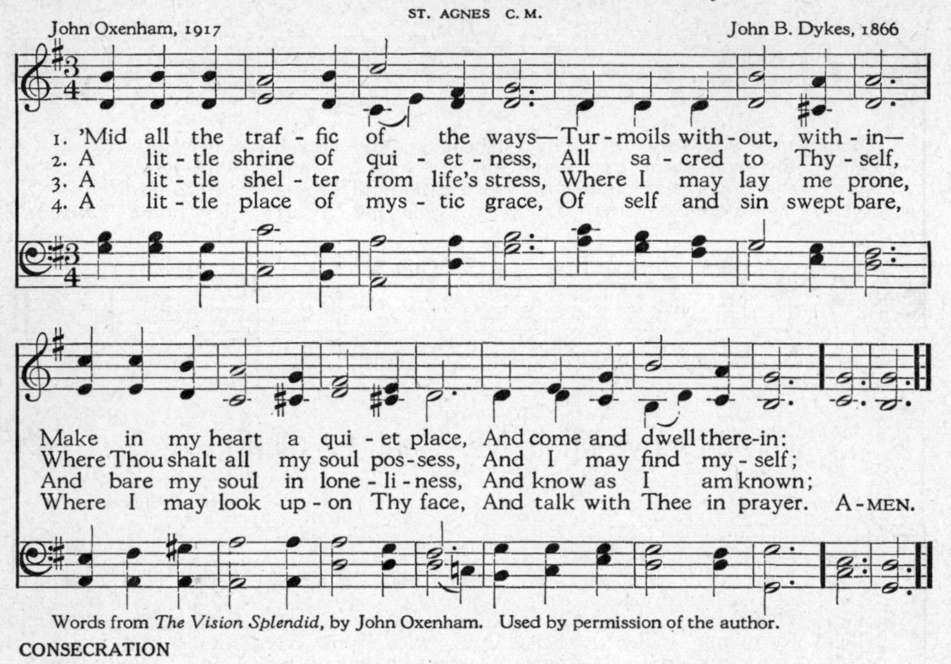
1. 'Mid all the traf - fic of the ways—Tur - moils with - out, with - in—
2. A lit - tle shrine of qui - et - ness, All sa - cred to Thy - self,
3. A lit - tle shel - ter from life's stress, Where I may lay me prone,
4. A lit - tle place of mys - tic grace, Of self and sin swept bare,
Make in my heart a qui - et place, And come and dwell there-in:
Where Thou shalt all my soul pos - sess, And I may find my - self;
And bare my soul in lone - li - ness, And know as I am known;
Where I may look up - on Thy face, And talk with Thee in prayer. A-MEN.

Words from *The Vision Splendid*, by John Oxenham. Used by permission of the author.

CONSECRATION

166 O Master, Let Me Walk with Thee

MARYTON L. M.

Washington Gladden, 1879 — Henry Percy Smith, 1874

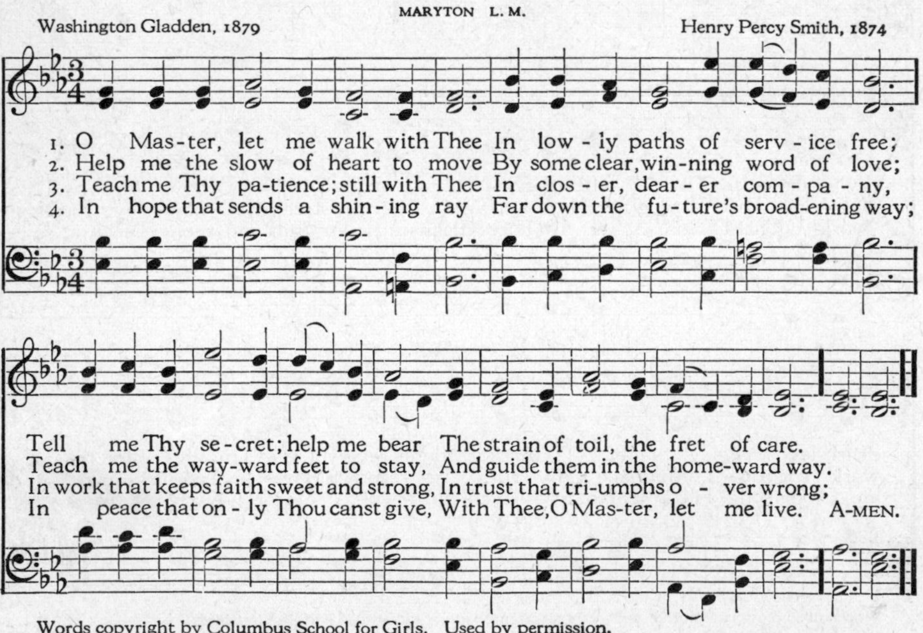
1. O Mas-ter, let me walk with Thee In low - ly paths of serv - ice free;
2. Help me the slow of heart to move By some clear, win-ning word of love;
3. Teach me Thy pa-tience; still with Thee In clos - er, dear - er com - pa - ny,
4. In hope that sends a shin - ing ray Far down the fu - ture's broad-ening way;
Tell me Thy se - cret; help me bear The strain of toil, the fret of care.
Teach me the way-ward feet to stay, And guide them in the home-ward way.
In work that keeps faith sweet and strong, In trust that tri - umphs o - ver wrong;
In peace that on - ly Thou canst give, With Thee, O Mas-ter, let me live. A-MEN.

Words copyright by Columbus School for Girls. Used by permission.
Music used by permission of M. Morley Horder.

Thou Didst Leave Thy Throne

167

MARGARET Irregular
Emily E. S. Elliott, 1864
Timothy R. Matthews, 1876
1. Thou didst leave Thy throne and Thy king - ly crown When Thou cam - est to
2. Heav-en's arch - es rang, when the an - gels sang, Pro - claim-ing Thy
3. The fox - es found rest and the bird had its nest In the shade of the
4. Thou cam - est, O Lord, with the liv - ing Word That should set Thy
5. When the heavens shall ring, and the an - gels sing At Thy com - ing to
earth for me; But in Beth - le-hem's home there was found no room
roy - al de - gree; But in low - ly birth didst Thou come to earth,
for - est tree; But Thy couch was the sod, O Thou Son of God,
chil - dren free; But with mock - ing scorn and with crown of thorn
vic - to - ry, Let Thy voice call me home, say - ing, "Yet there is room,
For Thy ho - ly na - tiv - i - ty. O come to my
And in great hu - mil - i - ty. O come to my
In the des - ert of Gal - i - lee. O come to my
They bore Thee to Cal - va - ry. O come to my
There is room at My side for thee." And my heart shall re -
heart, Lord Je - sus: There is room in my heart for Thee!
heart, Lord Je - sus: There is room in my heart for Thee!
heart, Lord Je - sus: There is room in my heart for Thee!
heart, Lord Je - sus: There is room in my heart for Thee!
joice, Lord Je - sus: When Thou com - est and call - est for me! A - MEN.

168 Take Thou Our Minds, Dear Lord

HALL 10. 10. 10. 10.
William H. Foulkes, 1918
Calvin W. Laufer, 1918
1. Take Thou our minds, dear Lord, we hum - bly pray;
2. Take Thou our hearts, O Christ—they are Thine own;
3. Take Thou our wills, Most High! Hold Thou full sway;
4. Take Thou our - selves, O Lord, heart, mind, and will;
Give us the mind of Christ each pass - ing day;
Come Thou with - in our souls and claim Thy throne;
Have in our in - most souls Thy per - fect way;
Through our sur - ren - dered souls Thy plans ful - fill.
Teach us to know the truth that sets us free;
Help us to shed a - broad Thy death - less love;
Guard Thou each sa - cred hour from self - ish ease;
We yield our - selves to Thee— time, tal - ents, all;
Grant us in all our thoughts to hon - or Thee.
Use us to make the earth like heaven a - bove.
Guide Thou our or - dered lives as Thou dost please.
We hear, and hence - forth heed, Thy sov - ereign call.
A-MEN.

Now in the Days of Youth

DIADEMATA S. M. D.
Walter J. Mathams, 1913
George J. Elvey, 1868
1. Now in the days of youth, When life flows fresh and free,
2. Teach us wher - e'er we live, To act as in Thy sight,
3. Teach us to love the true, The beau - ti - ful and pure,
4. Spir - it of Christ, do Thou Our first bright days in - spire,
Thou Lord of all our hearts and lives, We give our - selves to Thee;
And do what Thou wouldst have us do With ra - di - ant de - light;
And let us not for one short hour An e - vil thought en - dure.
That we may live the life of love And loft - i - est de - sire;
Our fer - vent gift re - ceive, And fit us to ful - fill,
Not choos - ing what is great, Nor spurn - ing what is small,
But give us grace to stand De - cid - ed, brave, and strong,
And be by Thee pre - pared For lar - ger years to come;
Through all our days, in all our ways, Our heaven-ly Fa - ther's will.
But tak - ing from Thy hands our tasks To glo - ri - fy them all.
The lov - ers of all ho - ly things, The foes of all things wrong.
And for the life in - ef - fa - ble, With-in the Fa - ther's home. A-MEN.

170 Just As I Am, Without One Plea

WOODWORTH L. M.
Charlotte Elliott, 1836
William B. Bradbury, 1849
1. Just as I am, with-out one plea But that Thy blood was shed for me,
2. Just as I am, and wait-ing not To rid my soul of one dark blot,
3. Just as I am, though tossed a-bout With man-y a con-flict, man-y a doubt,
4. Just as I am, poor, wretch-ed, blind; Sight, rich-es, heal-ing of the mind,
5. Just as I am! Thou wilt re-ceive, Wilt wel-come, par-don, cleanse, re-lieve;
6. Just as I am! Thy love un-known Has bro-ken ev-ery bar-rier down;
And that Thou bidd'st me come to Thee, O Lamb of God, I come, I come!
To Thee, whose blood can cleanse each spot, O Lamb of God, I come, I come!
Fight-ings and fears with-in, with-out, O Lamb of God, I come, I come!
Yea, all I need, in Thee to find, O Lamb of God, I come, I come!
Be-cause Thy prom-ise I be-lieve, O Lamb of God, I come, I come!
Now to be Thine, yea, Thine a-lone, O Lamb of God, I come, I come! A-MEN.
171 Just As I Am, Thine Own to Be
JUST AS I AM 8. 8. 8. 6.
Marianne Hearn Farningham, 1887
Joseph Barnby, 1893
1. Just as I am, Thine own to be, Friend of the young, who lov-est me,
2. In the glad morn-ing of my day, My life to give, my vows to pay,
3. I would live ev-er in the light; I would work ev-er for the right;
4. Just as I am, young, strong, and free, To be the best that I can be
To con-se-crate my-self to Thee, O Je-sus Christ, I come.
With no re-serve and no de-lay, With all my heart I come.
I would serve Thee with all my might; There-fore, to Thee I come.
For truth, and right-eous-ness, and Thee, Lord of my life, I come. A-MEN.

My Jesus, As Thou Wilt! 172

JEWETT 6.6.6.6. D.
Benjamin Schmolck, c. 1704
Trans. by Jane Laurie Borthwick, 1854
Carl Maria von Weber (1786–1826)
Arr. by Joseph P. Holbrook, 1862
1. My Je - sus, as Thou wilt! O may Thy will be mine!
2. My Je - sus, as Thou wilt! Though seen through many a tear,
3. My Je - sus, as Thou wilt! All shall be well for me;
In - to Thy hand of love I would my all re - sign.
Let not my star of hope Grow dim or dis - ap - pear.
Each chan - ging fu - ture scene I glad - ly trust with Thee.
Through sor - row or through joy, Con - duct me as Thine own;
Since Thou on earth hast wept, And sor - rowed oft a - lone,
Straight to my home a - bove I trav - el calm - ly on,
And help me still to say, "My Lord, Thy will be done."
If I must weep with Thee, My Lord, Thy will be done.
And sing, in life or death, "My Lord, Thy will be done." A-MEN.

173 Beneath the Cross of Jesus

ST. CHRISTOPHER 7. 6. 8. 6. 8. 6. 8. 6.
Elizabeth C. Clephane, Published 1872
Frederick C. Maker, 1881
1. Be - neath the cross of Je - sus I fain would take my stand—
2. Up - on the cross of Je - sus Mine eye at times can see
3. I take, O cross, thy shad - ow For my a - bid - ing place:
The shad - ow of a might - y Rock With - in a wea - ry land;
The ver - y dy - ing form of One Who suf - fered there for me:
I ask no oth - er sun - shine than The sun - shine of His face;
A home with - in the wil - der - ness, A rest up - on the way,
And from my strick - en heart with tears Two won - ders I con - fess—
Con - tent to let the world go by, To know no gain nor loss:
From the burn - ing of the noon - tide heat, And the bur - den of the day.
The won - ders of re - deem - ing love And my un - worth - i - ness.
My sin - ful self my on - ly shame, My glo - ry all, the cross. A-MEN.

O Jesus, I Have Promised

ANGEL'S STORY 7. 6. 7. 6. D.
John E. Bode, 1869
Arthur H. Mann, 1883
1. O Je - sus, I have prom - ised To serve Thee to the end;
2. O let me feel Thee near me! The world is ev - er near;
3. O let me hear Thee speak - ing In ac - cents clear and still,
4. O Je - sus, Thou hast prom - ised To all who fol - low Thee
Be Thou for - ev - er near me, My Mas - ter and my Friend:
I see the sights that daz - zle, The tempt - ing sounds I hear;
A - bove the storms of pas - sion, The mur - murs of self - will!
That where Thou art in glo - ry There shall Thy serv - ant be;
I shall not fear the bat - tle If Thou art by my side,
My foes are ev - er near me, A - round me and with - in;
O speak to re - as - sure me, To has - ten or con - trol!
And, Je - sus, I have prom - ised To serve Thee to the end;
Nor wan - der from the path - way If Thou wilt be my Guide.
But, Je - sus, draw Thou near - er, And shield my soul from sin.
O speak, and make me lis - ten, Thou Guard - ian of my soul!
O give me grace to fol - low My Mas - ter and my Friend! A - MEN.

175 Take My Life, and Let It Be

HENDON 7. 7. 7. 7. 7.
Frances Ridley Havergal, 1874
H. A. César Malan, 1827
1. Take my life, and let it be Con-se-crat-ed, Lord, to Thee.
2. Take my hands, and let them move At the im-pulse of Thy love.
3. Take my sil-ver and my gold; Not a mite would I with-hold.
4. Take my will, and make it Thine; It shall be no long-er mine.
5. Take my love; my Lord, I pour At Thy feet its treas-ure store.
Take my mo-ments and my days; Let them flow in
Take my lips, and let them be Filled with mes-sa-
Take my in-tel-lect, and use Ev-ery power as
Take my heart, it is Thine own; It shall be Thy
Take my-self, and I will be Ev-er, on-ly,
cease-less praise, Let them flow in cease-less praise.
ges from Thee, Filled with mes-sa-ges from Thee.
Thou shalt choose, Ev-ery power as Thou shalt choose.
roy-al throne, It shall be Thy roy-al throne.
all for Thee, Ev-er, on-ly, all for Thee.
A-MEN.

Give of Your Best to the Master

BARNARD 8. 7. 8. 7. D.
Howard B. Grose
Mrs. Charles Barnard (1830-1869)
1. Give of your best to the Mas-ter; Give of the strength of your youth;
2. Give of your best to the Mas-ter; Give Him first place in your heart;
3. Give of your best to the Mas-ter; Nought else is wor-thy His love;
REF. Give of your best to the Mas-ter; Give of the strength of your youth;
Fine
Throw your soul's fresh, glow-ing ar-dor In-to the bat-tle for truth.
Give Him first place in your serv-ice, Con-se-crate ev-ery part.
He gave Him-self for your ran-som, Gave up His glo-ry a-bove:
Clad in sal-va-tion's full ar-mor, Join in the bat-tle for truth.
Je-sus has set the ex-am-ple; Daunt-less was He, young and brave;
Give, and to you shall be giv-en; God His be-lov-ed Son gave;
Laid down His life with-out mur-mur, You from sin's ru-in to save;
rall.
D.C.
Give Him your loy-al de-vo-tion, Give Him the best that you have.
Grate-ful-ly seek-ing to serve Him, Give Him the best that you have.
Give Him your heart's ad-o-ra-tion, Give Him the best that you have.

177 Truehearted, Wholehearted

TRUEHEARTED 11.10.11.10. with Refrain
Frances Ridley Havergal, 1874
George C. Stebbins, 1890
1. True-heart-ed, whole-heart-ed, faith-ful and loy-al, King of our lives, by Thy grace we will be; Un-der the stand-ard ex-alt-ed and roy-al, Strong in Thy strength we will bat-tle for Thee.
2. True-heart-ed, whole-heart-ed, full-est al-le-giance Yield-ing hence-forth to our glo-ri-ous King; Val-iant en-deav-or and lov-ing o-be-dience, Free-ly and joy-ous-ly now would we bring.
3. True-heart-ed, whole-heart-ed, Sav-iour all-glo-rious! Take Thy great pow-er and reign there a-lone, O-ver our wills and af-fec-tions vic-to-rious, Free-ly sur-ren-dered and whol-ly Thine own.
REFRAIN
Peal out the watch-word! Si-lence it nev-er! Song of our
Peal
Si-lence
Song

Truehearted, Wholehearted (Concluded)

spir - its re - joi - cing and free; Peal out the watch-word!
re - joi - cing and free; Peal
Loy - al for - ev - er, King of our lives, by Thy grace we will be. A-MEN.
Loy - al King

God, Who Touchest Earth with Beauty 178

BULLINGER 8.5.8.5.

Mary S. Edgar, 1925, 1939

Ethelbert W. Bullinger, 1874; Alt.

1. God, who touch - est earth with beau - ty, Make my heart a - new;
2. Like Thy springs and run - ning wa - ters Make me crys - tal pure;
3. Like Thy dan - cing waves in sun - light Make me glad and free;
4. Like the arch - ing of the heav - ens Lift my thoughts a - bove;
5. God, who touch - est earth with beau - ty, Make my heart a - new;
With Thy Spir - it re - cre - ate me, Pure and strong and true.
Like Thy rocks of tow - ering gran - deur Make me strong and sure.
Like the straight - ness of the pine trees Let me up - right be.
Turn my dreams to no - ble ac - tion—Min - is - tries of love.
Keep me ev - er, by Thy Spir - it, Pure and strong and true. A-MEN.

179 God of Our Youth, to Whom We Yield

COVERT 8. 8. 8. 8. 8. 8.

William Byron Forbush, 1911; Alt. Calvin W. Laufer, 1928

1. God of our youth, to whom we yield The tribute of our eager praise, Upon the well-contested field, And 'mid the glory of these days, God of our youth, be with us yet, Lest we forget, lest we forget.
2. Sturdy of limb, with bounding health, Eager to play the hero's part, Grant to us each that greater wealth, An undefiled and loyal heart, God of our youth, be Thou our might, To do the right, to do the right.
3. When from the field of mimic strife Of strength with strength and speed with speed, We face the sterner fights of life, As then our strength in time of need, God of our youth, inspire us still, To do Thy will, to do Thy will. A-MEN.

Alternative tune, "St. Catherine," number 224.

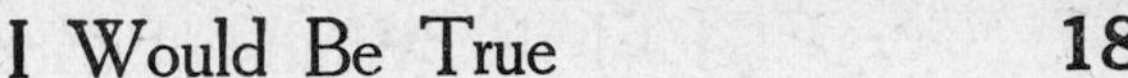
I Would Be True
180

PEEK 11. 10. 11. 10.
Howard Arnold Walter (1883–1918)
Joseph Yates Peek, 1911
1. I would be true, for there are those who trust me; I would be pure, for there are those who care; I would be strong, for there is much to suf - fer; I would be brave, for there is much to dare, I would be brave, for there is much to dare.
2. I would be friend of all— the foe, the friend - less; I would be giv - ing, and for - get the gift; I would be hum - ble, for I know my weak - ness; I would look up, and laugh, and love, and lift, I would look up, and laugh, and love, and lift.
A-MEN.

181 I Feel the Winds of God Today

MOUNT VERNON C. M. D.
Jessie Adams, 1907
Charles S. Brown, 1906
1. I feel the winds of God to-day; To-day my sail I lift,
2. It is the wind of God that dries My vain, re-gret-ful tears,
3. If ev-er I for-get Thy love And how that love was shown,
Though heav-y oft with drench-ing spray, And torn with man-y a rift:
Un-til with brav-er thoughts shall rise The pur-er, bright-er years:
Lift high the blood-red flag a-bove: It bears Thy Name a-lone.
If hope but light the wa-ter's crest, And Christ my bark will use,
If cast on shores of self-ish ease Or pleas-ure I should be,
Great Pi-lot of my on-ward way, Thou wilt not let me drift:
I'll seek the seas at His be-hest And brave an-oth-er cruise.
Lord, let me feel Thy fresh-ening breeze And I'll put back to sea.
I feel the winds of God to-day, To-day my sail I lift. A-MEN.

O Jesus, Prince of Life and Truth

ALL SAINTS NEW C. M. D.
Anon.
Henry S. Cutler, 1872
1. O Je - sus, Prince of life and truth, Be - neath Thy ban - ner bright,
2. In ser - ried ranks, with fear - less tread, O Cap - tain of us all,
3. O Je - sus, once a Naz - areth boy, And tempt-ed like as we,
We ded - i - cate our strength and youth To bat - tle for the right;
Thy glo - ry on our ban - ners shed, We an - swer to Thy call;
All in - ward foes help us de - stroy, And spot - less all to be.
We give our lives with glad in - tent To serve the world and Thee,
And where the fier - cest bat - tles press A - gainst the hosts of sin,
We trust Thee for the grace to win The high, vic - to - rious goal,
To die, to suf - fer and be spent, To set our broth-ers free.
To res - cue those in dire dis-tress We glad - ly en - ter in.
Where pu - ri - ty shall con - quer sin In Christ-like self - con - trol. A-MEN.

183 Father, Lead Me Day by Day

LYNE 7.7.7.7.

John Page Hopps (1834–1912) — *Magdalen Chapel Hymns*, c. 1760

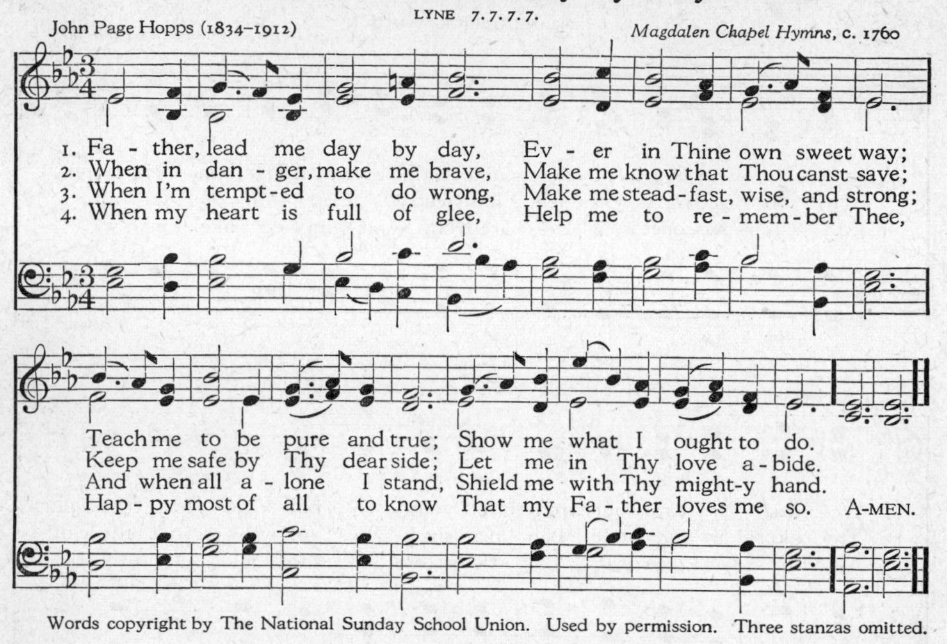
1. Fa - ther, lead me day by day, Ev - er in Thine own sweet way;
2. When in dan - ger, make me brave, Make me know that Thou canst save;
3. When I'm tempt-ed to do wrong, Make me stead-fast, wise, and strong;
4. When my heart is full of glee, Help me to re - mem - ber Thee,
Teach me to be pure and true; Show me what I ought to do.
Keep me safe by Thy dear side; Let me in Thy love a - bide.
And when all a - lone I stand, Shield me with Thy might-y hand.
Hap - py most of all to know That my Fa - ther loves me so. A-MEN.

 Three stanzas omitted.

184 I Know that My Redeemer Lives

BRADFORD C. M.

Harold I. Donnelly, 1928 — Arr. from Georg Friedrich Handel, 1741

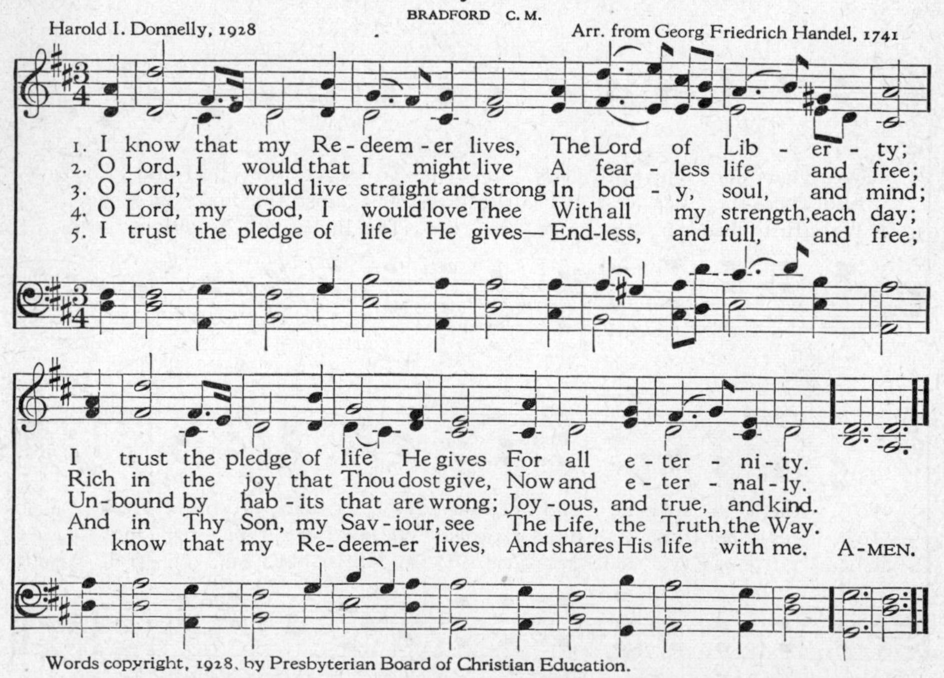
1. I know that my Re - deem - er lives, The Lord of Lib - er - ty;
2. O Lord, I would that I might live A fear - less life and free;
3. O Lord, I would live straight and strong In bod - y, soul, and mind;
4. O Lord, my God, I would love Thee With all my strength, each day;
5. I trust the pledge of life He gives— End-less, and full, and free;
I trust the pledge of life He gives For all e - ter - ni - ty.
Rich in the joy that Thou dost give, Now and e - ter - nal - ly.
Un - bound by hab - its that are wrong; Joy - ous, and true, and kind.
And in Thy Son, my Sav - iour, see The Life, the Truth, the Way.
I know that my Re - deem-er lives, And shares His life with me. A-MEN.

Temper My Spirit, O Lord

AGNI Irregular

Jean Starr Untermeyer, 1921

Grace Wilbur Conant, 1927

Tem - per my spir - it, O Lord, Keep it long in the fire;
Make it one with the flame, let it share That up - reach-ing de - sire.
Grasp it, Thy - self, O my God, Swing it straight-er and high - er!
Tem-per my spir-it, O Lord, Tem-per my spir - it, O Lord.
A-MEN.

186 Great Master, Touch Us

CONISBOROUGH 10. 10. 10. 10.

Horatius Bonar (1808-1889) — Wilfrid Sanderson, 1919

1. Great Mas-ter, touch us with Thy skill-ful hands; Let not the music that is in us die: Great Sculp-tor, hew and pol-ish us, nor let, Hid-den and lost, Thy form with-in us lie.
2. Spare not the stroke; do with us what Thou wilt; Let there be nought un-fin-ished, bro-ken, marred; Com-plete Thy pur-pose that we may be-come Thy per-fect im-age—Thou our God and Lord. A-MEN.

187 The Body, Lord, Is Ours to Keep

DOLUT 8. 8. 8. 8. 8. 5.

Eleanor B. Stock, 1929 — Sebastian W. Meyer, 1909

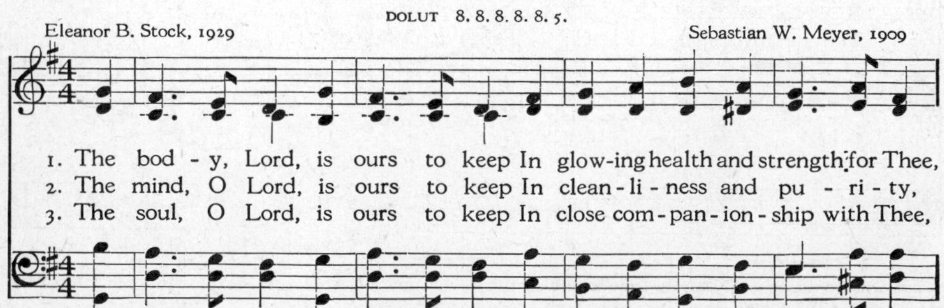

1. The bod-y, Lord, is ours to keep In glow-ing health and strength for Thee,
2. The mind, O Lord, is ours to keep In clean-li-ness and pu-ri-ty,
3. The soul, O Lord, is ours to keep In close com-pan-ion-ship with Thee,

The Body, Lord, Is Ours to Keep (Concluded)

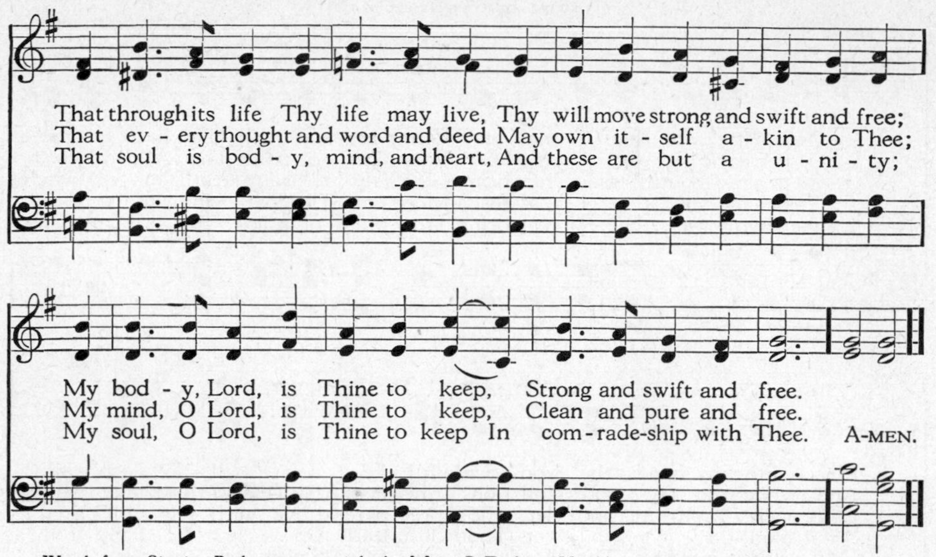
That through its life Thy life may live, Thy will move strong and swift and free;
That ev - ery thought and word and deed May own it - self a - kin to Thee;
That soul is bod - y, mind, and heart, And these are but a u - ni - ty;
My bod - y, Lord, is Thine to keep, Strong and swift and free.
My mind, O Lord, is Thine to keep, Clean and pure and free.
My soul, O Lord, is Thine to keep In com - rade-ship with Thee. A-MEN.

Words from *Singing Pathways*, copyright by Mary S. Dickie. Used by permission of Eleanor B. Stock.
Music used by permission of the Trustees of *The Fellowship Hymn Book*.

Teach Me, O Lord, Thy Holy Way 188

RIMINGTON L. M.

William T. Matson, 1866 — Francis Duckworth, 1904

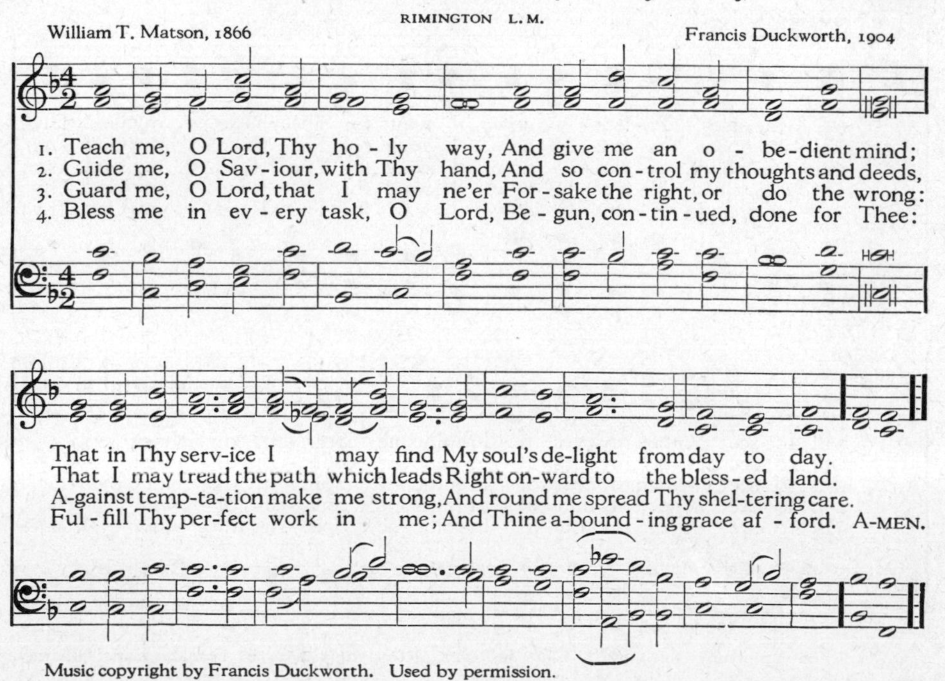
1. Teach me, O Lord, Thy ho - ly way, And give me an o - be - dient mind;
2. Guide me, O Sav - iour, with Thy hand, And so con - trol my thoughts and deeds,
3. Guard me, O Lord, that I may ne'er For - sake the right, or do the wrong:
4. Bless me in ev - ery task, O Lord, Be - gun, con - tin - ued, done for Thee:
That in Thy serv - ice I may find My soul's de - light from day to day.
That I may tread the path which leads Right on - ward to the bless - ed land.
A - gainst temp - ta - tion make me strong, And round me spread Thy shel - tering care.
Ful - fill Thy per - fect work in me; And Thine a - bound - ing grace af - ford. A-MEN.

Music copyright by Francis Duckworth. Used by permission.

189 Open My Eyes, that I May See

OPEN MY EYES Irregular

Clara H. Scott, 1896 — Clara H. Scott, 1896

1. O-pen my eyes, that I may see Glimp-ses of truth Thou hast for me; Place in my hands the won-der-ful key That shall un-clasp, and set me free. Si-lent-ly now I wait for Thee, Read-y, my God, Thy will to see; O-pen my eyes, il-lu-mine me, Spir-it di-vine!
2. O-pen my ears, that I may hear Voi-ces of truth Thou send-est clear; And while the wave notes fall on my ear, Ev-ery-thing false will dis-ap-pear. Si-lent-ly now I wait for Thee, Read-y, my God, Thy will to see; O-pen my ears, il-lu-mine me, Spir-it di-vine!
3. O-pen my mouth, and let me bear Glad-ly the warm truth ev-ery-where; O-pen my heart, and let me pre-pare Love with Thy chil-dren thus to share. Si-lent-ly now I wait for Thee, Read-y, my God, Thy will to see; O-pen my heart, il-lu-mine me, Spir-it di-vine!
4. O-pen my mind, that I may read More of Thy love in word and deed; What shall I fear while yet Thou dost lead? On-ly for light from Thee I plead. Si-lent-ly now I wait for Thee, Read-y, my God, Thy will to see; O-pen my mind, il-lu-mine me, Spir-it di-vine!
5. O-pen my way, that I may bring Tro-phies of grace to Christ, my King; Ech-oed in love Thy Word shall out-ring Sweet as the note that an-gels sing. Si-lent-ly now I wait for Thee, Read-y, my God, Thy will to see; O-pen my way, il-lu-mine me, Spir-it di-vine!
A-MEN.

I've Found a Friend

FRIEND 8. 7. 8. 7. D.
James Gridley Small, 1866
George C. Stebbins, 1878
1. I've found a Friend; oh, such a Friend! He loved me ere I knew Him;
He drew me with the cords of love, And thus He bound me to Him;
And round my heart still close-ly twine Those ties which nought can sev-er,
For I am His, and He is mine, For-ev-er and for-ev-er.
2. I've found a Friend; oh, such a Friend! He bled, He died to save me;
And not a-lone the gift of life, But His own self He gave me.
Nought that I have my own I call, I hold it for the Giv-er;
My heart, my strength, my life, my all, Are His, and His for-ev-er.
3. I've found a Friend; oh, such a Friend! So kind, and true, and ten-der!
So wise a Coun-se-lor and Guide, So might-y a De-fend-er!
From Him who loves me now so well What power my soul can sev-er?
Shall life or death, or earth or hell? No: I am His for-ev-er.
A-MEN.

191 More Love to Thee, O Christ

MORE LOVE TO THEE 6. 4. 6. 4. 6. 6. 4.
Elizabeth Prentiss, 1869
William Howard Doane (1832–1916)
1. More love to Thee, O Christ, More love to Thee!
2. Once earth - ly joy I craved, Sought peace and rest;
3. Let sor - row do its work, Send grief and pain;
4. Then shall my lat - est breath Whis - per Thy praise;
Hear Thou the prayer I make On bend - ed knee;
Now Thee a - lone I seek; Give what is best:
Sweet are Thy mes - sen - gers, Sweet their re - frain,
This be the part - ing cry My heart shall raise;
This is my ear - nest plea, More love, O Christ, to Thee,
This all my prayer shall be, More love, O Christ, to Thee,
When they can sing with me, More love, O Christ, to Thee,
This still its prayer shall be, More love, O Christ, to Thee,
More love to Thee, More love to Thee!
More love to Thee, More love to Thee!
More love to Thee, More love to Thee!
More love to Thee, More love to Thee!
A - MEN.

O Love That Wilt Not Let Me Go

ST. MARGARET 8. 8. 8. 8. 6.
George Matheson, 1882
Albert L. Peace, 1885
1. O Love that wilt not let me go, I rest my wea - ry soul in Thee; I give Thee back the life I owe, That in Thine o - cean depths its flow May rich - er, full - er be.
2. O Light that fol - lowest all my way, I yield my flick - ering torch to Thee; My heart re - stores its bor - rowed ray, That in Thy sun-shine's blaze its day May bright-er, fair - er be.
3. O Joy that seek - est me through pain, I can - not close my heart to Thee; I trace the rain - bow through the rain, And feel the prom - ise is not vain That morn shall tear - less be.
4. O Cross that lift - est up my head, I dare not ask to fly from Thee; I lay in dust life's glo - ry dead, And from the ground there blos-soms red Life that shall end - less be.
A-MEN.

193 I Love to Tell the Story

I LOVE TO TELL THE STORY 7. 6. 7. 6. D. with Refrain

Katherine Hankey, 1866; Refrain Added — William G. Fischer, 1869

1. I love to tell the sto - ry Of un - seen things a - bove,
2. I love to tell the sto - ry; More won - der - ful it seems
3. I love to tell the sto - ry; 'T is pleas - ant to re - peat
4. I love to tell the sto - ry; For those who know it best
Of Je - sus and His glo - ry, Of Je - sus and His love.
Than all the gold - en fan - cies Of all our gold - en dreams.
What seems, each time I tell it, More won - der - ful - ly sweet.
Seem hun - ger - ing and thirst - ing To hear it, like the rest.
I love to tell the sto - ry, Be - cause I know it's true;
I love to tell the sto - ry, It did so much for me;
I love to tell the sto - ry, For some have nev - er heard
And when, in scenes of glo - ry, I sing the new, new song,
It sat - is - fies my long - ings As noth - ing else could do.
And that is just the rea - son I tell it now to thee.
The mes - sage of sal - va - tion From God's own ho - ly Word.
'T will be the old, old sto - ry, That I have loved so long.

I Love to Tell the Story (Concluded)

REFRAIN
I love to tell the sto - ry, 'T will be my theme in glo - ry
To tell the old, old sto - ry Of Je - sus and His love. A-MEN.

Jesus, the Very Thought of Thee 194

ST. AGNES C. M.

From the Latin, Eleventh Century
Trans. by Edward Caswall, 1849

John B. Dykes, 1866

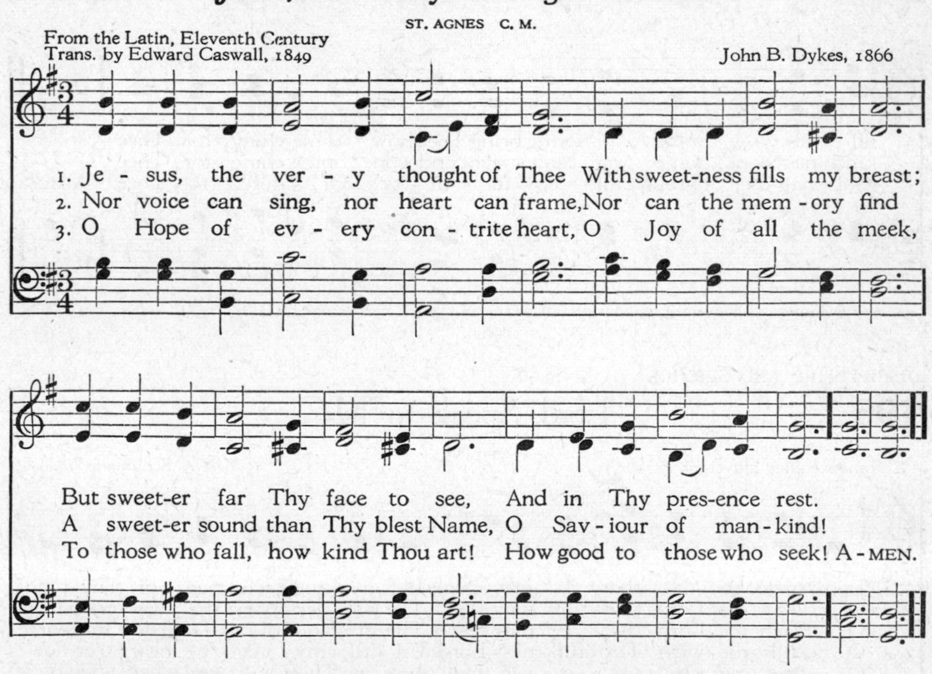
1. Je - sus, the ver - y thought of Thee With sweet-ness fills my breast;
2. Nor voice can sing, nor heart can frame, Nor can the mem - ory find
3. O Hope of ev - ery con - trite heart, O Joy of all the meek,
But sweet-er far Thy face to see, And in Thy pres-ence rest.
A sweet-er sound than Thy blest Name, O Sav - iour of man - kind!
To those who fall, how kind Thou art! How good to those who seek! A - MEN.

4. But what to those who find? Ah, this
Nor tongue nor pen can show:
The love of Jesus, what it is
None but His loved ones know.

5. Jesus, our only Joy be Thou,
As Thou our Prize wilt be;
Jesus, be Thou our Glory now,
And through eternity.

195 Saviour! Thy Dying Love

SOMETHING FOR JESUS 6. 4. 6. 4. 6. 6. 6. 4.

S. Dryden Phelps, 1862
Stanzas 2, 3 Alt.

Robert Lowry, 1872

1. Sav - iour! Thy dy - ing love Thou gav - est me, Nor should I
2. Give me a faith - ful heart, Guid - ed by Thee, That each de -
3. All that I am and have— Thy gifts so free— In joy, in
aught with-hold, Dear Lord, from Thee: In love my soul would bow, My heart ful -
part - ing day Hence-forth may see Some work of love be-gun, Some deed of
grief, through life, Dear Lord, for Thee; And when Thy face I see, My ran-somed
fill its vow, Some of - fering bring Thee now, Some-thing for Thee.
kind - ness done, Some wan-derer sought and won, Some-thing for Thee.
soul shall be, Through all e - ter - ni - ty, Of - fered to Thee. A-MEN.

DISCIPLESHIP AND SERVICE

196 Lord, Speak to Me

CANONBURY L. M.

Frances Ridley Havergal, 1872

Robert A. Schumann, 1839

1. Lord, speak to me, that I may speak In liv - ing ech - oes of Thy tone;
2. O lead me, Lord, that I may lead The wan-dering and the wa-vering feet;
3. O teach me, Lord, that I may teach The pre-cious things Thou dost im - part;
4. O fill me with Thy full - ness, Lord, Un - til my ver - y heart o'er-flow
5. O use me, Lord, use e - ven me, Just as Thou wilt, and when, and where;

Lord, Speak to Me (Concluded)

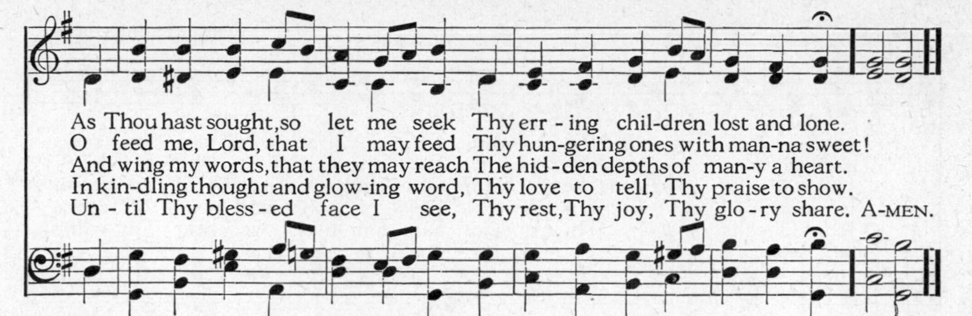
As Thou hast sought, so let me seek Thy err - ing chil-dren lost and lone.
O feed me, Lord, that I may feed Thy hun-gering ones with man-na sweet!
And wing my words, that they may reach The hid - den depths of man-y a heart.
In kin-dling thought and glow-ing word, Thy love to tell, Thy praise to show.
Un - til Thy bless - ed face I see, Thy rest, Thy joy, Thy glo - ry share. A-MEN.

O Son of Man, Thou Madest Known 197

BROOKFIELD L. M.

Milton S. Littlefield, 1916 Thomas B. Southgate, 1855

1. O Son of Man, Thou mad - est known, Through qui - et
2. O Work - man true, may we ful - fill In dai - ly
3. Thou Mas - ter Work - man, grant us grace The chal - lenge
4. And thus we pray in deed and word, Thy King - dom
work in shop and home, The sa - cred - ness of
life Thy Fa - ther's will; In du - ty's call, Thy
of our tasks to face; By loy - al scorn of
come on earth, O Lord; In work that gives ef -
com - mon things, The chance of life that each day brings.
call we hear To full - er life, through work sin - cere.
sec - ond best, By ef - fort true, to meet each test.
fect to prayer Thy pur - pose for Thy world we share. A - MEN.

198 Jesus Calls Us: O'er the Tumult

GALILEE 8.7.8.7.

Cecil Frances Alexander, 1852
Stanza 2 Alt.

William H. Jude, 1887

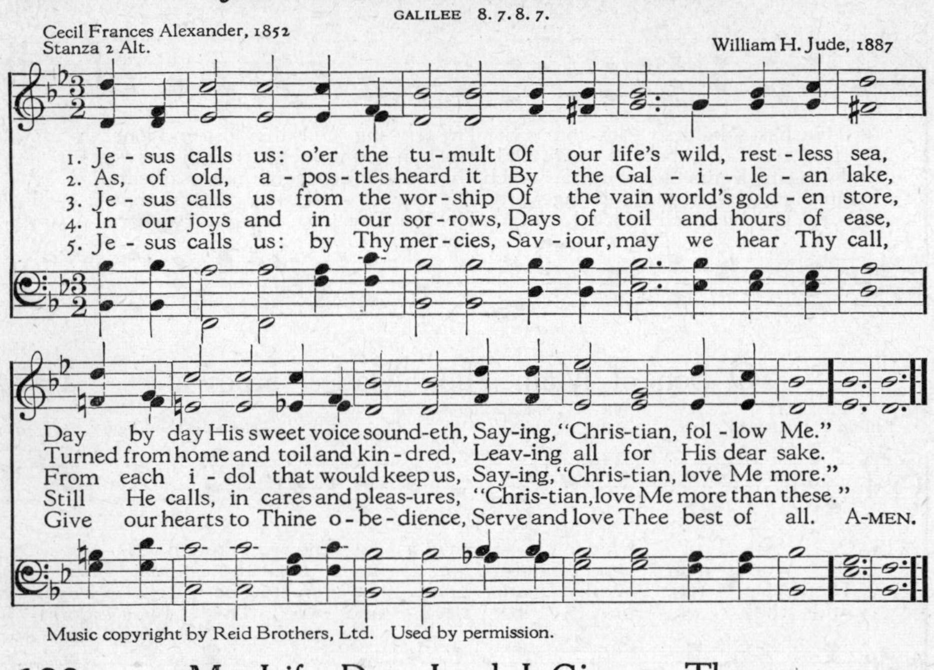
1. Je - sus calls us: o'er the tu - mult Of our life's wild, rest - less sea,
2. As, of old, a - pos - tles heard it By the Gal - i - le - an lake,
3. Je - sus calls us from the wor - ship Of the vain world's gold - en store,
4. In our joys and in our sor - rows, Days of toil and hours of ease,
5. Je - sus calls us: by Thy mer - cies, Sav - iour, may we hear Thy call,
Day by day His sweet voice sound-eth, Say-ing, "Chris-tian, fol - low Me."
Turned from home and toil and kin - dred, Leav-ing all for His dear sake.
From each i - dol that would keep us, Say-ing, "Chris-tian, love Me more."
Still He calls, in cares and pleas-ures, "Chris-tian, love Me more than these."
Give our hearts to Thine o - be - dience, Serve and love Thee best of all. A-MEN.

199 My Life, Dear Lord, I Give to Thee

LITTLEFIELD L. M.

Calvin W. Laufer, 1918

Calvin W. Laufer, 1918

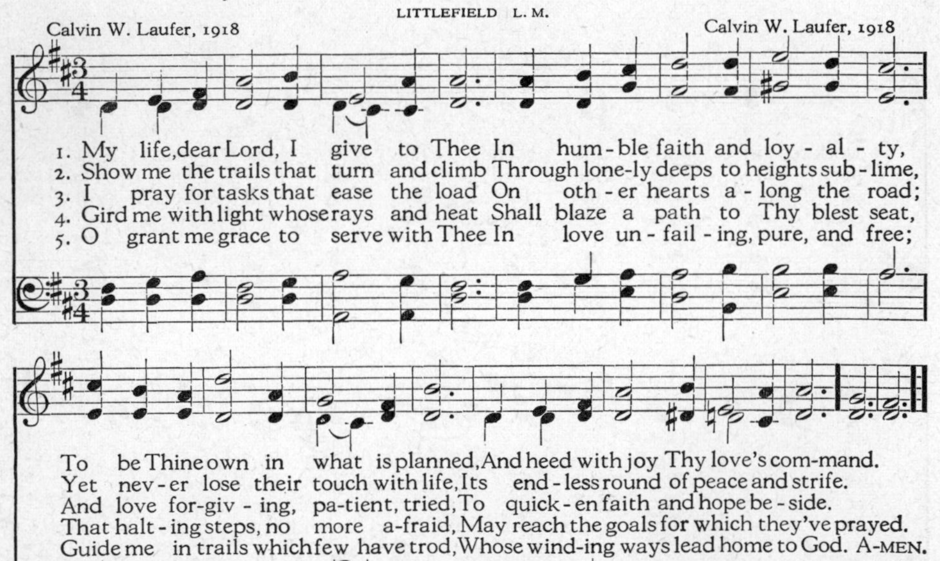
1. My life, dear Lord, I give to Thee In hum - ble faith and loy - al - ty,
2. Show me the trails that turn and climb Through lone-ly deeps to heights sub - lime,
3. I pray for tasks that ease the load On oth - er hearts a - long the road;
4. Gird me with light whose rays and heat Shall blaze a path to Thy blest seat,
5. O grant me grace to serve with Thee In love un - fail - ing, pure, and free;
To be Thine own in what is planned, And heed with joy Thy love's com-mand.
Yet nev - er lose their touch with life, Its end - less round of peace and strife.
And love for - giv - ing, pa - tient, tried, To quick - en faith and hope be - side.
That halt - ing steps, no more a - fraid, May reach the goals for which they've prayed.
Guide me in trails which few have trod, Whose wind-ing ways lead home to God. A-MEN.

Jesus, Thou Divine Companion

LOVE DIVINE [Le Jeune] 8. 7. 8. 7. D.

Henry van Dyke, 1909

George F. Le Jeune, 1872

1. Je - sus, Thou di - vine Com - pan - ion, By Thy low - ly hu - man birth
2. They who tread the path of la - bor Fol - low where Thy feet have trod;
3. Ev - ery task, how - ev - er sim - ple, Sets the soul that does it free;
Thou hast come to join the work - ers, Bur - den bear - ers of the earth.
They who work with - out com - plain - ing Do the ho - ly will of God.
Ev - ery deed of love and kind - ness Done to man is done to Thee.
Thou, the Car - pen - ter of Naz - areth, Toil - ing for Thy dai - ly food,
Thou, the Peace that pass - eth knowl-edge, Dwell-est in the dai - ly strife;
Je - sus, Thou di - vine Com - pan - ion, Help us all to work our best;
By Thy pa-tience and Thy cour - age, Thou hast taught us toil is good.
Thou, the Bread of heaven, art bro - ken In the sac - ra - ment of life.
Bless us in our dai - ly la - bor, Lead us to our Sab-bath rest. A-MEN.

201 O Jesus, Thou Art Standing

ST. EDITH (ST. HILDA) 7.6.7.6.D.
Justin H. Knecht, 1799
W. Walsham How, 1867
Arr. by Edward Husband, 1871
1. O Je - sus, Thou art stand - ing Out - side the fast-closed door,
2. O Je - sus, Thou art knock - ing; And lo, that hand is scarred,
3. O Je - sus, Thou art plead - ing In ac - cents meek and low,
In low - ly pa - tience wait - ing To pass the thresh - old o'er:
And thorns Thy brow en - cir - cle, And tears Thy face have marred:
"I died for you, My chil - dren, And will ye treat Me so?"
Shame on us, Chris - tian broth - ers, His Name and sign who bear,
O love that pass - eth knowl - edge, So pa - tient - ly to wait!
O Lord, with shame and sor - row We o - pen now the door;
O shame, thrice shame up - on us, To keep Him stand - ing there!
O sin that hath no e - qual, So fast to bar the gate!
Dear Sav - iour, en - ter, en - ter, And leave us nev - er - more!
A-MEN.

The Voice of God Is Calling

202

WEBB 7. 6. 7. 6. D.
John Haynes Holmes, 1913
George J. Webb, 1837
1. The voice of God is call - ing Its sum - mons un - to men;
2. I hear My peo - ple cry - ing In cot and mine and slum;
3. We heed, O Lord, Thy sum - mons, And an - swer, "Here are we!"
4. From ease and pleas - ure save us, From pride of place ab - solve;
As once He spoke in Zi - on, So now He speaks a - gain.
No field or mart is si - lent, No cit - y street is dumb.
Send us up - on Thine er - rand, Let us Thy serv - ants be.
Purge us of low de - sire, Lift us to high re - solve.
Whom shall I send to suc - cor My peo - ple in their need?
I see My peo - ple fall - ing In dark - ness and de - spair,
Our strength is dust and ash - es, Our years a pass - ing hour—
Take us, and make us ho - ly, Teach us Thy will and way,
Whom shall I send to loos - en The bonds of lust and greed?
Whom shall I send to shat - ter The fet - ters which they bear?
But Thou canst use our weak - ness, To mag - ni - fy Thy power.
Speak, and be - hold! we an - swer, Com - mand, and we o - bey! A-MEN.

Words used by permission of John Haynes Holmes.

203 We Thank Thee, Lord, Thy Paths of Service Lead

FIELD 10. 10. 10. 10.
Calvin W. Laufer, 1919
Calvin W. Laufer, 1919
1. We thank Thee, Lord, Thy paths of serv - ice lead
2. We've sought and found Thee in the se - cret place
3. We've felt Thy touch in sor - row's dark - ened way
4. We've seen Thy glo - ry like a man - tle spread
5. Show us the paths in which Thou would - est lead
To bla - zoned heights and down the slopes of need;
And mar - veled at the ra - diance of Thy face;
A - bound with love and sol - ace for the day;
O'er hill and dale in saf - fron flame and red;
To bla - zoned heights or down the slopes of need;
They reach Thy throne, en - com - pass land and sea,
But of - ten in some far - off Gal - i - lee
And, 'neath the bur - dens there, Thy sov - reign - ty
But in the eyes of men, re - deemed and free,
For both a - like en - com - pass land and sea,
And he who jour - neys in them walks with Thee.
Be - held Thee fair - er yet while serv - ing Thee.
Has held our hearts en-thralled while serv - ing Thee.
A splen - dor great - er yet while serv - ing Thee.
And he who jour - neys in them walks with Thee.
A-MEN.

We Would Be Building

FINLANDIA 10. 10. 10. 10. 10. 10.

Purd E. Deitz, 1935

Jean Sibelius (1865-)
Arr. for *The Hymnal* (1933)

May be sung in unison
1. We would be build-ing; tem-ples still un-done O'er crum-bling
2. Teach us to build; up-on the sol-id rock We set the
3. O keep us build-ing, Mas-ter; may our hands Ne'er fal-ter
walls their cross-es scarce-ly lift; Wait-ing till love can raise the bro-ken stone,
dream that hard-ens in-to deed, Ribbed with the steel that time and change doth mock,
when the dream is in our hearts, When to our ears there come di-vine com-mands
And hearts cre-a-tive bridge the hu-man rift; We would be build-ing,
Th'un-fail-ing pur-pose of our no-blest creed; Teach us to build; O
And all the pride of sin-ful will de-parts; We build with Thee, O
Mas-ter, let Thy plan Re-veal the life that God would give to man.
Mas-ter, lend us sight To see the tow-ers gleam-ing in the light.
grant en-dur-ing worth Un-til the heaven-ly King-dom comes on earth. A-MEN.

205 I Bind My Heart This Tide

FEALTY 6. 7. 7. 7. D.
Lauchlan MacLean Watt (1867-)
Grace Wilbur Conant, 1927
1. I bind my heart this tide To the Gal - i - le - an's side,
2. I bind my heart in thrall To the God, the Lord of all,
To the wounds of Cal - va - ry, To the Christ who died for me.
To the God, the poor man's Friend, And the Christ whom He did send.
I bind my soul this day To the broth - er far a - way,
I bind my - self to peace, To make strife and en - vy cease;
And the broth - er near at hand, In this town, and in this land.
God, knit Thou sure the cord Of my thrall-dom to my Lord! A - MEN.

Brightly Beams Our Father's Mercy 206

LOWER LIGHTS 8. 7. 8. 7. with Refrain

Philip P. Bliss, 1877 Philip P. Bliss, 1877

1. Bright-ly beams our Fa-ther's mer-cy From His light-house ev-er-more,
2. Dark the night of sin has set-tled, Loud the an-gry bil-lows roar;
3. Trim your fee-ble lamp, my broth-er; Some poor sail-or, tem-pest-tossed,
But to us He gives the keep-ing Of the lights a-long the shore.
Ea-ger eyes are watch-ing, long-ing, For the lights a-long the shore.
Try-ing now to make the har-bor, In the dark-ness may be lost.
REFRAIN
Let the low-er lights be burn-ing! Send a gleam a-cross the wave!

Some poor faint-ing, strug-gling sea-man You may res-cue, you may save. A-MEN.

207 Lord, We Come with Hearts Aflame

ST. ATHANASIUS 7.7.7.7.7.7.

Berton Braley (1882–) Edward J. Hopkins, 1872

1. Lord, we come with hearts a-flame, Seek-ing serv-ice in Thy Name;
2. Lord of hosts, we ask Thine aid, Keep us ev-er un-a-fraid;
3. Lord of all, we take our stand, Giv-ing help at Thy com-mand;
All our youth and strength are Thine, Given to help Thy work di-vine;
Hold us loy-al, hold us true To the task we have to do;
Ea-ger, joy-ful, blithe, and strong, Thrilled with love and filled with song;
All our love and faith we bring, They are Thine, O heaven-ly King.
Lead us on to vic-to-ry, We shall tri-umph prais-ing Thee.
Lord, we come with hearts a-flame, Seek-ing serv-ice in Thy Name. A-MEN.

Words from *Twice 55 Community Songs* (The Brown Book). Used by permission of the author and C. C. Birchard & Company, publishers.

208 Immortal Love, Forever Full

SERENITY C. M.

John Greenleaf Whittier, 1866 Arr. from William V. Wallace, 1856

1. Im-mor-tal Love, for-ev-er full, For-ev-er flow-ing free,
2. We may not climb the heaven-ly steeps To bring the Lord Christ down;
3. But warm, sweet, ten-der, ev-en yet A pres-ent help is He;
4. The heal-ing of His seam-less dress Is by our beds of pain;
5. O Lord and Mas-ter of us all, What-e'er our name or sign,

Immortal Love, Forever Full (Concluded)

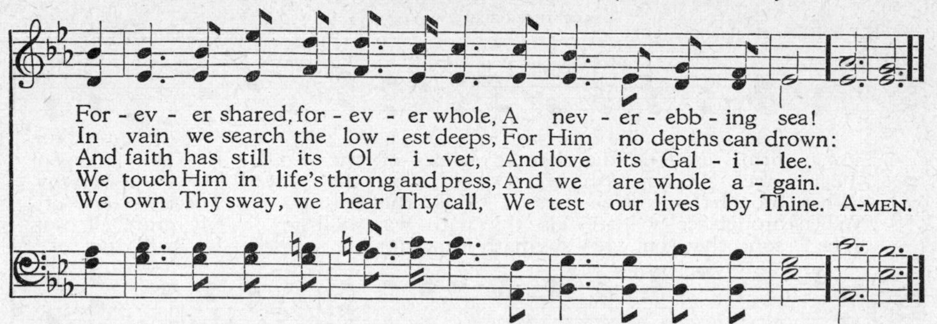
For - ev - er shared, for - ev - er whole, A nev - er - ebb - ing sea!
In vain we search the low - est deeps, For Him no depths can drown:
And faith has still its Ol - i - vet, And love its Gal - i - lee.
We touch Him in life's throng and press, And we are whole a - gain.
We own Thy sway, we hear Thy call, We test our lives by Thine. A-MEN.

Words used by permission of the authorized publishers, Houghton Mifflin Company.

Steal Away to Jesus

209

STEAL AWAY Irregular

Negro Spiritual
Harmonized by Lawrence Curry, 1939

Steal a - way, steal a - way, steal a - way to Je - sus;
Fine
Steal a - way, steal a - way home, I ain't got long to stay here.
1. My Lord calls me, He calls me by the thun - der; The
2. Green trees are bend - ing, Poor sin - ner stands a - trem-bling; The
3. My Lord calls me, He calls me by the light - ning; The
D.C. al Fine
trum-pet sounds with - in - a my soul! I ain't got long to stay here.

210 How Firm a Foundation

ADESTE FIDELES 11.11.11.11.
"K," in Rippon's Selection, 1787
From J. F. Wade's Cantus Diversi, 1751
1. How firm a foun-da-tion, ye saints of the Lord, Is laid for your
2. "Fear not, I am with thee, O be not dis-mayed; For I am thy
3. "When through the deep wa-ters I call thee to go, The riv-ers of
4. "When through fier-y tri-als thy path-way shall lie, My grace, all-suf-
5. "The soul that on Je-sus hath leaned for re-pose, I will not, I
faith in His ex-cel-lent Word! What more can He say than to
God, and will still give thee aid; I'll strength-en thee, help thee, and
woe shall not thee o-ver-flow; For I will be with thee thy
fi-cient, shall be thy sup-ply; The flame shall not hurt thee; I
will not de-sert to his foes; That soul, though all hell should en-
you He hath said, Who un-to the Sav-iour for ref-uge have fled?
cause thee to stand, Up-held by My right-eous, om-nip-o-tent hand,
trou-bles to bless, And sanc-ti-fy to thee thy deep-est dis-tress,
on-ly de-sign Thy dross to con-sume, and thy gold to re-fine,
deav-or to shake, I'll nev-er, no, nev-er, no, nev-er for-sake,
Who un-to the Sav-iour for ref-uge have fled?
Up-held by My right-eous, om-nip-o-tent hand.
And sanc-ti-fy to thee thy deep-est dis-tress.
Thy dross to con-sume, and thy gold to re-fine.
I'll nev-er, no, nev-er, no, nev-er for-sake." A-MEN.

My Faith Looks Up to Thee

211

OLIVET 6. 6. 4. 6. 6. 6. 4.
Ray Palmer, 1830
Lowell Mason, 1832
1. My faith looks up to Thee, Thou Lamb of Cal - va - ry, Sav - iour di - vine: Now hear me while I pray, Take all my guilt a - way, O let me from this day Be whol - ly Thine!
2. May Thy rich grace im - part Strength to my faint - ing heart, My zeal in - spire; As Thou hast died for me, O may my love to Thee Pure, warm, and change - less be, A liv - ing fire!
3. While life's dark maze I tread, And griefs a - round me spread, Be Thou my Guide; Bid dark - ness turn to day, Wipe sor - row's tears a - way, Nor let me ev - er stray From Thee a - side.
4. When ends life's tran - sient dream, When death's cold, sul - len stream Shall o'er me roll, Blest Sav - iour, then, in love, Fear and dis - trust re - move; O bear me safe a - bove, A ran - somed soul!
A-MEN.

212 Strong Son of God, Immortal Love

ST. CRISPIN L. M.

Alfred Tennyson, 1850 — George J. Elvey, 1862

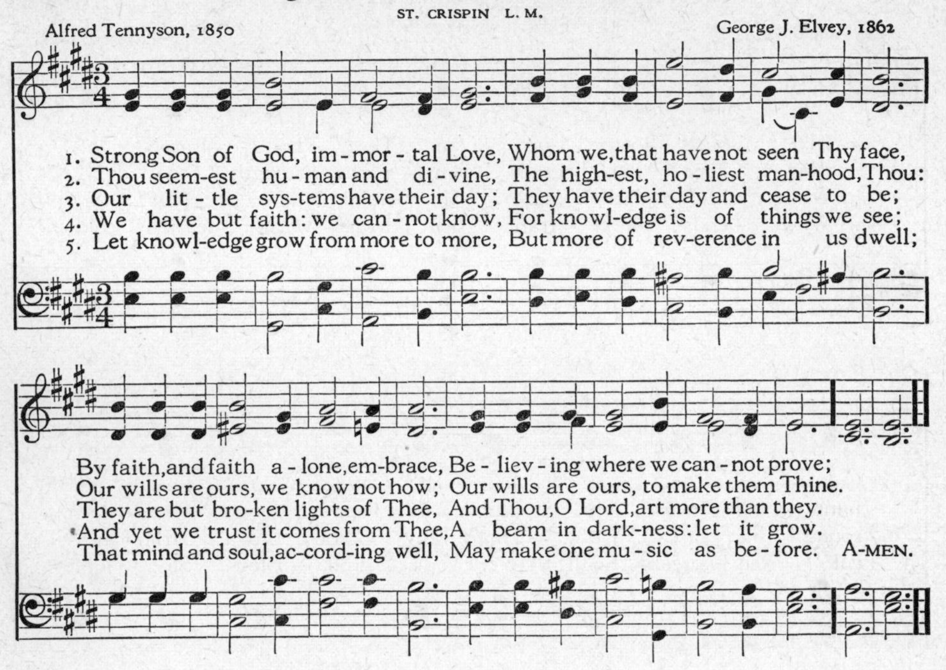
1. Strong Son of God, im-mor-tal Love, Whom we, that have not seen Thy face,
2. Thou seem-est hu-man and di-vine, The high-est, ho-liest man-hood, Thou:
3. Our lit-tle sys-tems have their day; They have their day and cease to be;
4. We have but faith: we can-not know, For knowl-edge is of things we see;
5. Let knowl-edge grow from more to more, But more of rev-erence in us dwell;
By faith, and faith a-lone, em-brace, Be-liev-ing where we can-not prove;
Our wills are ours, we know not how; Our wills are ours, to make them Thine.
They are but bro-ken lights of Thee, And Thou, O Lord, art more than they.
And yet we trust it comes from Thee, A beam in dark-ness: let it grow.
That mind and soul, ac-cord-ing well, May make one mu-sic as be-fore. A-MEN.

213 I Know Not How That Bethlehem's Babe

EXETER C. M.

Harry Webb Farrington, 1910 — Henry Lowell Mason, 1923

1. I know not how that Beth-lehem's Babe Could in the God-head be;
2. I know not how that Cal-vary's cross A world from sin could free;
3. I know not how that Jo-seph's tomb Could solve death's mys-ter-y;
I on-ly know the Man-ger Child Has brought God's life to me.
I on-ly know its match-less love Has brought God's love to me.
I on-ly know a liv-ing Christ, Our im-mor-tal-i-ty. A-MEN.

Thou Art the Way

214

ST. JAMES C. M.

George W. Doane, 1824

Raphael Courteville, d. 1772

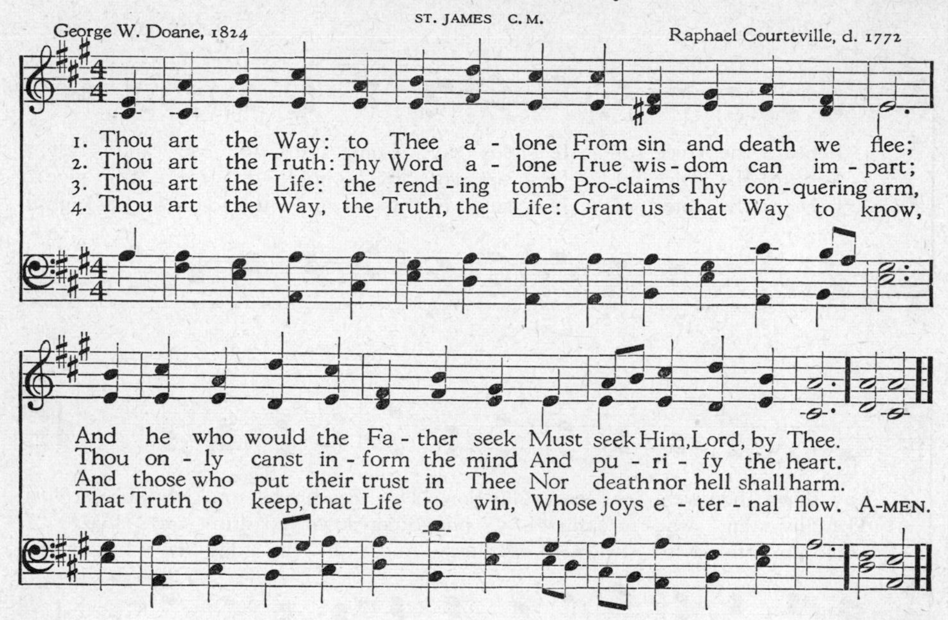
1. Thou art the Way: to Thee a - lone From sin and death we flee;
2. Thou art the Truth: Thy Word a - lone True wis - dom can im - part;
3. Thou art the Life: the rend - ing tomb Pro-claims Thy con - quering arm,
4. Thou art the Way, the Truth, the Life: Grant us that Way to know,
And he who would the Fa - ther seek Must seek Him, Lord, by Thee.
Thou on - ly canst in - form the mind And pu - ri - fy the heart.
And those who put their trust in Thee Nor death nor hell shall harm.
That Truth to keep, that Life to win, Whose joys e - ter - nal flow. A-MEN.

I Am Trusting Thee, Lord Jesus

215

BULLINGER 8. 5. 8. 3.

Frances Ridley Havergal, 1874

Ethelbert W. Bullinger, 1874

1. I am trust - ing Thee, Lord Je - sus, Trust - ing on - ly Thee;
2. I am trust - ing Thee for par - don; At Thy feet I bow;
3. I am trust - ing Thee for cleans - ing In the crim - son flood;
4. I am trust - ing Thee to guide me; Thou a - lone shalt lead,
5. I am trust - ing Thee, Lord Je - sus; Nev - er let me fall;
Trust - ing Thee for full sal - va - tion, Great and free.
For Thy grace and ten - der mer - cy, Trust - ing now.
Trust - ing Thee to make me ho - ly By Thy blood.
Ev - ery day and hour sup - ply - ing All my need.
I am trust - ing Thee for - ev - er, And for all. A - MEN.

216 I Heard the Voice of Jesus Say

VOX DILECTI C. M. D.
Horatius Bonar, 1846
John B. Dykes, 1868
1. I heard the voice of Je - sus say, "Come un - to Me and rest;
2. I heard the voice of Je - sus say, "Be - hold, I free - ly give
3. I heard the voice of Je - sus say, "I am this dark world's Light;
Lay down, thou wea - ry one, lay down Thy head up - on My breast."
The liv - ing wa - ter; thirst - y one, Stoop down and drink, and live."
Look un - to Me, thy morn shall rise, And all thy day be bright."
I came to Je - sus as I was, Wea - ry and worn and sad,
I came to Je - sus, and I drank Of that life - giv - ing stream;
I looked to Je - sus, and I found In Him my Star, my Sun;
I found in Him a rest - ing place, And He has made me glad.
My thirst was quenched, my soul re-vived, And now I live in Him.
And in that Light of life I'll walk, Till trav-eling days are done. A-MEN.

I Want to Be a Christian

217

I WANT TO BE A CHRISTIAN Irregular

Negro Spiritual
Harmonized by Lawrence Curry, 1939

1. Lord, I want to be a Chris-tian in-a my heart, in-a my heart; Lord, I want to be a Chris-tian in-a my heart.
2. Lord, I want to be more lov-ing in-a my heart, in-a my heart; Lord, I want to be more lov-ing in-a my heart.
3. Lord, I want to be like Je-sus in-a my heart, in-a my heart; Lord, I want to be like Je-sus in-a my heart.
Refrain
In-a my heart, ... In-a my heart, ...
In-a my heart, In-a my heart,
Lord, I want to be a Chris-tian in-a my heart.
Lord, I want to be more lov-ing in-a my heart.
Lord, I want to be like Je-sus in-a my heart.

218 Jesus, and Shall It Ever Be

FEDERAL STREET L. M.

Joseph Grigg, 1765
Alt. by Benjamin Francis, 1787

Henry K. Oliver, 1832

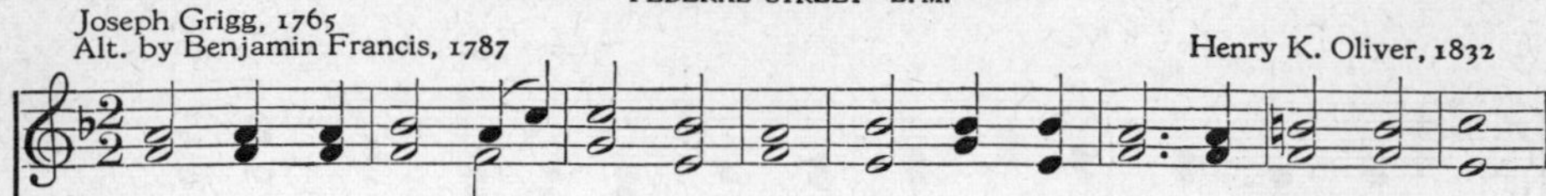

1. Je - sus, and shall it ev - er be, A mor - tal man a-shamed of Thee:
2. A-shamed of Je - sus! soon - er far Let eve-ning blush to own a star:
3. A-shamed of Je - sus! just as soon Let mid-night be a-shamed of noon:
4. A-shamed of Je - sus, that dear Friend On whom my hopes of heaven de - pend?
5. Till then—nor is my boast-ing vain— Till then I boast a Sav - iour slain;

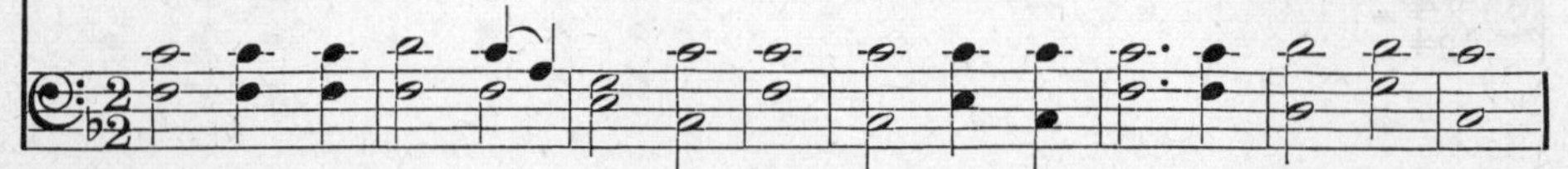

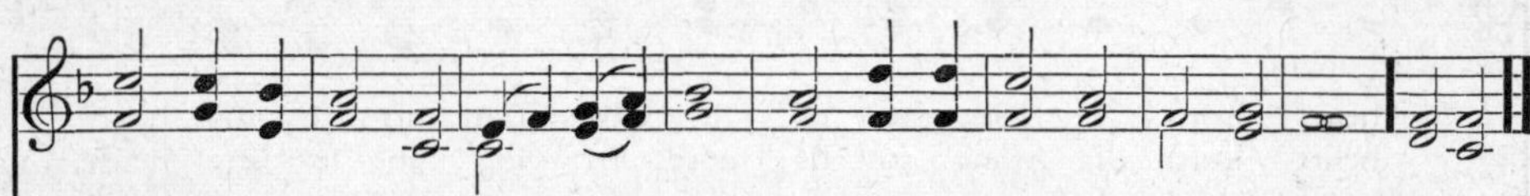

A-shamed of Thee, whom an - gels praise, Whose glo-ries shine through end-less days?
He sheds the beams of light di - vine O'er this be-night-ed soul of mine.
'T is mid-night with my soul till He, Bright Morn-ing Star, bids dark-ness flee.
No; when I blush, be this my shame, That I no more re - vere His Name.
And O may this my glo - ry be, That Christ is not a-shamed of me. A-MEN.

219 Jacob's Ladder

JACOB'S LADDER 8. 8. 8. 5.

Negro Spiritual
Harmonized by Lawrence Curry, 1941

1. We are climb-ing Ja-cob's lad-der, We are climb-ing Ja-cob's lad-der,
2. Ev - ery round goes high - er, high - er, Ev - ery round goes high - er, high - er,
3. Sin-ner, do you love my Je - sus? Sin-ner, do you love my Je - sus?
4. If you love Him, why not serve Him? If you love Him, why not serve Him?
5. Do you think I'd make a sol - dier? Do you think I'd make a sol - dier?
6. We are climb-ing high - er, high - er, We are climb-ing high - er, high - er,

Jacob's Ladder (Concluded)

We are climb - ing Ja - cob's lad - der, Sol - dier of the cross.
Ev - ery round goes high - er, high - er, Sol - dier of the cross.
Sin - ner, do you love my Je - sus? Sol - dier of the cross.
If you love Him, why not serve Him? Sol - dier of the cross.
Do you think I'd make a sol - dier? Sol - dier of the cross.
We are climb - ing high - er, high - er, Sol - dier of the cross.

Soldiers of Christ, Arise 220

SOLDIERS OF CHRIST S. M.

Charles Wesley, 1749 — William Pierson Merrill, 1895

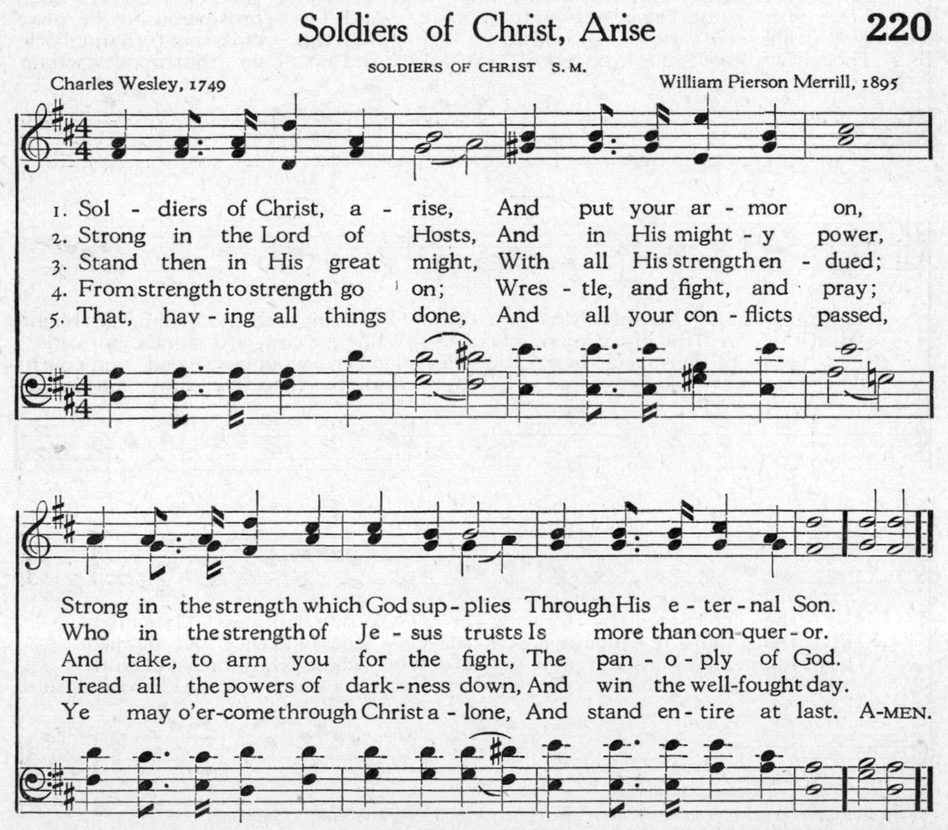
1. Sol - diers of Christ, a - rise, And put your ar - mor on,
2. Strong in the Lord of Hosts, And in His might - y power,
3. Stand then in His great might, With all His strength en - dued;
4. From strength to strength go on; Wres - tle, and fight, and pray;
5. That, hav - ing all things done, And all your con - flicts passed,
Strong in the strength which God sup - plies Through His e - ter - nal Son.
Who in the strength of Je - sus trusts Is more than con - quer - or.
And take, to arm you for the fight, The pan - o - ply of God.
Tread all the powers of dark - ness down, And win the well-fought day.
Ye may o'er-come through Christ a - lone, And stand en - tire at last. A-MEN.

221 Once to Every Man and Nation

TON-Y BOTEL 8.7.8.7.D.
James Russell Lowell, 1845; Alt.
Thomas John Williams
Unison
1. Once to ev-ery man and na-tion Comes the mo-ment to de-cide,
2. Then to side with truth is no-ble, When we share her wretch-ed crust,
3. By the light of burn-ing mar-tyrs, Je-sus' bleed-ing feet I track,
4. Though the cause of e-vil pros-per, Yet 'tis truth a-lone is strong;
In the strife of truth with false-hood, For the good or e-vil side;
Ere her cause bring fame and prof-it, And 't is pros-perous to be just;
Toil-ing up new Cal-varies ev-er With the cross that turns not back;
Though her por-tion be the scaf-fold, And up-on the throne be wrong,
Some great cause, God's new Mes-si-ah, Of-fering each the bloom or blight,
Then it is the brave man choos-es, While the cow-ard stands a-side
New oc-ca-sions teach new du-ties, Time makes an-cient good un-couth;
Yet that scaf-fold sways the fu-ture, And, be-hind the dim un-known,
And the choice goes by for-ev-er 'Twixt that dark-ness and that light.
Till the mul-ti-tude make vir-tue Of the faith they had de-nied.
They must up-ward still and on-ward, Who would keep a-breast of truth.
Stand-eth God with-in the shad-ow Keep-ing watch a-bove His own. A-MEN.

Who Is on the Lord's Side? 222

ARMAGEDDON 6. 5. 6. 5. 6. 5. D.

Frances Ridley Havergal, 1877

German Melody
Arr. by John Goss, 1871

1. Who is on the Lord's side? Who will serve the King? Who will be His help-ers,
2. Not for weight of glo-ry, Not for crown or palm, En-ter we the ar-my,
3. Je-sus, Thou hast bought us, Not with gold or gem, But with Thine own life-blood,
4. Fierce may be the con-flict, Strong may be the foe, But the King's own ar-my
Oth-er lives to bring? Who will leave the world's side? Who will face the foe?
Raise the war-rior psalm; But for Love that claim-eth Lives for whom He died:
For Thy di-a-dem: With Thy bless-ing fill-ing Each who comes to Thee,
None can o-ver-throw: Round His stand-ard ran-ging, Vic-tory is se-cure;
Who is on the Lord's side? Who for Him will go? By Thy call of mer-cy,
He whom Je-sus nam-eth Must be on His side. By Thy love con-strain-ing,
Thou hast made us will-ing, Thou hast made us free. By Thy grand re-demp-tion,
For His truth un-chan-ging Makes the tri-umph sure. Joy-ful-ly en-list-ing
By Thy grace di-vine, We are on the Lord's side, Sav-iour, we are Thine.
By Thy grace di-vine, We are on the Lord's side, Sav-iour, we are Thine.
By Thy grace di-vine, We are on the Lord's side, Sav-iour, we are Thine.
By Thy grace di-vine, We are on the Lord's side, Sav-iour, we are Thine. A-MEN.

223 Dare to Be Brave, Dare to Be True

DARE TO BE BRAVE 8. 10. 9. 10. with Refrain

W. J. Rooper; Alt. — Duncan Hume

1. Dare to be brave, dare to be true; Strive for the right, for the Lord is with you; Fight with sin bravely, fight and be strong; Christ is your Captain; fear only what's wrong.
2. Dare to be brave, dare to be true; God is your Father: He watches o'er you; He knows your trials; when your heart quails, Ask Him to help you; His grace never fails.
3. Dare to be brave, dare to be true; God grant you courage to carry you through; Try to help others; ever be kind; Let all the erring a friend in you find.
REFRAIN
Fight then, good soldiers, fight and be brave; Christ is your Captain, mighty to save. A-MEN.

Faith of Our Fathers! Living Still

ST. CATHERINE 8. 8. 8. 8. 8. 8.
Frederick W. Faber, 1849
Stanzas 2, 3 Alt.
Henri F. Hemy, 1865
Alt. by James G. Walton, 1871
1. Faith of our fa - thers! liv - ing still In spite of dun - geon, fire, and sword, O how our hearts beat high with joy When - e'er we hear that glo - rious word: Faith of our fa - thers, ho - ly faith! We will be true to thee till death.
2. Our fa - thers, chained in pris - ons dark, Were still in heart and con - science free; And blest would be their chil - dren's fate If they, like them, should die for thee: Faith of our fa - thers, ho - ly faith! We will be true to thee till death.
3. Faith of our fa - thers! God's great power Shall win all na - tions un - to thee; And through the truth that comes from God Man - kind shall then be tru - ly free: Faith of our fa - thers, ho - ly faith! We will be true to thee till death.
4. Faith of our fa - thers! we will love Both friend and foe in all our strife, And preach thee, too, as love knows how By kind - ly words and vir - tuous life: Faith of our fa - thers, ho - ly faith! We will be true to thee till death.
A - MEN.

225 Stand Up, Stand Up for Jesus

WEBB 7.6.7.6. D.

George Duffield, 1858 — George J. Webb, 1837

1. Stand up, stand up for Je - sus, Ye sol - diers of the cross;
2. Stand up, stand up for Je - sus, The trump - et call o - bey;
3. Stand up, stand up for Je - sus, Stand in His strength a - lone;
4. Stand up, stand up for Je - sus, The strife will not be long;
Lift high His roy - al ban - ner, It must not suf - fer loss:
Forth to the might - y con - flict, In this His glo - rious day:
The arm of flesh will fail you, Ye dare not trust your own:
This day the noise of bat - tle, The next the vic - tor's song:
From vic - tory un - to vic - tory His ar - my He shall lead,
Ye that are men now serve Him A - gainst un - num - bered foes;
Put on the gos - pel ar - mor, Each piece put on with prayer;
To him that o - ver - com - eth A crown of life shall be;
Till ev - ery foe is van-quished, And Christ is Lord in - deed.
Let cour - age rise with dan - ger, And strength to strength op - pose.
Where du - ty calls, or dan - ger, Be nev - er want - ing there.
He with the King of Glo - ry Shall reign e - ter - nal - ly.
A-MEN.

Lead On, O King Eternal

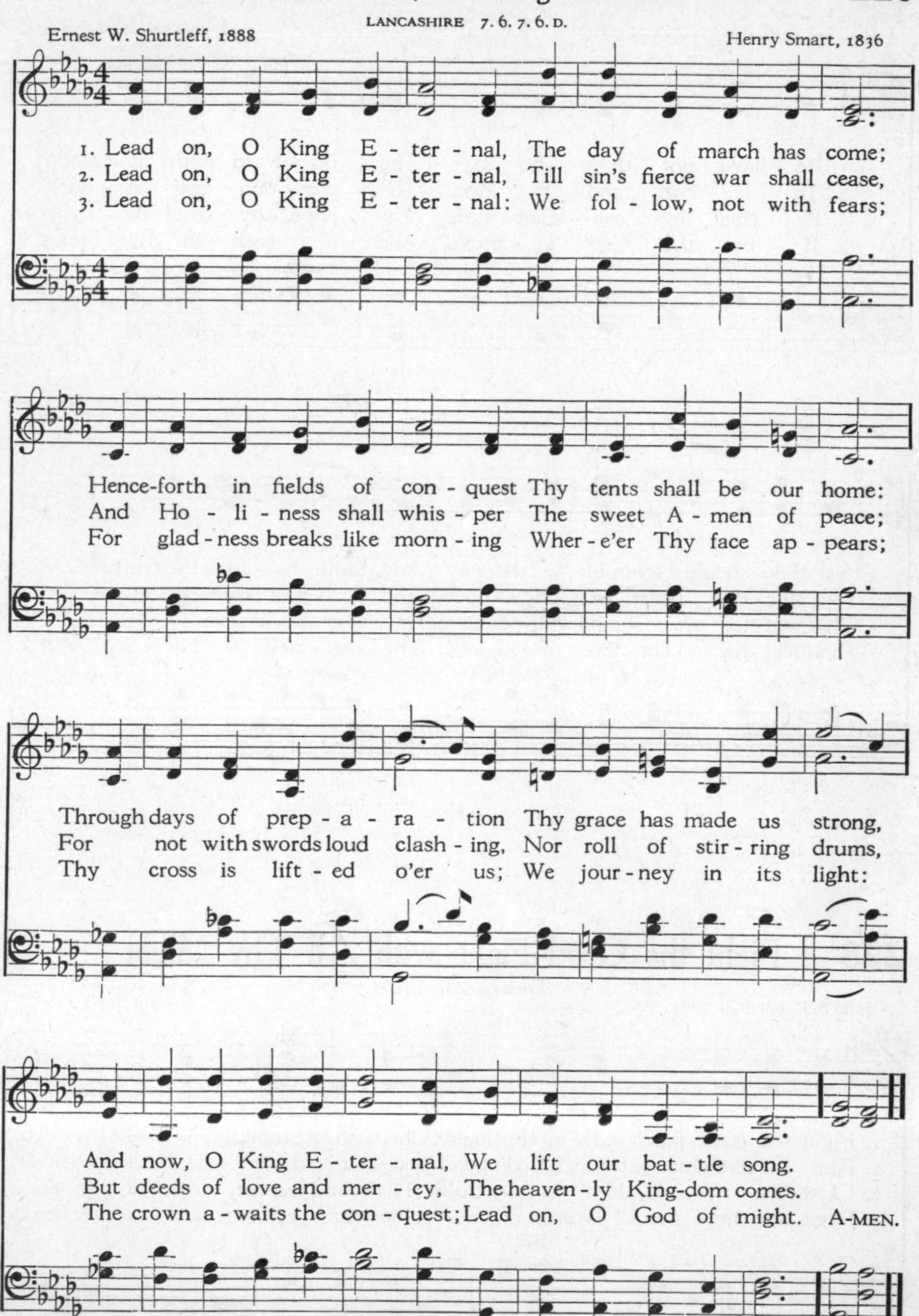
LANCASHIRE 7. 6. 7. 6. D.
Ernest W. Shurtleff, 1888
Henry Smart, 1836
1. Lead on, O King E - ter - nal, The day of march has come;
2. Lead on, O King E - ter - nal, Till sin's fierce war shall cease,
3. Lead on, O King E - ter - nal: We fol - low, not with fears;
Hence-forth in fields of con - quest Thy tents shall be our home:
And Ho - li - ness shall whis - per The sweet A - men of peace;
For glad - ness breaks like morn - ing Wher - e'er Thy face ap - pears;
Through days of prep - a - ra - tion Thy grace has made us strong,
For not with swords loud clash - ing, Nor roll of stir - ring drums,
Thy cross is lift - ed o'er us; We jour - ney in its light:
And now, O King E - ter - nal, We lift our bat - tle song.
But deeds of love and mer - cy, The heaven - ly King-dom comes.
The crown a - waits the con - quest; Lead on, O God of might. A-MEN.

227 Believe Not Those Who Say

FESTAL SONG S. M.

Anne Brontë, 1850 — William H. Walter, 1894

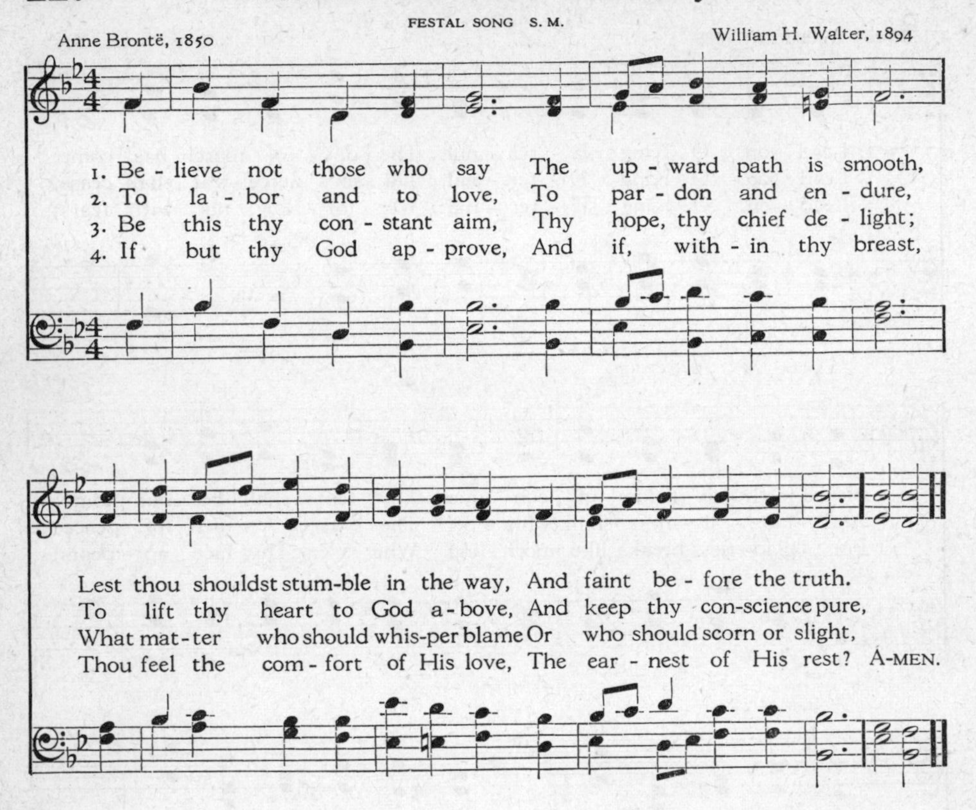
1. Be - lieve not those who say The up - ward path is smooth,
2. To la - bor and to love, To par - don and en - dure,
3. Be this thy con - stant aim, Thy hope, thy chief de - light;
4. If but thy God ap - prove, And if, with - in thy breast,
Lest thou shouldst stum-ble in the way, And faint be - fore the truth.
To lift thy heart to God a - bove, And keep thy con-science pure,
What mat - ter who should whis-per blame Or who should scorn or slight,
Thou feel the com - fort of His love, The ear - nest of His rest? A-MEN.

228 Fight the Good Fight with All Thy Might

PENTECOST L. M.

John S. B. Monsell, 1863 — William Boyd, 1863

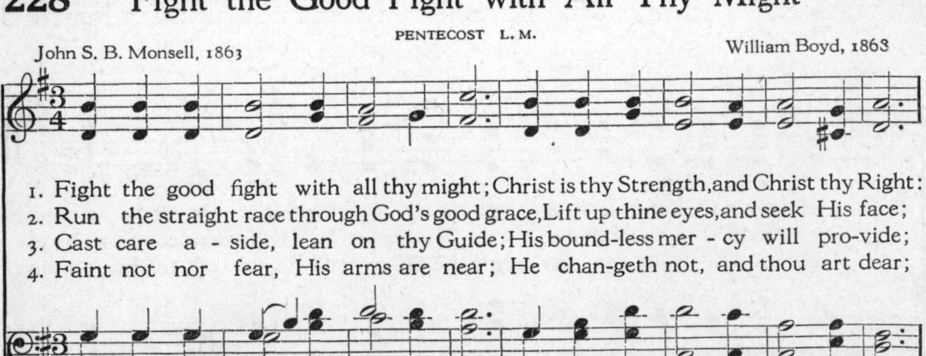
1. Fight the good fight with all thy might; Christ is thy Strength, and Christ thy Right:
2. Run the straight race through God's good grace, Lift up thine eyes, and seek His face;
3. Cast care a - side, lean on thy Guide; His bound-less mer - cy will pro-vide;
4. Faint not nor fear, His arms are near; He chan-geth not, and thou art dear;

Fight the Good Fight (Concluded)

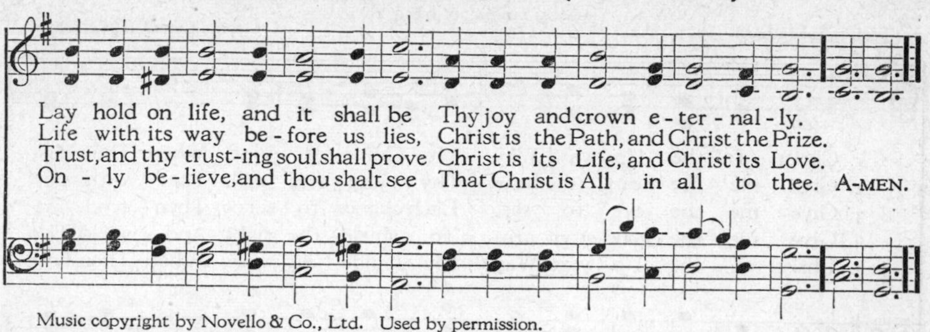
Lay hold on life, and it shall be Thy joy and crown e - ter - nal - ly.
Life with its way be - fore us lies, Christ is the Path, and Christ the Prize.
Trust, and thy trust-ing soul shall prove Christ is its Life, and Christ its Love.
On - ly be - lieve, and thou shalt see That Christ is All in all to thee. A-MEN.

Music copyright by Novello & Co., Ltd. Used by permission.

Be Strong! 229

HAROLD 2. 10. 10. 10.

Maltbie D. Babcock, 1901 Carl F. Price, 1921

1. Be strong! We are not here to play, to dream, to drift; We
2. Be strong! Say not the days are e - vil—who's to blame? And
3. Be strong! It mat - ters not how deep in - trenched the wrong, How
have hard work to do and loads to lift; Shun not the strug - gle:
fold the hands and ac - qui - esce—O shame! Stand up, speak out, and
hard the bat - tle goes, the day, how long; Faint not, fight on! To -
face it, 't is God's gift. Be strong, be strong, be strong!
brave - ly, in God's Name. Be strong, be strong, be strong!
mor - row comes the song. Be strong, be strong, be strong! A-MEN.

Words from *Thoughts for Every-Day Living*. Copyright, 1901, by Charles Scribner's Sons. Used by permission.
Music copyright, 1921, by Carl F. Price. Used by permission.

230 Christ of the Upward Way

SURSUM CORDA 6. 4. 6. 4. 10. 10.

Walter J. Mathams (1853–1932) George Lomas (1834–1884)

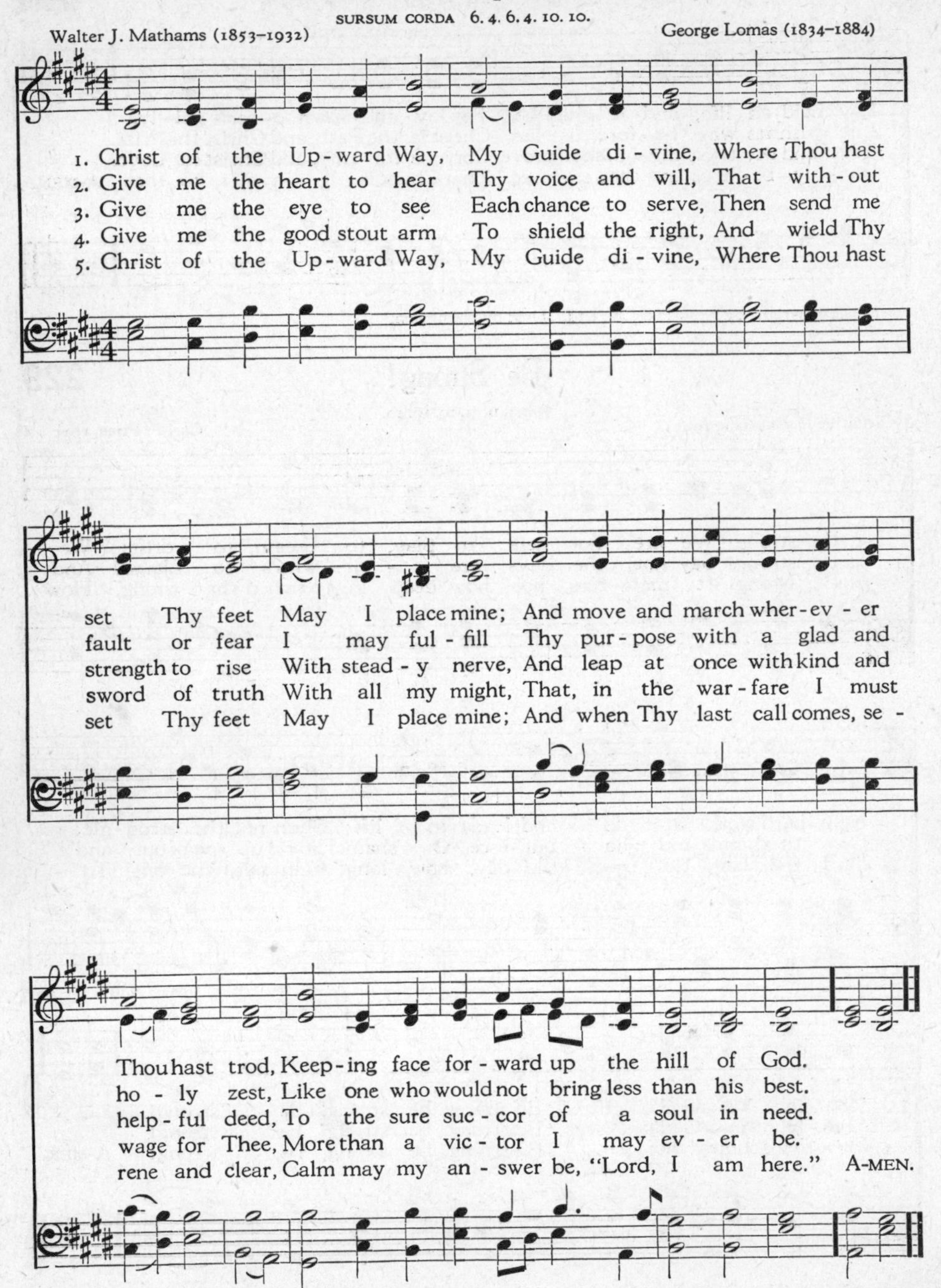

1. Christ of the Up-ward Way, My Guide di-vine, Where Thou hast set Thy feet May I place mine; And move and march wher-ev-er Thou hast trod, Keep-ing face for-ward up the hill of God.
2. Give me the heart to hear Thy voice and will, That with-out fault or fear I may ful-fill Thy pur-pose with a glad and ho-ly zest, Like one who would not bring less than his best.
3. Give me the eye to see Each chance to serve, Then send me strength to rise With stead-y nerve, And leap at once with kind and help-ful deed, To the sure suc-cor of a soul in need.
4. Give me the good stout arm To shield the right, And wield Thy sword of truth With all my might, That, in the war-fare I must wage for Thee, More than a vic-tor I may ev-er be.
5. Christ of the Up-ward Way, My Guide di-vine, Where Thou hast set Thy feet May I place mine; And when Thy last call comes, se-rene and clear, Calm may my an-swer be, "Lord, I am here." A-MEN.

Music used by permission of M. Morley Horder.

Onward, Christian Soldiers

ST. GERTRUDE 6. 5. 6. 5. D. with Refrain
Sabine Baring-Gould, 1865
Arthur S. Sullivan, 1871
1. On - ward, Chris-tian sol-diers, March - ing as to war, With the cross of Je - sus
2. Like a might-y ar - my Moves the Church of God; Broth-ers, we are tread-ing
3. Crowns and thrones may per-ish, King-doms rise and wane, But the Church of Je - sus
4. On - ward, then, ye peo - ple, Join our hap-py throng, Blend with ours your voi - ces
Go - ing on be - fore: Christ the roy - al Mas - ter Leads a-gainst the foe;
Where the saints have trod; We are not di - vid - ed, All one bod - y we,
Con - stant will re - main; Gates of hell can nev - er 'Gainst that Church pre-vail;
In the tri-umph song; Glo - ry, laud, and hon - or Un - to Christ the King;
REFRAIN
For - ward in - to bat - tle, See, His ban-ners go. On-ward, Chris-tian sol - diers,
One in hope and doc - trine, One in char - i - ty.
We have Christ's own prom-ise, And that can-not fail.
This through count-less a - ges Men and an - gels sing.
March-ing as to war, With the cross of Je - sus Go - ing on be - fore. A-MEN.

232 Follow the Gleam

FOLLOW THE GLEAM Irregular
Helen Hill Miller
Bryn Mawr Silver Bay Prize Song, 1920
Sallie Hume Douglas, 1915
Unison
1. To the knights in the days of old, Keep-ing watch on the
2. And we who would serve the King, And loy-al-ly
mount-tain height, Came a vi-sion of Ho-ly Grail
Him o-bey, In the con-se-crate si-lence know
And a voice through the wait-ing night: Fol-low, fol-low,
That the chal-lenge still holds to-day. Fol-low, fol-low,
fol-low the gleam; Ban-ners un-furled o'er all the world; Fol-low, fol-
fol-low the gleam; Stand-ards of worth o'er all the earth; Fol-low, fol-
low, fol-low the gleam Of the chal-ice that is the Grail.
low, fol-low the gleam Of the light that shall bring the dawn.

He Who Would Valiant Be

ST. DUNSTAN'S 6. 5. 6. 5. 6. 6. 6. 5.

John Bunyan (1628–1688); Alt.

Winfred Douglas, 1917

1. He who would val - iant be 'Gainst all dis - as - ter,
2. Who - so be - set him round With dis - mal sto - ries,
3. Since, Lord, Thou dost de - fend Us with Thy Spir - it,
Let him in con - stan - cy Fol - low the Mas - ter.
Do but them - selves con - found—His strength the more is.
We know we at the end Shall life in - her - it.
There's no dis - cour - age - ment Shall make him once re - lent
No foes shall stay his might; Though he with gi - ants fight,
Then, fan - cies, flee a - way! I'll fear not what men say,
His first a - vowed in - tent To be a pil - grim.
He will make good his right To be a pil - grim.
I'll la - bor night and day To be a pil - grim. A - MEN.

234 March On, O Soul, with Strength!

ARTHUR'S SEAT 6. 6. 6. 6. 8. 8.
George T. Coster, 1900
John Goss, 1874
1. March on, O soul, with strength! Like those strong men of old
2. The sons of fa - thers we By whom our faith is taught
3. March on, O soul, with strength, As strong the bat - tle rolls!
4. Not long the con - flict: soon The ho - ly war shall cease,
Who 'gainst en - thron - ed wrong Stood con - fi - dent and bold;
To fear no ill, to fight The ho - ly fight they fought:
'Gainst lies and lusts and wrongs, Let cour - age rule our souls:
Faith's war - fare end - ed, won The home of end - less peace!
Who, thrust in prison or cast to flame,
He - ro - ic war - riors, ne'er from Christ
In keen - est strife, Lord, may we stand,
Look up! the vic - tor's crown at length!
Still made their glo - ry in Thy Name.
By an - y lure or guile en - ticed.
Up - held and strength - ened by Thy hand.
March on, O soul, march on, with strength! A-MEN.

Heralds of Christ

NATIONAL HYMN 10. 10. 10. 10.
Laura S. Copenhaver (1868–1940)
George William Warren, 1892
Trumpets, before each stanza
1. Heralds of Christ who bear the King's commands,
Immortal tidings in your mortal hands,
Pass on and carry swift the news ye bring,
Make straight, make straight the highway of the King.
2. Through desert ways, dark fen, and deep morass,
Through jungles, sluggish seas, and mountain pass,
Build ye the road, and falter not nor stay;
Prepare across the earth the King's highway.
3. Where once the twisting trail in darkness wound
Let marching feet and joyous song resound,
Where burned the funeral pyres, let children sing,
Make straight, make straight the highway of the King.
4. Lord, give us faith and strength the road to build,
To see the promise of the day fulfilled,
When war shall be no more and strife shall cease
Upon the highway of the Prince of Peace. A-MEN.

236 God of Grace and God of Glory

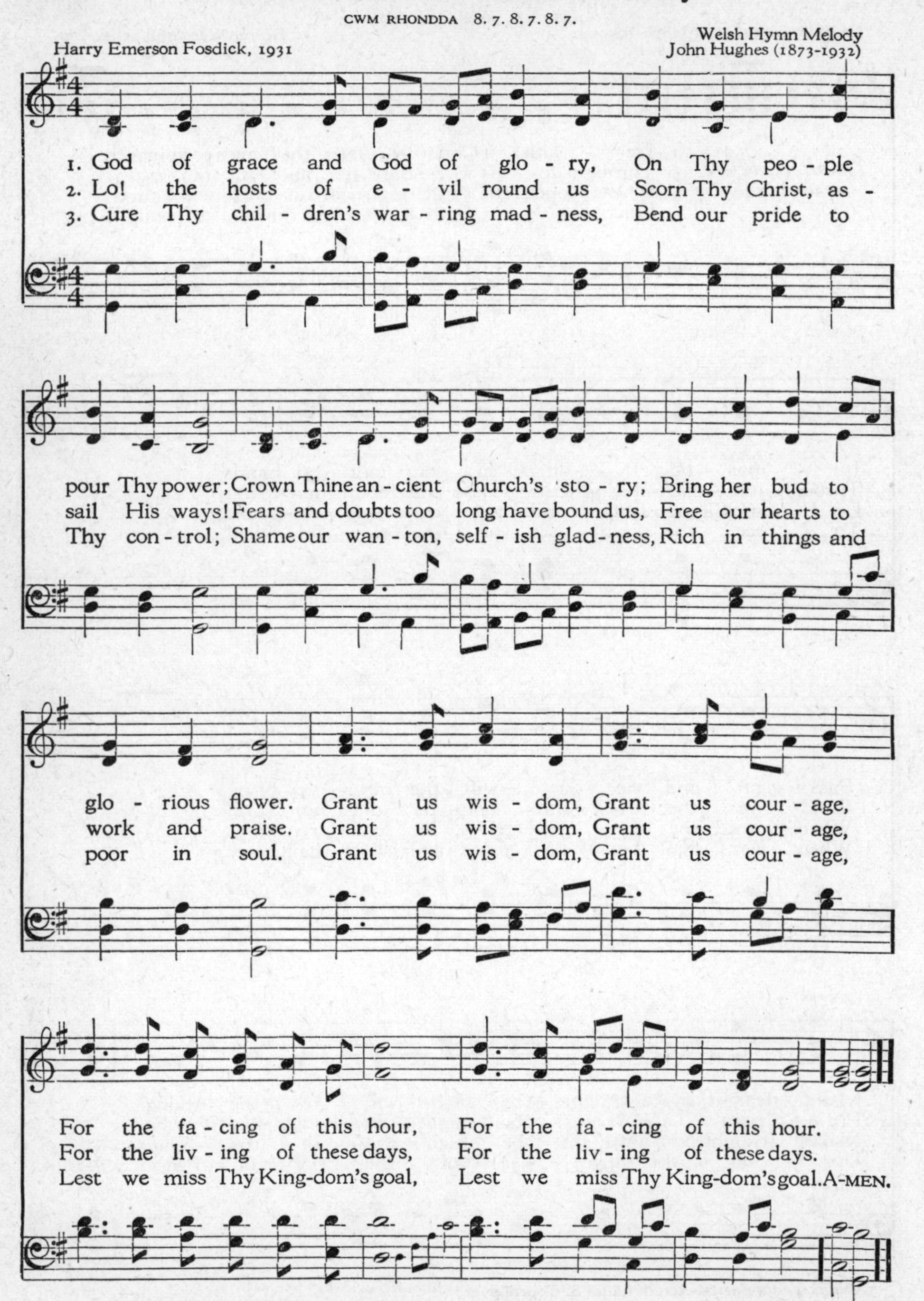
CWM RHONDDA 8. 7. 8. 7. 8. 7.
Harry Emerson Fosdick, 1931
Welsh Hymn Melody
John Hughes (1873-1932)
1. God of grace and God of glo - ry, On Thy peo - ple
2. Lo! the hosts of e - vil round us Scorn Thy Christ, as -
3. Cure Thy chil - dren's war - ring mad - ness, Bend our pride to
pour Thy power; Crown Thine an - cient Church's sto - ry; Bring her bud to
sail His ways! Fears and doubts too long have bound us, Free our hearts to
Thy con - trol; Shame our wan - ton, self - ish glad - ness, Rich in things and
glo - rious flower. Grant us wis - dom, Grant us cour - age,
work and praise. Grant us wis - dom, Grant us cour - age,
poor in soul. Grant us wis - dom, Grant us cour - age,
For the fa - cing of this hour, For the fa - cing of this hour.
For the liv - ing of these days, For the liv - ing of these days.
Lest we miss Thy King-dom's goal, Lest we miss Thy King-dom's goal. A-MEN.

God of Grace and God of Glory (Concluded)

4. Set our feet on lofty places;
Gird our lives that they may be
Armored with all Christlike graces
In the fight to set men free.
Grant us wisdom,
Grant us courage,
That we fail not man nor Thee!

5. Save us from weak resignation
To the evils we deplore;
Let the search for Thy salvation
Be our glory evermore.
Grant us wisdom,
Grant us courage,
Serving Thee whom we adore.

That Cause Can Neither Be Lost nor Stayed 237

GOD'S PLAN 9.9.10.10.

Christian Ostergaard
Trans. by J. A. Aaberg

Danish Folk Tune
Harmonized by Lawrence Curry, 1939

1. That cause can nei - ther be lost nor stayed Which takes the
2. Each no - ble serv - ice that men have wrought Was first con -
3. There - by it - self like a tree it shows: That high it
4. Be then no more by a storm dis - mayed, For by it
course of what God has made; And is not trust - ing in walls and
ceived as a fruit - ful thought; Each wor - thy cause with a fu - ture
reach - es, as deep it grows; And when the storms are its branch - es
the full-grown seeds are laid; And though the tree by its might it
tow - ers, But slow - ly grow - ing from seeds to flow - ers.
glo - rious By qui - et grow - ing be - comes vic - to - rious.
shak - ing, It deep - er root in the soil is tak - ing.
shat - ters, What then, if thou - sands of seeds it scat - ters?

238 We've a Story to Tell to the Nations

MESSAGE 10. 8. 8. 7. 7. with Refrain
Colin Sterne, 1896
H. Ernest Nichol, 1896
1. We've a sto - ry to tell to the na - tions, That shall turn their
2. We've a song to be sung to the na - tions, That shall lift their
3. We've a mes - sage to give to the na - tions, That the Lord who
4. We've a Sav - iour to show to the na - tions, Who the path of
hearts to the right, A sto - ry of truth and mer - cy,
hearts to the Lord; A song that shall con - quer e - vil
reign - eth a - bove Hath sent us His Son to save us,
sor - row hath trod, That all of the world's great peo - ples
A sto - ry of peace and light, A sto - ry of peace and light.
And shat - ter the spear and sword, And shat - ter the spear and sword.
And show us that God is Love, And show us that God is Love.
Might come to the truth of God, Might come to the truth of God.
REFRAIN
For the dark-ness shall turn to dawn - ing, And the dawn-ing to noon-day bright,

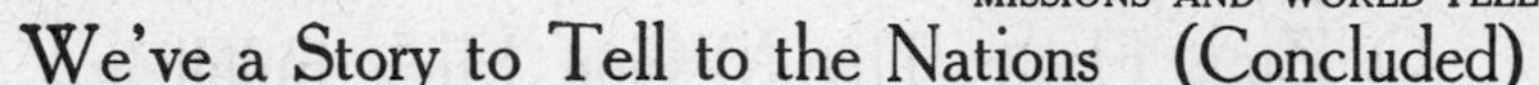

We've a Story to Tell to the Nations (Concluded)

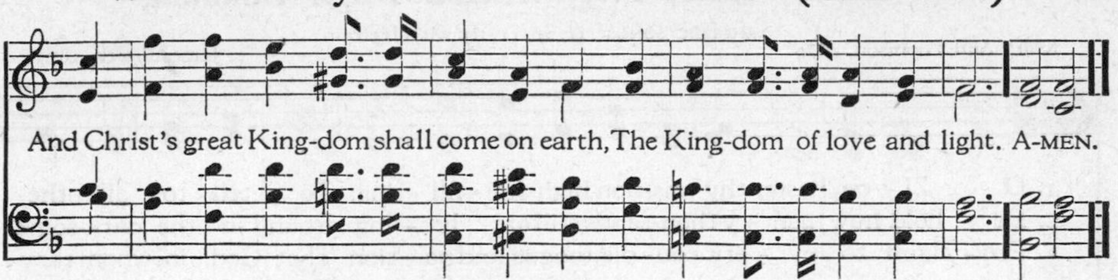
And Christ's great King-dom shall come on earth, The King-dom of love and light. A-MEN.

Words and music copyright by H. Ernest Nichol & Son, 342 Beverley Road, Hull, England. Used by permission.

239 The Morning Light Is Breaking

WEBB 7.6.7.6.D.

Samuel F. Smith, 1832

George J. Webb, 1837

1. The morn - ing light is break - ing, The dark - ness dis - ap - pears;
2. See dis - tant na - tions bend - ing Be - fore the God we love,
3. Blest riv - er of sal - va - tion, Pur - sue thy on - ward way;
The sons of earth are wak - ing To pen - i - ten - tial tears;
And thou - sand hearts as - cend - ing In grat - i - tude a - bove;
Flow thou to ev - ery na - tion, Nor in thy rich - ness stay:
Each breeze that sweeps the o - cean Brings ti - dings from a - far
While sin - ners, now con - fess - ing, The gos - pel call o - bey,
Stay not till all the low - ly Tri - um - phant reach their home;
Of na - tions in com - mo - tion, Pre - pared for Zi - on's war.
And seek the Sav - iour's bless - ing, A na - tion in a day.
Stay not till all the ho - ly Pro - claim, "The Lord is come." A-MEN.

240 O Zion, Haste, Thy Mission High Fulfilling

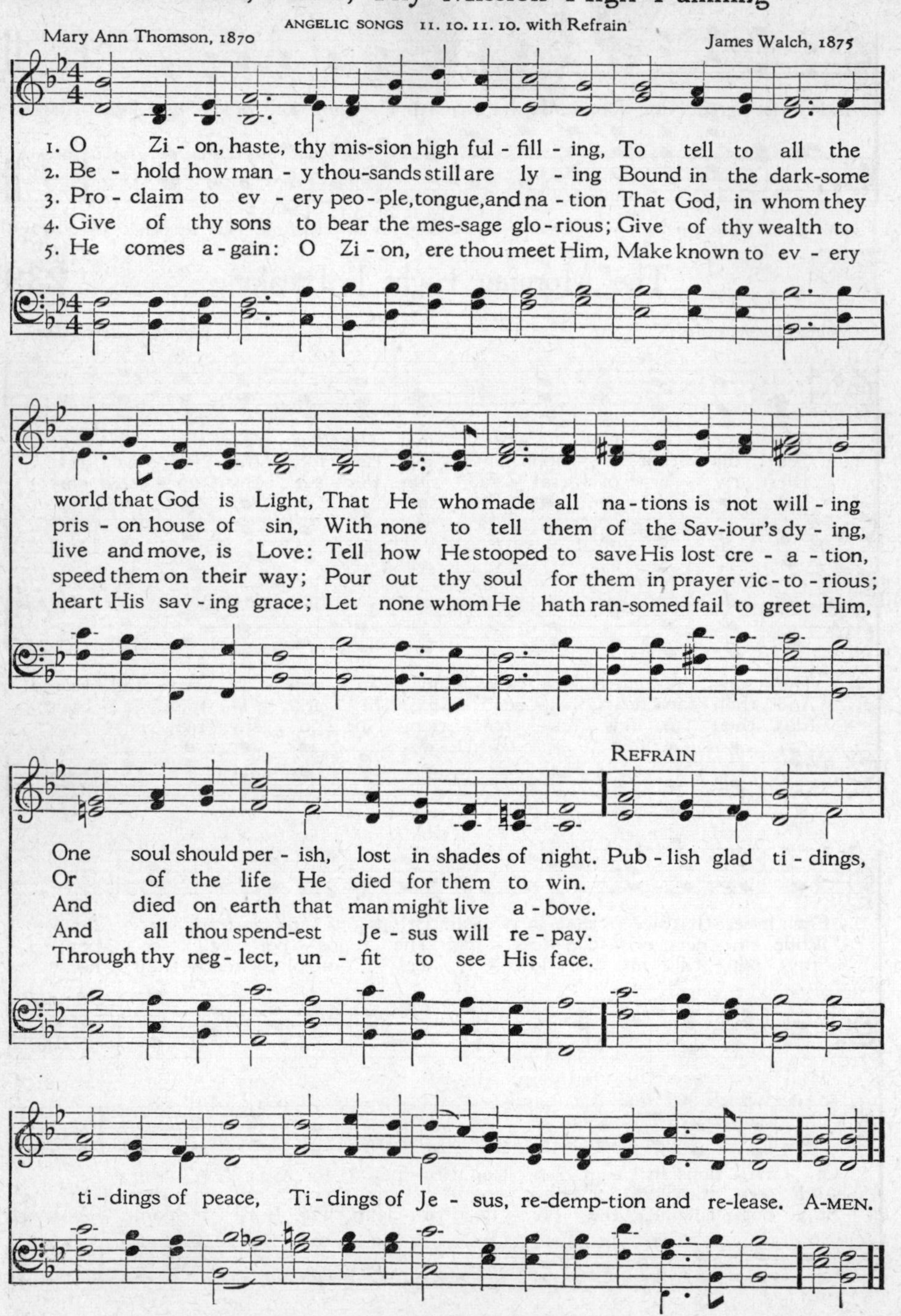
ANGELIC SONGS 11. 10. 11. 10. with Refrain
Mary Ann Thomson, 1870
James Walch, 1875
1. O Zi - on, haste, thy mis-sion high ful - fill - ing, To tell to all the
2. Be - hold how man - y thou-sands still are ly - ing Bound in the dark-some
3. Pro - claim to ev - ery peo - ple, tongue, and na - tion That God, in whom they
4. Give of thy sons to bear the mes-sage glo - rious; Give of thy wealth to
5. He comes a - gain: O Zi - on, ere thou meet Him, Make known to ev - ery
world that God is Light, That He who made all na - tions is not will - ing
pris - on house of sin, With none to tell them of the Sav-iour's dy - ing,
live and move, is Love: Tell how He stooped to save His lost cre - a - tion,
speed them on their way; Pour out thy soul for them in prayer vic - to - rious;
heart His sav - ing grace; Let none whom He hath ran-somed fail to greet Him,
One soul should per - ish, lost in shades of night.
Or of the life He died for them to win.
And died on earth that man might live a - bove.
And all thou spend-est Je - sus will re - pay.
Through thy neg - lect, un - fit to see His face.
REFRAIN
Pub - lish glad ti - dings, ti - dings of peace, Ti - dings of Je - sus, re-demp-tion and re-lease. A-MEN.

From Ocean Unto Ocean

TENNENT 7.6.7.6.D.
Robert Murray, 1880
Uzziah C. Burnap, 1895
1. From o - cean un - to o - cean Our land shall own Thee Lord,
2. O Christ, for Thine own glo - ry, And for our coun - try's weal,
3. Where er - ror smites with blind - ness, En - slaves and leads a - stray,
4. Our Sav - iour King, de - fend us, And guide where we should go;
And, filled with true de - vo - tion, O - bey Thy sov - ereign word.
We hum - bly plead be - fore Thee, Thy - self in us re - veal;
Do Thou in lov - ing - kind - ness Pro - claim Thy gos - pel day;
Forth with Thy mes - sage send us, Thy love and light to show;
Our prai - ries and our moun - tains, For - est and fer - tile field,
And may we know, Lord Je - sus, The touch of Thy dear hand;
Till all the tribes and ra - ces That dwell in this fair land,
Till, fired with true de - vo - tion, En - kin - dled by Thy word,
Our riv - ers, lakes, and foun - tains, To Thee shall trib - ute yield.
And, healed of our dis - eas - es, The Tempt - er's power with - stand.
A - dorned with Chris - tian gra - ces, With - in Thy courts shall stand.
From o - cean un - to o - cean Our land shall own Thee Lord.
A-MEN.

242 The Whole Wide World for Jesus!

THE WHOLE WIDE WORLD 7. 6. 7. 6. D. with Refrain

J. Dempster Hammond, 1880 John H. Maunder, 1894

1. The whole wide world for Je - sus! This shall our watch-word be;
2. The whole wide world for Je - sus In - spires us with the thought
3. The whole wide world for Je - sus! The march - ing or - der sound:
Up - on the high - est moun - tain, Down by the wid - est sea;
That all God's wan - dering chil - dren Have by His love been sought.
Go ye and preach the gos - pel Wher - ev - er man is found.
The whole wide world for Je - sus! To Him shall all men bow,
The whole wide world for Je - sus! O faint not by the way!
The whole wide world for Je - sus! Ride forth, O con-quering King,
In cit - y or in prai - rie— The world for Je - sus now!
The cross shall sure - ly con - quer In this our glo - rious day.
Through all the might - y na - tions The world to glo - ry bring!

The Whole Wide World for Jesus! (Concluded)

Refrain
The whole wide world, The whole wide world—Pro-claim the gos-pel ti-dings through
The whole wide world; Lift up the cross for Je-sus, His ban-ner be un-furled,
Till ev-ery tongue con-fess Him through The whole wide world! A-men.

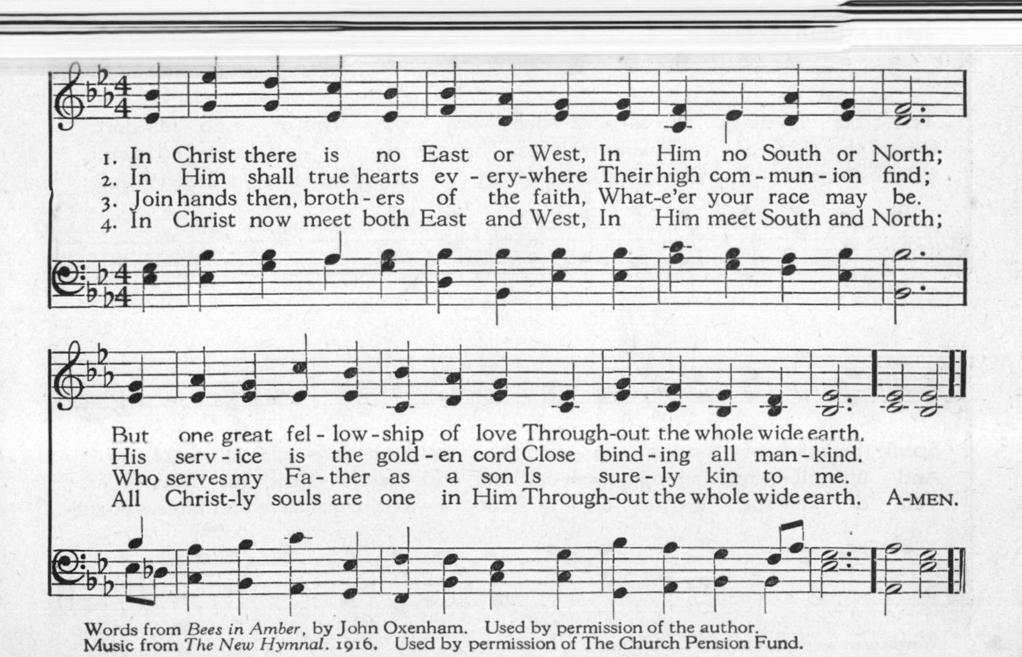
1. In Christ there is no East or West, In Him no South or North;
2. In Him shall true hearts ev-ery-where Their high com-mun-ion find;
3. Join hands then, broth-ers of the faith, What-e'er your race may be.
4. In Christ now meet both East and West, In Him meet South and North;
But one great fel-low-ship of love Through-out the whole wide earth.
His serv-ice is the gold-en cord Close bind-ing all man-kind.
Who serves my Fa-ther as a son Is sure-ly kin to me.
All Christ-ly souls are one in Him Through-out the whole wide earth. A-men.

Words from *Bees in Amber*, by John Oxenham. Used by permission of the author.
Music from *The New Hymnal*. 1916. Used by permission of The Church Pension Fund.

244 Sow the Seed Beside All Waters

CRUCIFER 8. 7. 8. 7. D.

Robert Murray, 1897 — Henry Smart, 1867

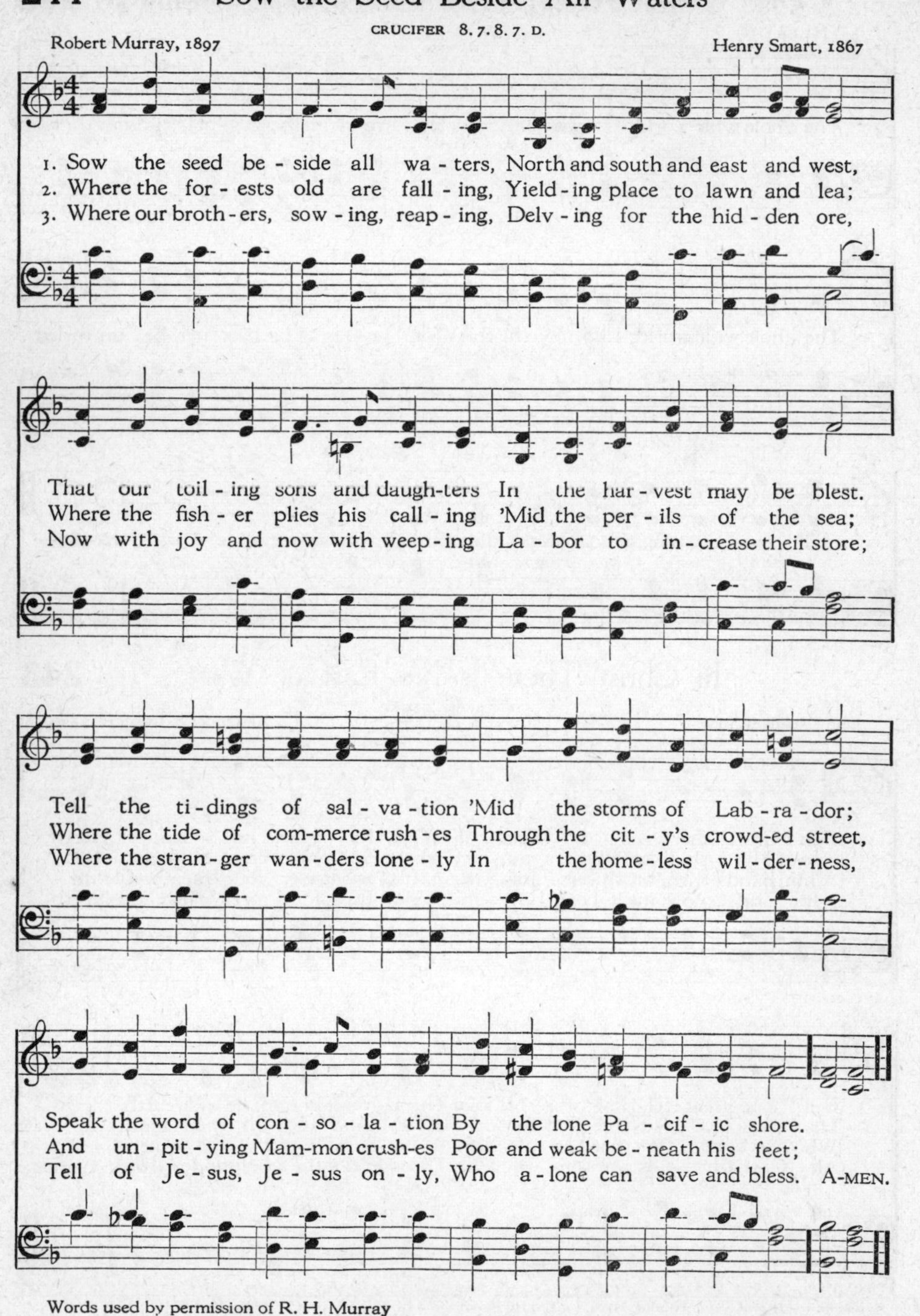
1. Sow the seed be-side all wa-ters, North and south and east and west,
2. Where the for-ests old are fall-ing, Yield-ing place to lawn and lea;
3. Where our broth-ers, sow-ing, reap-ing, Delv-ing for the hid-den ore,
That our toil-ing sons and daugh-ters In the har-vest may be blest.
Where the fish-er plies his call-ing 'Mid the per-ils of the sea;
Now with joy and now with weep-ing La-bor to in-crease their store;
Tell the ti-dings of sal-va-tion 'Mid the storms of Lab-ra-dor;
Where the tide of com-merce rush-es Through the cit-y's crowd-ed street,
Where the stran-ger wan-ders lone-ly In the home-less wil-der-ness,
Speak the word of con-so-la-tion By the lone Pa-cif-ic shore.
And un-pit-ying Mam-mon crush-es Poor and weak be-neath his feet;
Tell of Je-sus, Je-sus on-ly, Who a-lone can save and bless. A-MEN.

Hail to the Brightness of Zion's Glad Morning! 245

WESLEY 11.10.11.10.
Thomas Hastings, 1832
Stanza 4, Line 2, Alt.
Lowell Mason, 1833
1. Hail to the bright - ness of Zi - on's glad morn - ing!
2. Hail to the bright - ness of Zi - on's glad morn - ing,
3. Lo, in the des - ert rich flow - ers are spring - ing,
4. See, from all lands, from the isles of the o - cean,
Joy to the lands that in dark - ness have lain!
Long by the proph - ets of Is - rael fore - told!
Streams ev - er co - pious are glid - ing a - long;
Praise to the Sav - iour as - cend - ing on high;
Hushed be the ac - cents of sor - row and mourn - ing;
Hail to the mil - lions from bond - age re - turn - ing!
Loud from the moun - tain - tops ech - oes are ring - ing,
Fall - en the en - gines of war and com - mo - tion,
Zi - on in tri - umph be - gins her mild reign.
Gen - tiles and Jews the blest vi - sion be - hold.
Wastes rise in ver - dure, and min - gle in song.
Shouts of sal - va - tion are rend - ing the sky.
A - MEN.

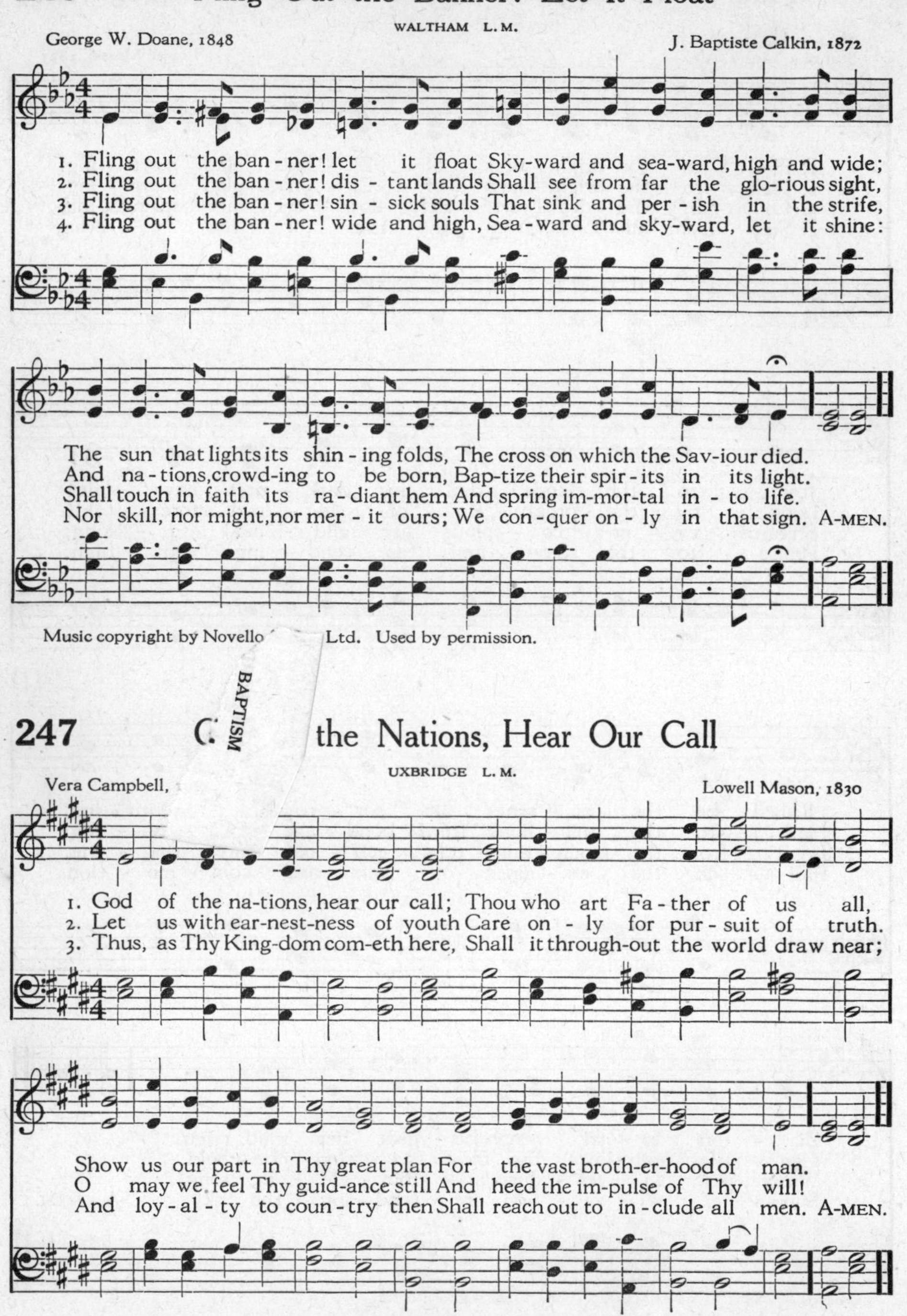
246 Fling Out the Banner! Let It Float
WALTHAM L. M.
George W. Doane, 1848
J. Baptiste Calkin, 1872
1. Fling out the ban - ner! let it float Sky-ward and sea-ward, high and wide;
2. Fling out the ban - ner! dis - tant lands Shall see from far the glo-rious sight,
3. Fling out the ban - ner! sin - sick souls That sink and per - ish in the strife,
4. Fling out the ban - ner! wide and high, Sea - ward and sky-ward, let it shine:
The sun that lights its shin - ing folds, The cross on which the Sav-iour died.
And na - tions, crowd-ing to be born, Bap-tize their spir - its in its light.
Shall touch in faith its ra - diant hem And spring im-mor-tal in - to life.
Nor skill, nor might, nor mer - it ours; We con - quer on - ly in that sign. A-MEN.
Music copyright by Novello Ltd. Used by permission.
BAPTISM
247 the Nations, Hear Our Call
UXBRIDGE L. M.
Vera Campbell,
Lowell Mason, 1830
1. God of the na-tions, hear our call; Thou who art Fa - ther of us all,
2. Let us with ear-nest-ness of youth Care on - ly for pur - suit of truth.
3. Thus, as Thy King-dom com-eth here, Shall it through-out the world draw near;
Show us our part in Thy great plan For the vast broth-er-hood of man.
O may we feel Thy guid-ance still And heed the im-pulse of Thy will!
And loy - al - ty to coun - try then Shall reach out to in - clude all men. A-MEN.

Jesus Shall Reign
248
DUKE STREET L. M.
From Psalm 72
Isaac Watts, 1719
John Hatton, d. 1793
1. Je - sus shall reign wher-e'er the sun Does his suc-ces - sive jour-neys run;
2. For Him shall end-less prayer be made, And prais-es throng to crown His head;
3. Peo - ple and realms of ev - ery tongue Dwell on His love with sweet-est song;
4. Bless-ings a-bound wher-e'er He reigns; The pris-oner leaps to lose his chains,
5. Let ev - ery crea-ture rise and bring Pe - cul - iar hon-ors to our King;
His King-dom stretch from shore to shore, Till moons shall wax and wane no more.
His Name, like sweet per - fume, shall rise With ev-ery morn - ing sac - ri - fice.
And in - fant voi - ces shall pro-claim Their ear-ly bless - ings on His Name.
The wea-ry find e - ter - nal rest, And all the sons of want are blest.
An - gels de - scend with songs a - gain, And earth re-peat the loud A - men! A-MEN.
Go, Labor On
249
PENTECOST L. M.
Horatius Bonar, 1843
William Boyd, 1868
1. Go, la - bor on: spend, and be spent, Thy joy to do the Fa-ther's will:
2. Go, la - bor on; 'tis not for nought; Thy earth - ly loss is heaven-ly gain:
3. Go, la - bor on while it is day: The world's dark night is has-tening on;
4. Toil on, faint not, keep watch and pray, Be wise the err - ing soul to win;
It is the way the Mas-ter went; Should not the serv-ant tread it still?
Men heed thee, love thee, praise thee not; The Mas-ter prais - es: what are men?
Speed, speed thy work, cast sloth a-way; It is not thus that souls are won.
Go forth in - to the world's high-way, Com - pel the wan-derer to come in. A-MEN.

250 Christ for the World We Sing

TRINITY (ITALIAN HYMN) 6. 6. 4. 6. 6. 6. 4.

Samuel Wolcott, 1869 — Felice de Giardini, 1769

1. Christ for the world we sing; The world to Christ we bring With lov - ing zeal; The poor and them that mourn, The faint and o - ver - borne, Sin - sick and sor - row - worn, Whom Christ doth heal.
2. Christ for the world we sing; The world to Christ we bring With fer - vent prayer; The way - ward and the lost, By rest - less pas - sions tossed, Re - deemed at count - less cost From dark de - spair.
3. Christ for the world we sing; The world to Christ we bring With one ac - cord; With us the work to share, With us re - proach to dare, With us the cross to bear, For Christ our Lord.
4. Christ for the world we sing; The world to Christ we bring With joy - ful song; The new - born souls whose days, Re - claimed from er - ror's ways, In - spired with hope and praise, To Christ be - long.
A - MEN.

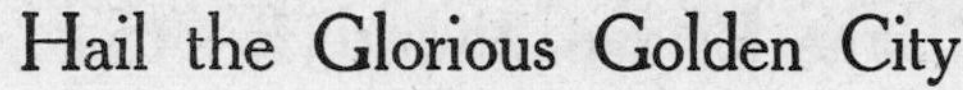

Hail the Glorious Golden City

AUSTRIAN HYMN 8.7.8.7.D.

Felix Adler (1851–1933) — Franz Joseph Haydn, 1797

1. Hail the glo-rious gold-en cit - y, Pic-tured by the seers of old!
2. We are build-ers of that cit - y; All our joys and all our groans
3. And the work that we have build-ed, Oft with bleed-ing hands and tears,
Ev - er-last - ing light shines o'er it, Won-drous tales of it are told:
Help to rear its shin - ing ram-parts; All our lives are build-ing stones:
Oft in er - ror, oft in an - guish, Will not per - ish with our years:
On - ly right-eous men and wom-en Dwell with-in its gleam-ing wall;
Wheth-er hum-ble or ex - alt - ed, All are called to task di-vine;
It will live and shine trans-fig - ured In the fi - nal reign of right;
Wrong is ban-ished from its bor-ders, Jus-tice reigns su-preme o'er all.
All must aid a-like to car - ry For-ward one sub-lime de-sign.
It will pass in-to the splen-dors Of the Cit - y of the Light. A-MEN.

252 The Fathers Built This City

PATMOS 7. 6. 8. 6. D.

William George Tarrant, 1895 — Henry J. Storer, 1891

1. The fa - thers built this cit - y In a - ges long a - go,
2. Yet still the cit - y stand - eth, A hive of toil - ing men,
3. Let all the peo - ple praise Thee, Give all Thy sav - ing health,
4. A com - mon-weal of broth - ers, U - nit - ed, great and small,
And, bus - y in its bus - y streets, They hur - ried to and fro;
And moth - er's love makes hap - py home For chil - dren now as then;
Or vain the la - borer's strong right arm And vain the mer-chant's wealth;
Up - on our ban - ner bla - zoned be The char - ter, "Each for all"!
The chil - dren played a - round them And sang the songs of yore,
O God of a - ges, help us Such cit - i - zens to be
Send forth Thy light to ban - ish The shad - ows and the shame,
Nor let us cease from bat - tle, Nor wea - ry sheathe the sword,
Till, one by one, they fell a - sleep, To work and play no more.
That chil-dren's chil - dren here may sing The songs of lib - er - ty!
Till all the civ - ic vir - tues shine A - round our cit - y's name.
Un - til this cit - y is be - come The cit - y of the Lord. A-MEN.

Words used by permission of Dorothy Tarrant.

Where Cross the Crowded Ways of Life 253

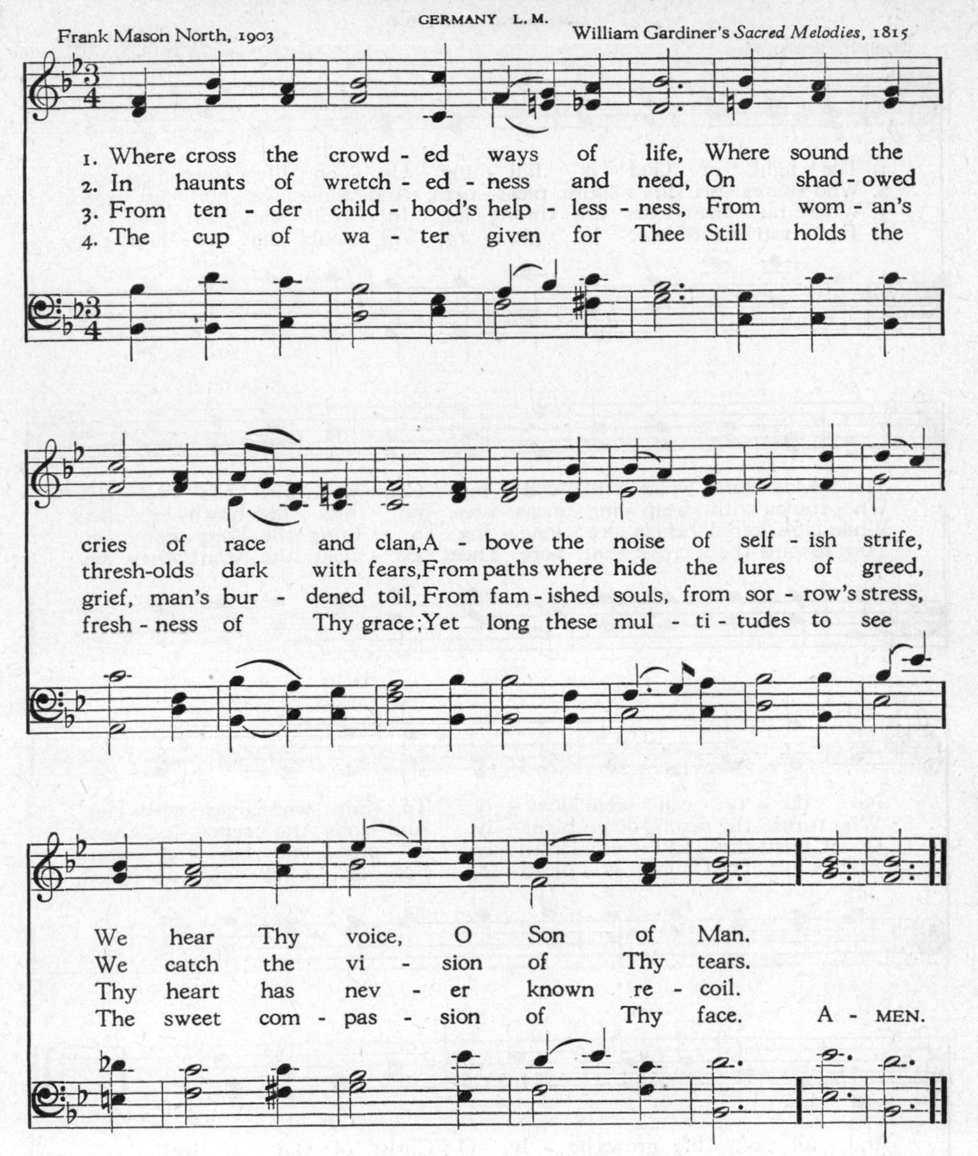
GERMANY L. M.
Frank Mason North, 1903
William Gardiner's Sacred Melodies, 1815
1. Where cross the crowd - ed ways of life, Where sound the
2. In haunts of wretch - ed - ness and need, On shad - owed
3. From ten - der child - hood's help - less - ness, From wom - an's
4. The cup of wa - ter given for Thee Still holds the
cries of race and clan, A - bove the noise of self - ish strife,
thresh-olds dark with fears, From paths where hide the lures of greed,
grief, man's bur - dened toil, From fam - ished souls, from sor - row's stress,
fresh - ness of Thy grace; Yet long these mul - ti - tudes to see
We hear Thy voice, O Son of Man.
We catch the vi - sion of Thy tears.
Thy heart has nev - er known re - coil.
The sweet com - pas - sion of Thy face. A - MEN.

5. O Master, from the mountainside,
Make haste to heal these hearts of pain;
Among these restless throngs abide,
O tread the city's streets again,

6. Till sons of men shall learn Thy love,
And follow where Thy feet have trod;
Till glorious from Thy heaven above
Shall come the City of our God.

254 The Light of God Is Falling

GREENLAND 7. 6. 7. 6. D.
Louis F. Benson, 1910
Arr. from J. Michael Haydn
In B. Jacob's National Psalmody, 1819
1. The light of God is fall - ing Up - on life's com - mon way;
2. Who shares his life's pure pleas - ures, And walks the hon - est road,
3. Where hu - man lives are throng - ing In toil and pain and sin,
4. Thy ran - somed host in glo - ry, All souls that sin and pray,
The Mas - ter's voice still call - ing, "Come, walk with Me to - day";
Who trades with heap - ing meas - ures, And lifts his broth - er's load,
While clois - tered hearts are long - ing To bring the King - dom in,
Turn toward the cross that bore Thee; "Be - hold the Man!" they say:
No du - ty can seem low - ly To him who lives with Thee,
Who turns the wrong down blunt - ly, And lends the right a hand,
O Christ, the Eld - er Broth - er Of proud and beat - en men,
And while Thy Church is plead - ing For all who would do good,
And all of life grows ho - ly, O Christ of Gal - i - lee!
He dwells in God's own coun - try, He tills the Ho - ly Land.
When they have found each oth - er, Thy King - dom will come then!
We hear Thy true voice lead - ing Our song of broth - er - hood.
A-MEN.

Words used by permission of Mrs. Robert F. Jefferys.

Come, Let Us Join with Faithful Souls

ELLACOMBE C. M. D.

William George Tarrant, 1892

Gesangbuch der Herzogl. Wirtembergischen Katholischen Hofkapelle, 1784

1. Come, let us join with faith-ful souls Our song of faith to sing,
One broth-er-hood in heart are we, And One our Lord and King.
Faith-ful are all who love the truth And dare the truth to tell,
Who stead-fast stand at God's right hand, And strive to serve Him well.

2. And faith-ful are the gen-tle hearts To whom the power is given
Of ev-ery hearth to make a home, Of ev-ery home a heaven.
O might-y host! no tongue can tell The num-bers of its throng;
No words can sound the mu-sic vast Of its grand bat-tle song.

3. From step to step it wins its way A-gainst a world of sin;
Part of the bat-tle-field is won, And part is yet to win.
O Lord of Hosts, our faith re-new, And grant us, in Thy love,
To sing the songs of vic-to-ry, With faith-ful souls a-bove. A-MEN.

256 Teach Us, O Lord, True Brotherhood

MARLOW C. M.

Marion Dutton Savage, 1913 — Arr. from John Chetham's *Book of Psalmody*, 1718

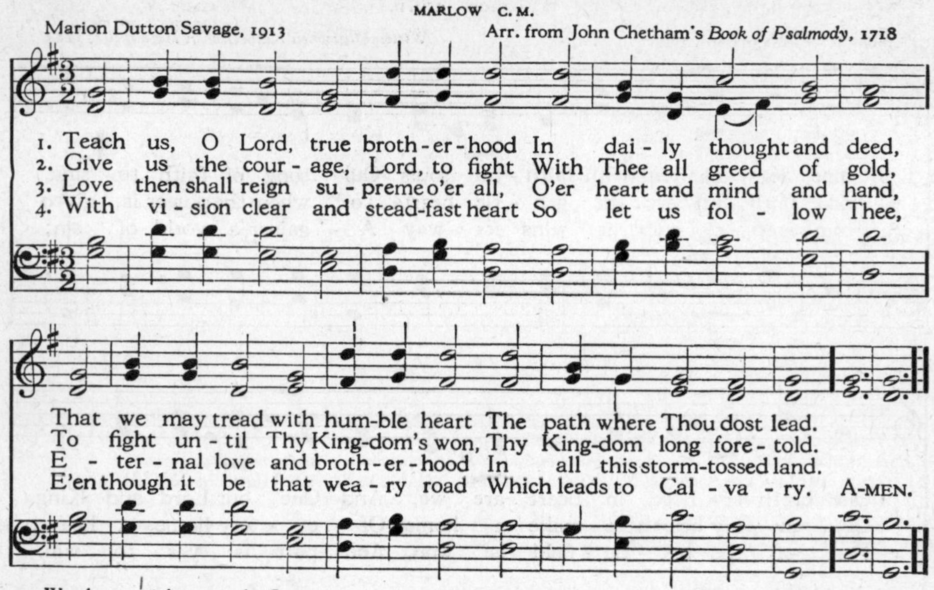
1. Teach us, O Lord, true broth-er-hood In dai-ly thought and deed,
2. Give us the cour-age, Lord, to fight With Thee all greed of gold,
3. Love then shall reign su-preme o'er all, O'er heart and mind and hand,
4. With vi-sion clear and stead-fast heart So let us fol-low Thee,
That we may tread with hum-ble heart The path where Thou dost lead.
To fight un-til Thy King-dom's won, Thy King-dom long fore-told.
E-ter-nal love and broth-er-hood In all this storm-tossed land.
E'en though it be that wea-ry road Which leads to Cal-va-ry. A-MEN.

257 When Thy Heart, with Joy O'erflowing

BULLINGER 8. 5. 8. 3.

Theodore C. Williams, 1891 — Ethelbert W. Bullinger, 1874

1. When thy heart, with joy o'er-flow-ing, Sings a thank-ful prayer,
2. When the har-vest sheaves in-gath-ered Fill thy barns with store,
3. If thy soul, with power up-lift-ed, Yearn for glo-rious deed,
4. Share with him thy bread of bless-ing, Sor-row's bur-den share;
In thy joy, O let thy broth-er With thee share.
To thy God and to thy broth-er Give the more.
Give thy strength to serve thy broth-er In his need.
When thy heart en-folds a broth-er God is there. A-MEN.

Rise Up, O Men of God! 258

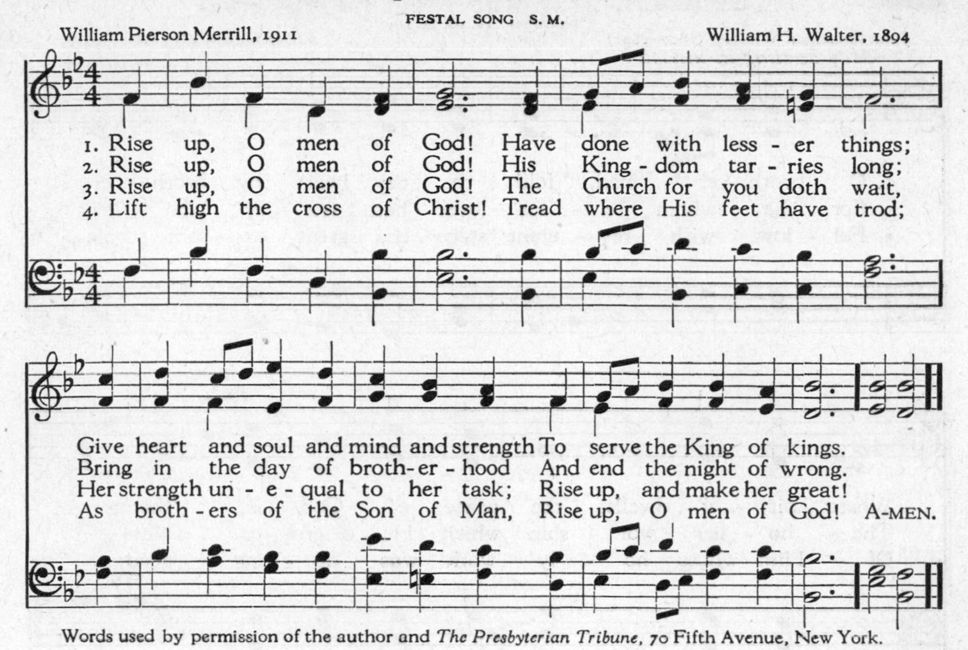
FESTAL SONG S. M.
William Pierson Merrill, 1911
William H. Walter, 1894
1. Rise up, O men of God! Have done with less - er things;
2. Rise up, O men of God! His King - dom tar - ries long;
3. Rise up, O men of God! The Church for you doth wait,
4. Lift high the cross of Christ! Tread where His feet have trod;
Give heart and soul and mind and strength To serve the King of kings.
Bring in the day of broth - er - hood And end the night of wrong.
Her strength un - e - qual to her task; Rise up, and make her great!
As broth - ers of the Son of Man, Rise up, O men of God! A-MEN.

Words used by permission of the author and *The Presbyterian Tribune*, 70 Fifth Avenue, New York.

Christian, Rise and Act Thy Creed 259

POSEN 7.7.7.7.

F. A. Rollo Russell, 1893

Georg C. Strattner
Arr. by J. A. Freylinghausen, 1705

1. Chris - tian, rise and act thy creed, Let thy prayer be in thy deed; Seek the right, per - form the true, Raise thy work and life a - new.
2. Hearts a - round thee sink with care; Thou canst help their load to bear, Thou canst bring in - spir - ing light, Arm their fal - tering wills to fight.
3. Let thine alms be hope and joy, And thy wor - ship God's em - ploy; Give Him thanks in hum - ble zeal, Learn - ing all His will to feel.
4. Come then, Law di - vine, and reign, Free - est faith as - sailed in vain, Per - fect love be - reft of fear, Born in heaven and ra - diant here. A-MEN.

260 O Brother Man, Fold to Thy Heart Thy Brother

WELWYN 11. 10. 11. 10.

John Greenleaf Whittier (1807–1892) Alfred Scott-Gatty (1847–1918)

May be sung in unison

1. O broth - er man, fold to thy heart thy broth - er;
2. For he whom Je - sus loved has tru - ly spo - ken:
3. Fol - low with rev - erent steps the great ex - am - ple
Where pit - y dwells, the peace of God is there;
The ho - lier wor - ship which He deigns to bless
Of Him whose ho - ly work was do - ing good;
To wor - ship right - ly is to love each oth - er,
Re - stores the lost, and binds the spir - it bro - ken,
So shall the wide earth seem our Fa - ther's tem - ple,
Each smile a hymn, each kind - ly deed a prayer.
And feeds the wid - ow and the fa - ther - less.
Each lov - ing life a psalm of grat - i - tude.
A-MEN.

When Wilt Thou Save the People? 261

COMMONWEALTH 7.6.7.6.8.8.8.5.

Ebenezer Elliott, 1850

Josiah Booth, 1888

1. When wilt Thou save the peo - ple? O God of mer - cy, when?
2. Shall crime bring crime for - ev - er, Strength aid - ing still the strong?
3. When wilt Thou save the peo - ple? O God of mer - cy, when?
Not kings and lords, but na - tions! Not thrones and crowns, but men!
Is it Thy will, O Fa - ther, That man shall toil for wrong?
The peo - ple, Lord, the peo - ple, Not thrones and crowns, but men!
Flowers of Thy heart, O God, are they; Let them not pass, like weeds, a - way,
"No," say Thy moun-tains; "No," Thy skies; Man's cloud-ed sun shall bright-ly rise,
God save the peo - ple; Thine they are, Thy chil-dren, as Thine an - gels fair;
Their her - it - age a sun - less day. God save the peo - ple!
And songs as - cend, in - stead of sighs. God save the peo - ple!
From vice, op - pres - sion, and de - spair, God save the peo - ple! A-MEN.

Music used by permission of Clifford Booth.

262 O Happy Home

WELWYN 11. 10. 11. 10.
Carl J. P. Spitta, 1833
Trans., Arr., and Alt. by Sarah L. Findlater, 1858
Alfred Scott-Gatty (1847–1918)
1. O hap - py home, where Thou art loved the dear - est,
2. O hap - py home, where each one serves Thee, low - ly,
3. O hap - py home, where Thou art not for - got - ten,
Thou lov - ing Friend and Sav - iour of our race,
What - ev - er his ap - point - ed work may be,
Where joy is o - ver - flow - ing, full and free,
And where a - mong the guests there nev - er com - eth
Till ev - ery com - mon task seems great and ho - ly,
O hap - py home, where ev - ery wound - ed spir - it
One who can hold such high and hon - ored place!
When it is done, O Lord, as un - to Thee!
Is brought, Phy - si - cian, Com - fort - er, to Thee.
A-MEN.

O Thou Whose Feet Have Climbed Life's Hill 263

ST. MAGNUS C.M.

Louis F. Benson, 1894, 1911 — Jeremiah Clark (1670-1707)

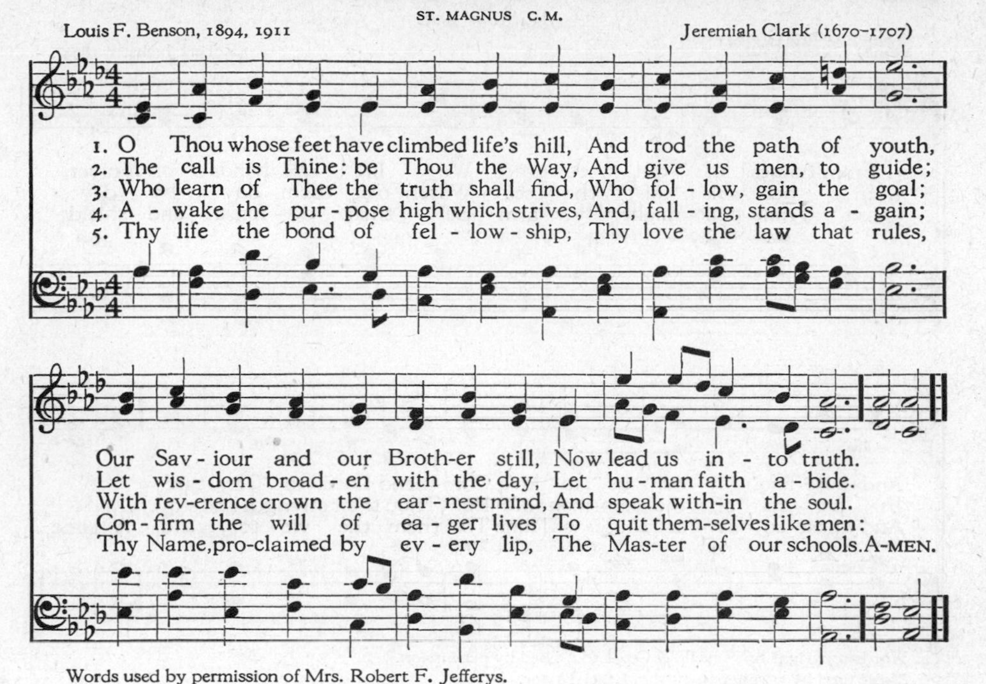
1. O Thou whose feet have climbed life's hill, And trod the path of youth,
2. The call is Thine: be Thou the Way, And give us men, to guide;
3. Who learn of Thee the truth shall find, Who fol - low, gain the goal;
4. A - wake the pur - pose high which strives, And, fall - ing, stands a - gain;
5. Thy life the bond of fel - low - ship, Thy love the law that rules,
Our Sav - iour and our Broth-er still, Now lead us in - to truth.
Let wis - dom broad - en with the day, Let hu - man faith a - bide.
With rev-erence crown the ear - nest mind, And speak with-in the soul.
Con - firm the will of ea - ger lives To quit them-selves like men:
Thy Name, pro-claimed by ev - ery lip, The Mas-ter of our schools. A-MEN.

Words used by permission of Mrs. Robert F. Jefferys.

Lord and Saviour, True and Kind 264

ORIENTIS PARTIBUS 7.7.7.7.

Handley C. G. Moule (1841-1920) — Medieval French Melody, Attributed to Pierre de Corbeil

1. Lord and Sav - iour, true and kind, Be the Mas - ter of my mind;
2. Let Thy gra - cious pres - ence rule All I think and speak at school;
3. Here I train for life's swift race; Let me do it in Thy grace:
4. Thou hast made me mind and soul; I for Thee would use the whole:
Bless, and guide, and strength-en still All my powers of thought and will.
Keep me faith - ful, prompt, and keen, At Thy side, my King un - seen.
Here I arm me for life's fight; Let me do it in Thy might.
Thou hast died that I might live; All my powers to Thee I give. A-MEN.

Words used by permission of the Trustees of Bishop Moule's Estate.

265 From Homes of Quiet Peace

TRENTHAM S. M.

William Henry Draper, 1900
Stanza 2, Line 3, Alt.

Robert Jackson, 1894

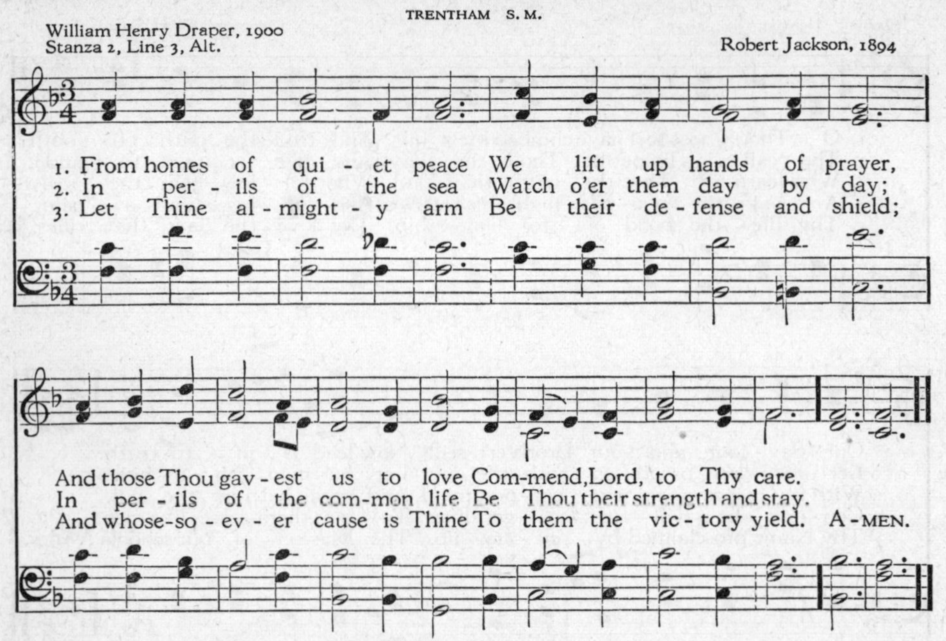
1. From homes of qui - et peace We lift up hands of prayer,
2. In per - ils of the sea Watch o'er them day by day;
3. Let Thine al - might - y arm Be their de - fense and shield;
And those Thou gav - est us to love Com-mend, Lord, to Thy care.
In per - ils of the com - mon life Be Thou their strength and stay.
And whose - so - ev - er cause is Thine To them the vic - tory yield. A - MEN.

266 O Thou Whose Gracious Presence Blessed

REST 8. 6. 8. 8. 6.

Louis F. Benson, 1925

Frederick C. Maker, 1887

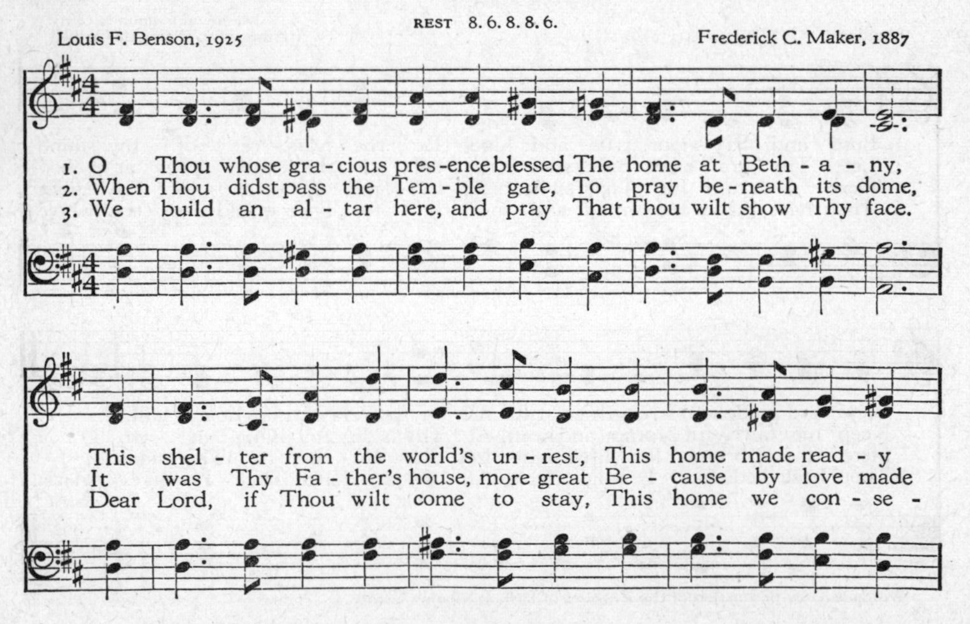
1. O Thou whose gra - cious pres - ence blessed The home at Beth - a - ny,
2. When Thou didst pass the Tem - ple gate, To pray be - neath its dome,
3. We build an al - tar here, and pray That Thou wilt show Thy face.
This shel - ter from the world's un - rest, This home made read - y
It was Thy Fa - ther's house, more great Be - cause by love made
Dear Lord, if Thou wilt come to stay, This home we con - se -

O Thou Whose Gracious Presence Blessed (Concluded)

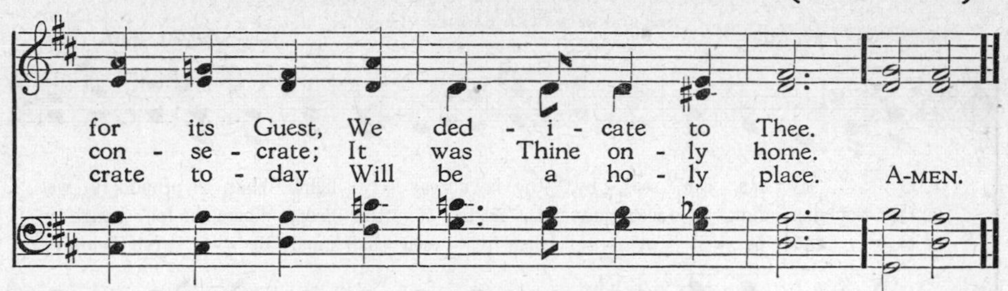
for its Guest, We ded - i - cate to Thee.
con - se - crate; It was Thine on - ly home.
crate to - day Will be a ho - ly place. A-MEN.

My Country, 'Tis of Thee 267

AMERICA 6. 6. 4. 6. 6. 6. 4.

Samuel F. Smith, 1832 — Source Unknown

1. My coun - try, 'tis of thee, Sweet land of lib - er - ty,
2. My na - tive coun - try, thee, Land of the no - ble free,
3. Let mu - sic swell the breeze, And ring from all the trees
4. Our fa - thers' God, to Thee, Au - thor of lib - er - ty,
Of thee I sing; Land where my fa - thers died, Land of the pil-grims' pride,
Thy name I love; I love thy rocks and rills, Thy woods and tem - pled hills;
Sweet free-dom's song: Let mor - tal tongues a-wake; Let all that breathe par-take;
To Thee we sing: Long may our land be bright With free-dom's ho - ly light;
From ev - ery moun - tain - side Let free - dom ring.
My heart with rap - ture thrills Like that a - bove.
Let rocks their si - lence break, The sound pro - long.
Pro - tect us by Thy might, Great God, our King. A - MEN.

268 The Star-spangled Banner

THE STAR-SPANGLED BANNER Irregular

Francis Scott Key, 1814

John Stafford Smith, 1778

1. O say, can you see, by the dawn's ear - ly light, What so proud - ly we
2. On the shore, dim - ly seen through the mists of the deep, Where the foe's haugh-ty
3. O thus be it ev - er, when free - men shall stand Be - tween their loved
hailed at the twi - light's last gleam - ing, Whose broad stripes and bright stars, through the
host in dread si - lence re - pos - es, What is that which the breeze, o'er the
home and the war's des - o - la - tion; Blest with vic - tory and peace, may the
per - il - ous fight, O'er the ram - parts we watched were so gal - lant - ly stream - ing?
tow - er - ing steep, As it fit - ful - ly blows, half con - ceals, half dis - clos - es?
heaven-res - cued land Praise the Power that hath made and pre - served us a na - tion!
And the rock - et's red glare, the bombs burst-ing in air, Gave proof through the
Now it catch - es the gleam of the morn-ing's first beam, In full glo - ry re -
Then con - quer we must, when our cause it is just, And this be our

The Star-spangled Banner (Concluded)

Refrain
night that our flag was still there! O say, does that star-span-gled
flect-ed now shines on the stream! 'T is the star-span-gled ban-ner: O
mot-to: "In God is our trust!" And the star-span-gled ban-ner in
ban-ner yet wave O'er the land of the free and the home of the brave?
long may it wave O'er the land of the free and the home of the brave!
tri-umph shall wave O'er the land of the free and the home of the brave!

Now Praise We Great and Famous Men 269

ACH GOTT UND HERR 8. 7. 8. 7.

William George Tarrant (1853–1928)

Melody in *Neu Leipziger Gesangbuch*, 1682
Arr. by Johann Sebastian Bach

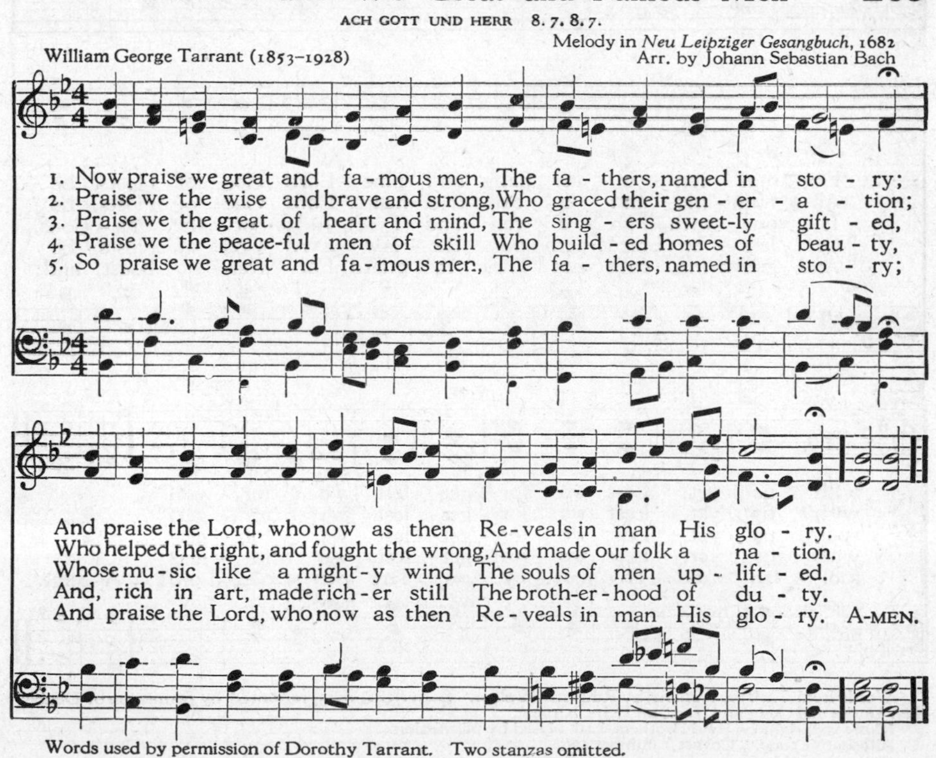
1. Now praise we great and fa-mous men, The fa-thers, named in sto-ry;
2. Praise we the wise and brave and strong, Who graced their gen-er-a-tion;
3. Praise we the great of heart and mind, The sing-ers sweet-ly gift-ed,
4. Praise we the peace-ful men of skill Who build-ed homes of beau-ty,
5. So praise we great and fa-mous men, The fa-thers, named in sto-ry;
And praise the Lord, who now as then Re-veals in man His glo-ry.
Who helped the right, and fought the wrong, And made our folk a na-tion.
Whose mu-sic like a might-y wind The souls of men up-lift-ed.
And, rich in art, made rich-er still The broth-er-hood of du-ty.
And praise the Lord, who now as then Re-veals in man His glo-ry. A-MEN.

 Two stanzas omitted.

270 God of Our Fathers, Known of Old

LEST WE FORGET 8. 8. 8. 8. 8. 8.

Rudyard Kipling, 1897 George F. Blanchard, 1898

1. God of our fa - thers, known of old, Lord of our far - flung
2. The tu - mult and the shout - ing dies; The cap - tains and the
3. Far-called, our na - vies melt a - way; On dune and head - land
4. If, drunk with sight of power, we loose Wild tongues that have not
5. For hea - then heart that puts her trust In reek - ing tube and
bat - tle line, Be - neath whose aw - ful hand we hold
kings de - part: Still stands Thine an - cient sac - ri - fice,
sinks the fire: Lo, all our pomp of yes - ter - day
Thee in awe, Such boast - ings as the Gen - tiles use,
i - ron shard, All val - iant dust that builds on dust,
Do - min - ion o - ver palm and pine— Lord God of Hosts, be
An hum - ble and a con - trite heart. Lord God of Hosts, be
Is one with Nin - e - veh and Tyre! Judge of the na - tions,
Or less - er breeds with - out the law— Lord God of Hosts, be
And, guard - ing, calls not Thee to guard, For fran - tic boast and
with us yet, Lest we for - get— lest we for - get!
with us yet, Lest we for - get— lest we for - get!
spare us yet, Lest we for - get— lest we for - get!
with us yet, Lest we for - get— lest we for - get!
fool - ish word— Thy mer - cy on Thy peo - ple, Lord! A - MEN.

Alternative tune, "Covert," number 179.

God of Our Fathers, Whose Almighty Hand 271

NATIONAL HYMN 10. 10. 10. 10.
Daniel C. Roberts, 1876
George William Warren, 1892
Trumpets, before each stanza
1. God of our fa - thers, whose al - might - y hand
Leads forth in beau - ty all the star - ry band
Of shin - ing worlds in splen - dor through the skies,
Our grate - ful songs be - fore Thy throne a - rise.
2. Thy love di - vine hath led us in the past;
In this free land by Thee our lot is cast;
Be Thou our Rul - er, Guard - ian, Guide, and Stay;
Thy word our law, Thy paths our chos - en way.
3. From war's a - larms, from dead - ly pes - ti - lence,
Be Thy strong arm our ev - er sure de - fense;
Thy true re - li - gion in our hearts in - crease,
Thy boun - teous good - ness nour - ish us in peace.
4. Re - fresh Thy peo - ple on their toil - some way,
Lead us from night to nev - er - end - ing day;
Fill all our lives with love and grace di - vine,
And glo - ry, laud, and praise be ev - er Thine.
A - MEN.

272 America the Beautiful

MATERNA C. M. D.
Katharine Lee Bates, 1893, 1904
Samuel A. Ward, 1882
1. O beau - ti - ful for spa - cious skies, For am - ber waves of grain,
2. O beau - ti - ful for pil - grim feet, Whose stern, im - pas-sioned stress
3. O beau - ti - ful for he - roes proved In lib - er - at - ing strife,
4. O beau - ti - ful for pa - triot dream That sees be - yond the years
For pur - ple moun-tain maj - es - ties A - bove the fruit - ed plain!
A thor - ough-fare for free - dom beat A - cross the wil - der - ness!
Who more than self their coun - try loved, And mer - cy more than life!
Thine al - a - bas - ter cit - ies gleam Un - dimmed by hu - man tears!
A - mer - i - ca! A - mer - i - ca! God shed His grace on thee
A - mer - i - ca! A - mer - i - ca! God mend thine ev - ery flaw,
A - mer - i - ca! A - mer - i - ca! May God thy gold re - fine
A - mer - i - ca! A - mer - i - ca! God shed His grace on thee
And crown thy good with broth - er - hood From sea to shin - ing sea!
Con - firm thy soul in self - con - trol, Thy lib - er - ty in law!
Till all suc - cess be no - ble - ness And ev - ery gain di - vine!
And crown thy good with broth - er - hood From sea to shin - ing sea! A-MEN.

God Save America!

RUSSIAN HYMN 11. 10. 11. 10.

William G. Ballantine, 1912

Alexis Lwoff, 1833

1. God save A - mer - i - ca! New world of glo - ry, New - born to
2. God save A - mer - i - ca! Here may all ra - ces Min - gle to -
3. God save A - mer - i - ca! Broth - er - hood ban - ish Wail of the
4. God save A - mer - i - ca! Bear - ing the ol - ive, Hers be the
5. God save A - mer - i - ca! 'Mid all her splen - dors, Save her from

free - dom and knowl - edge and power, Lift - ing the towers of her
geth - er as chil - dren of God, Found - ing an em - pire on
work - er and curse of the crushed; Joy break in songs from her
bless - ing the peace - mak - ers prove, Call - ing the na - tions to
pride and from lux - u - ry; Throne in her heart the un -

light - ning - lit cit - ies Where the flood tides of hu - man - i - ty roar!
broth - er - ly kind - ness, E - qual in lib - er - ty, made of one blood!
ju - bi - lant mil - lions, Hail - ing the day when all dis - cords are hushed!
glad fed - er - a - tion, Lead - ing the world in the tri - umph of love!
seen and e - ter - nal; Right be her might and the truth make her free! A-MEN.

274 Not Alone for Mighty Empire

HYFRYDOL 8.7.8.7. D.
William Pierson Merrill, 1909
Rowland Hugh Prichard (1811-1887)
1. Not a-lone for might-y em-pire, Stretch-ing far o'er land and sea;
2. Not for bat-tle-ship and for-tress, Not for con-quests of the sword;
3. For the ar-mies of the faith-ful, Souls that passed and left no name;
4. God of jus-tice, save the peo-ple From the clash of race and creed,
Not a-lone for boun-teous har-vests, Lift we up our hearts to Thee.
But for con-quests of the spir-it Give we thanks to Thee, O Lord;
For the glo-ry that il-lu-mines Pa-triot lives of death-less fame;
From the strife of class and fac-tion: Make our na-tion free in-deed.
Stand-ing in the liv-ing pres-ent, Mem-o-ry and hope be-tween,
For the price-less gift of free-dom, For the home, the church, the school;
For our proph-ets and a-pos-tles, Loy-al to the liv-ing Word;
Keep her faith in sim-ple man-hood Strong as when her life be-gan,
Lord, we would with deep thanks-giv-ing Praise Thee most for things un-seen.
For the o-pen door to man-hood In a land the peo-ple rule.
For all he-roes of the Spir-it, Give we thanks to Thee, O Lord.
Till it find its full fru-i-tion In the broth-er-hood of man. A-MEN.

Words used by permission of William Pierson Merrill.

O God, Beneath Thy Guiding Hand 275

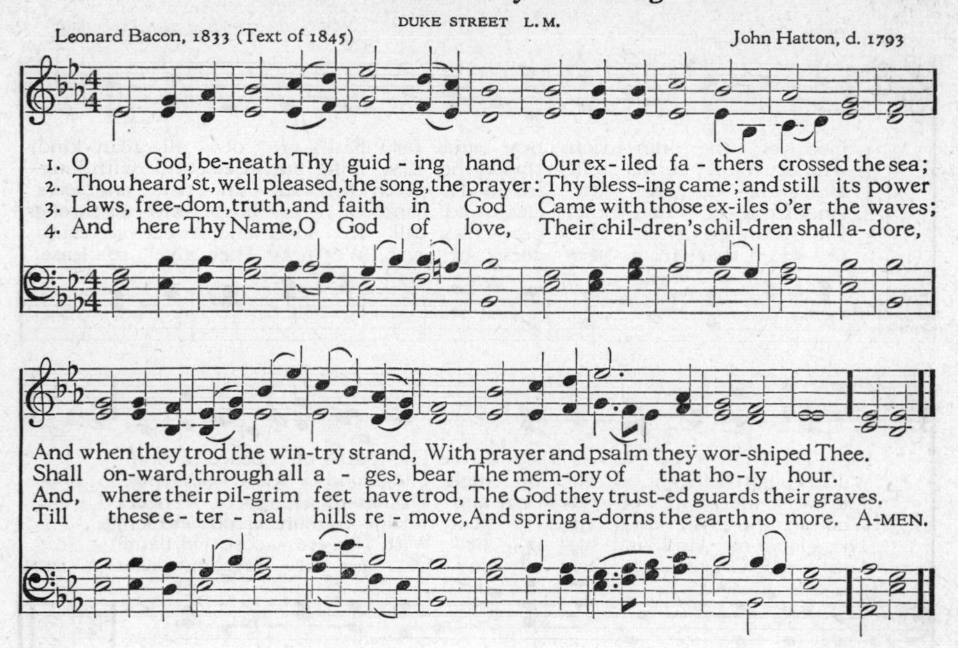
DUKE STREET L. M.
Leonard Bacon, 1833 (Text of 1845)
John Hatton, d. 1793
1. O God, be-neath Thy guid - ing hand Our ex - iled fa - thers crossed the sea;
2. Thou heard'st, well pleased, the song, the prayer: Thy bless-ing came; and still its power
3. Laws, free-dom, truth, and faith in God Came with those ex - iles o'er the waves;
4. And here Thy Name, O God of love, Their chil-dren's chil-dren shall a - dore,
And when they trod the win-try strand, With prayer and psalm they wor-shiped Thee.
Shall on-ward, through all a - ges, bear The mem-ory of that ho - ly hour.
And, where their pil-grim feet have trod, The God they trust-ed guards their graves.
Till these e - ter - nal hills re - move, And spring a-dorns the earth no more. A-MEN.

God Send Us Men Whose Aim 'Twill Be 276

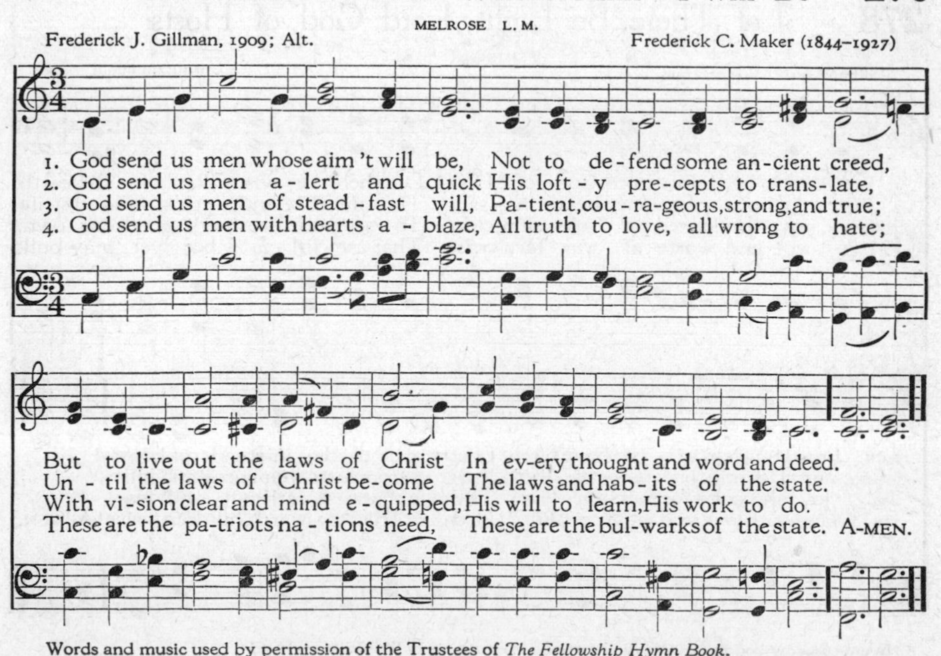
MELROSE L. M.
Frederick J. Gillman, 1909; Alt.
Frederick C. Maker (1844–1927)
1. God send us men whose aim 't will be, Not to de - fend some an - cient creed,
2. God send us men a - lert and quick His loft - y pre - cepts to trans - late,
3. God send us men of stead - fast will, Pa - tient, cou - ra - geous, strong, and true;
4. God send us men with hearts a - blaze, All truth to love, all wrong to hate;
But to live out the laws of Christ In ev - ery thought and word and deed.
Un - til the laws of Christ be - come The laws and hab - its of the state.
With vi - sion clear and mind e - quipped, His will to learn, His work to do.
These are the pa - triots na - tions need, These are the bul - warks of the state. A-MEN.

277 God of the Nations, Near and Far

ST. AGNES C.M.

John Haynes Holmes, 1911 — John B. Dykes, 1866

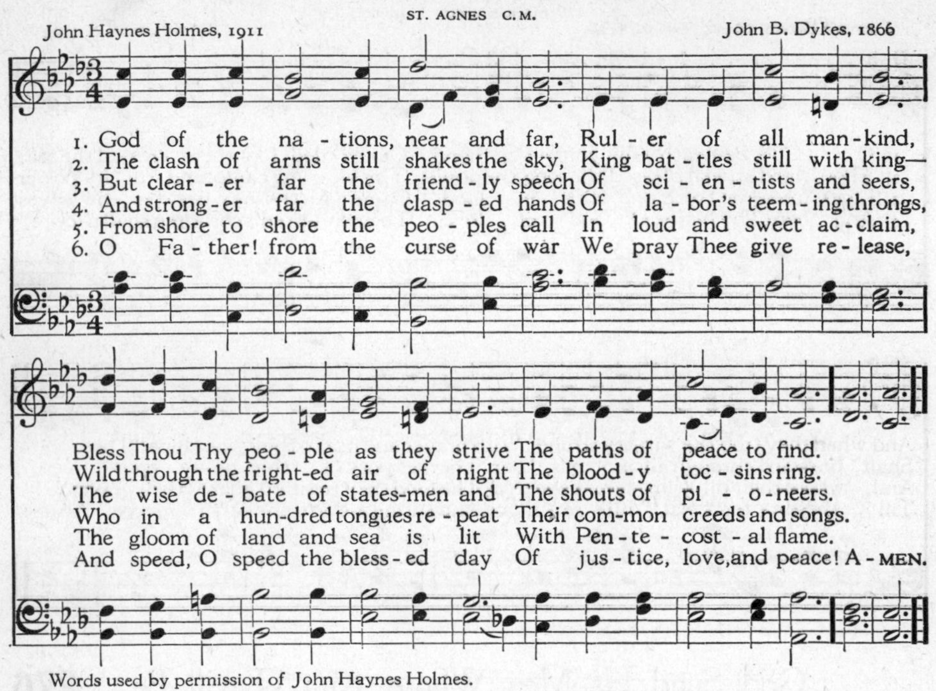
1. God of the na - tions, near and far, Rul - er of all man - kind, Bless Thou Thy peo - ple as they strive The paths of peace to find.
2. The clash of arms still shakes the sky, King bat - tles still with king— Wild through the fright-ed air of night The blood - y toc - sins ring.
3. But clear - er far the friend - ly speech Of sci - en - tists and seers, The wise de - bate of states-men and The shouts of pi - o - neers.
4. And strong - er far the clasp - ed hands Of la - bor's teem - ing throngs, Who in a hun-dred tongues re - peat Their com-mon creeds and songs.
5. From shore to shore the peo - ples call In loud and sweet ac - claim, The gloom of land and sea is lit With Pen - te - cost - al flame.
6. O Fa - ther! from the curse of war We pray Thee give re - lease, And speed, O speed the bless - ed day Of jus - tice, love, and peace! A - MEN.

Words used by permission of John Haynes Holmes.

278 Let There Be Light, Lord God of Hosts

PENTECOST L. M.

William Merrill Vories, 1908 — William Boyd, 1868

1. Let there be light, Lord God of Hosts, Let there be wis - dom on the earth! Let broad hu-man - i - ty have birth! Let there be deeds, in-stead of boasts!
2. With - in our pas-sioned hearts in - still The calm that end - eth strain and strife; Make us Thy min - is - ters of life; Purge us from lusts that curse and kill!
3. Give us the peace of vi - sion clear To see our broth-ers' good our own, To joy and suf - fer not a - lone—The love that cast - eth out all fear!
4. Let woe and waste of war - fare cease, That use - ful la - bor yet may build Its homes with love and laugh-ter filled! God give Thy way-ward chil-dren peace! A - MEN.

Words used by permission of The American Peace Society, Washington, D. C.

279 O God of Love, O King of Peace

CANNONS L. M.

Henry Williams Baker, 1861 — Georg Friedrich Handel (1685–1759)

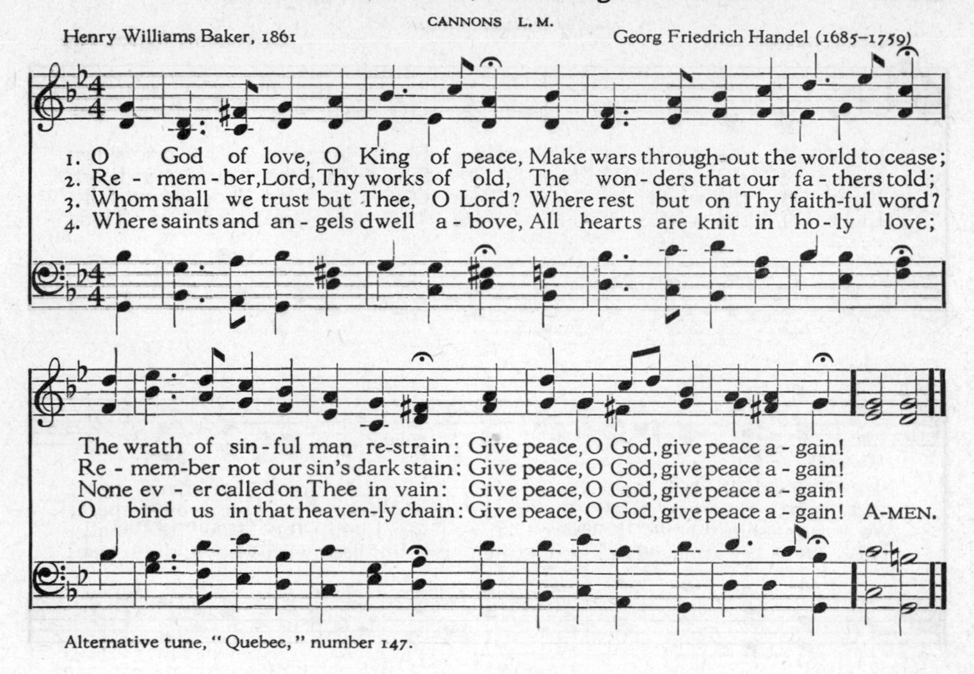
1. O God of love, O King of peace, Make wars through-out the world to cease;
2. Re - mem - ber, Lord, Thy works of old, The won - ders that our fa - thers told;
3. Whom shall we trust but Thee, O Lord? Where rest but on Thy faith-ful word?
4. Where saints and an - gels dwell a - bove, All hearts are knit in ho - ly love;
The wrath of sin - ful man re-strain: Give peace, O God, give peace a - gain!
Re - mem-ber not our sin's dark stain: Give peace, O God, give peace a - gain!
None ev - er called on Thee in vain: Give peace, O God, give peace a - gain!
O bind us in that heaven-ly chain: Give peace, O God, give peace a - gain! A-MEN.

Alternative tune, "Quebec," number 147.

280 Thy Kingdom Come, O Lord

ST. CECILIA 6. 6. 6. 6.

Frederick L. Hosmer, 1905 — Leighton G. Hayne, 1863

1. Thy King - dom come, O Lord, Wide - cir - cling as the sun;
2. One in the bond of peace, The serv - ice glad and free
3. Speed, speed the longed - for time Fore - told by rap - tured seers—
4. Till rise at last, to span Its firm foun - da - tions broad,
Ful - fill of old Thy word And make the na - tions one:
Of truth and right - eous - ness, Of love and eq - ui - ty.
The proph - e - cy sub - lime, The hope of all the years—
The com - mon - wealth of man, The Cit - y of our God. A-MEN.

281 Light of the World, We Hail Thee

SALVE DOMINE 7. 6. 7. 6. D.
John S. B. Monsell, 1863
Lawrence W. Watson, 1909
1. Light of the world, we hail Thee, Flush - ing the east - ern skies;
2. Light of the world, Thy beau - ty Steals in - to ev - ery heart,
3. Light of the world, be - fore Thee Our spir - its pros - trate fall;
4. Light of the world, il - lu - mine This dark - ened land of Thine,
Nev - er shall dark - ness veil Thee A - gain from hu - man eyes;
And glo - ri - fies with du - ty Life's poor - est, hum - blest part;
We wor - ship, we a - dore Thee, Thou Light, the Life of all;
Till ev - ery - thing that's hu - man Be filled with what's di - vine;
Too long, a - las, with - hold - en, Now spread from shore to shore;
Thou rob - est in Thy splen - dor The sim - ple ways of men,
With Thee is no for - get - ting Of all Thy hand hath made;
Till ev - ery tongue and na - tion, From sin's do - min - ion free,
Thy light, so glad and gold - en, Shall set on earth no more.
And help - est them to ren - der Light back to Thee a - gain.
Thy ris - ing hath no set - ting, Thy sun - shine hath no shade.
Rise in the new cre - a - tion Which springs from love and Thee. A-MEN.

Music used by permission of G. R. D. Watson.

Ring Out, Wild Bells 282

DEUS TUORUM MILITUM L. M.

Alfred Tennyson, 1849

Grenoble Church Melody

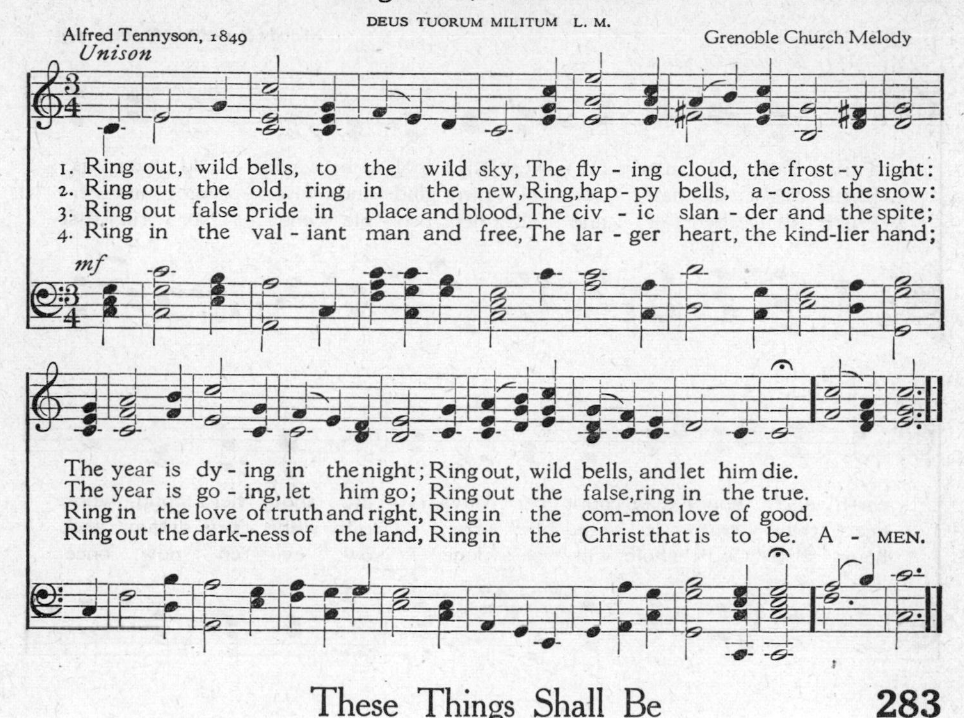
Unison
1. Ring out, wild bells, to the wild sky, The fly - ing cloud, the frost - y light:
2. Ring out the old, ring in the new, Ring, hap - py bells, a - cross the snow:
3. Ring out false pride in place and blood, The civ - ic slan - der and the spite;
4. Ring in the val - iant man and free, The lar - ger heart, the kind-lier hand;
mf
The year is dy - ing in the night; Ring out, wild bells, and let him die.
The year is go - ing, let him go; Ring out the false, ring in the true.
Ring in the love of truth and right, Ring in the com-mon love of good.
Ring out the dark-ness of the land, Ring in the Christ that is to be. A - MEN.

These Things Shall Be 283

DEPAUW L. M.

John Addington Symonds, 1880
Stanza 3, Line 2, Alt.

Robert G. McCutchan, 1930

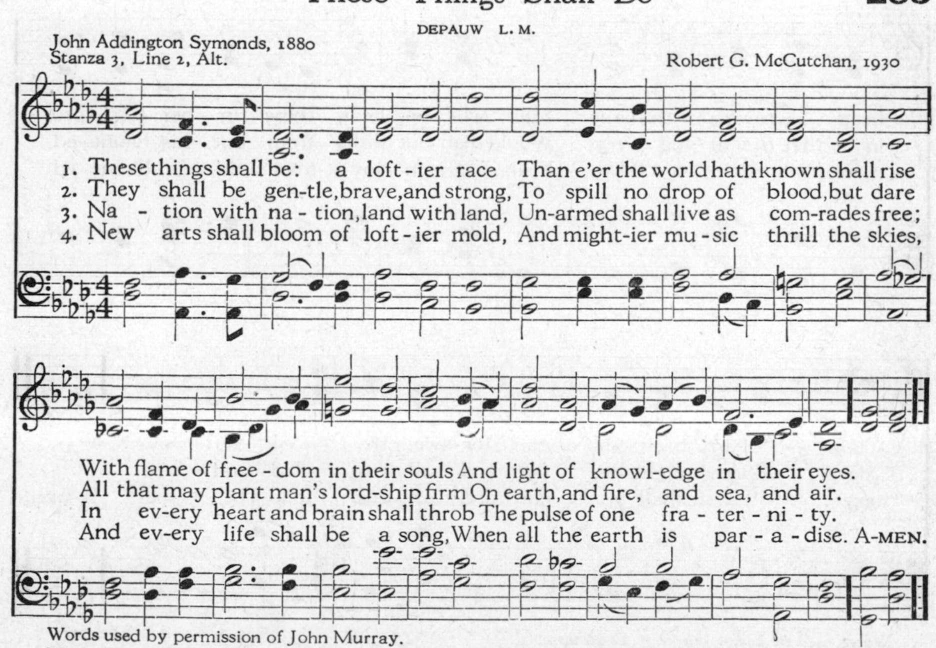
1. These things shall be: a loft - ier race Than e'er the world hath known shall rise
2. They shall be gen-tle, brave, and strong, To spill no drop of blood, but dare
3. Na - tion with na - tion, land with land, Un-armed shall live as com-rades free;
4. New arts shall bloom of loft - ier mold, And might-ier mu - sic thrill the skies,
With flame of free - dom in their souls And light of knowl-edge in their eyes.
All that may plant man's lord-ship firm On earth, and fire, and sea, and air.
In ev-ery heart and brain shall throb The pulse of one fra - ter - ni - ty.
And ev-ery life shall be a song, When all the earth is par - a - dise. A-MEN.

284 Turn Back, O Man

OLD 124TH 10. 10. 10. 10. 10.

Clifford Bax, 1919

Melody in *Genevan Psalter*, 1551

May be sung in unison

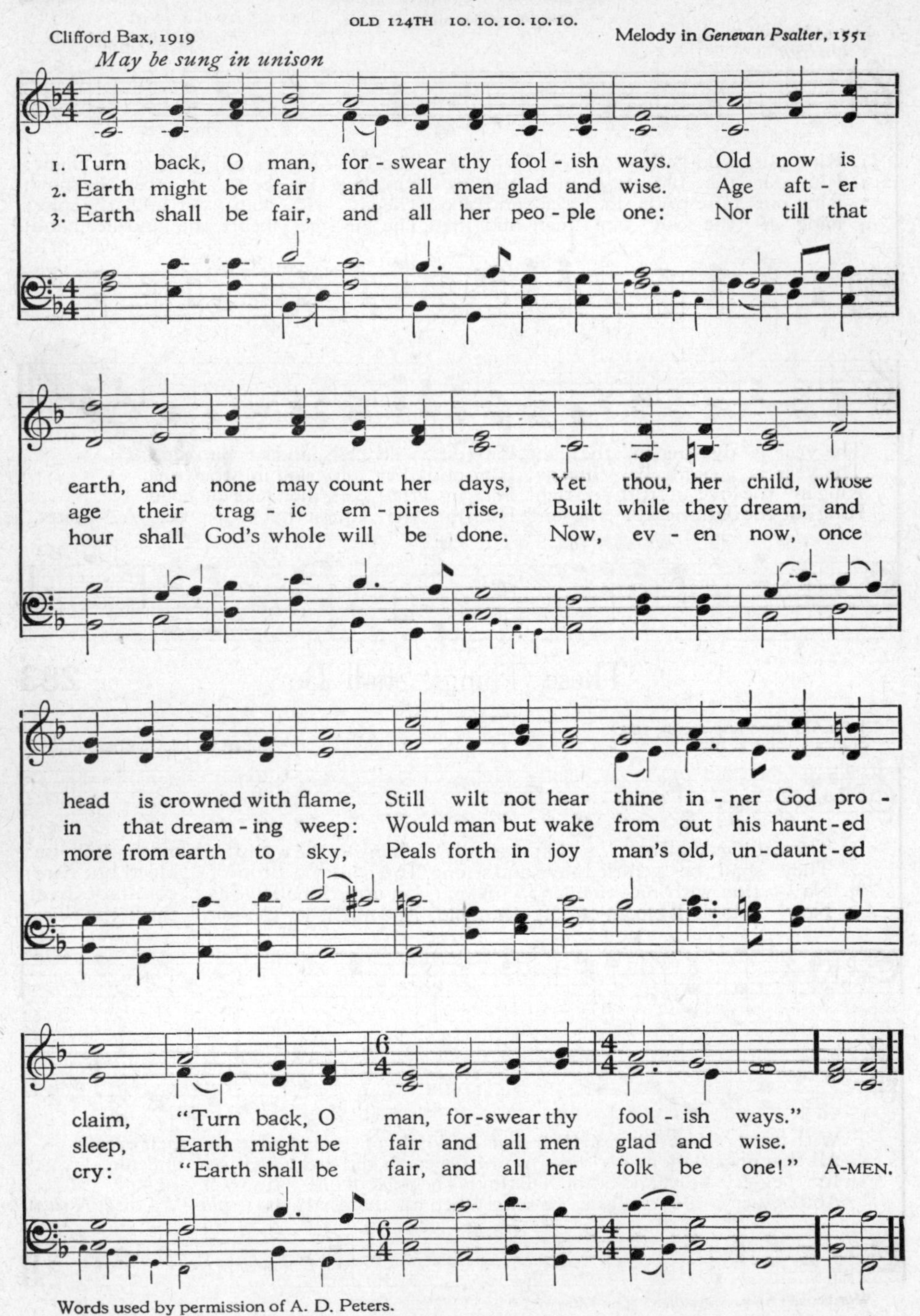

1. Turn back, O man, for-swear thy fool-ish ways. Old now is earth, and none may count her days, Yet thou, her child, whose head is crowned with flame, Still wilt not hear thine in-ner God pro-claim, "Turn back, O man, for-swear thy fool-ish ways."
2. Earth might be fair and all men glad and wise. Age aft-er age their trag-ic em-pires rise, Built while they dream, and in that dream-ing weep: Would man but wake from out his haunt-ed sleep, Earth might be fair and all men glad and wise.
3. Earth shall be fair, and all her peo-ple one: Nor till that hour shall God's whole will be done. Now, ev-en now, once more from earth to sky, Peals forth in joy man's old, un-daunt-ed cry: "Earth shall be fair, and all her folk be one!" A-MEN.

Words used by permission of A. D. Peters.

God the Omnipotent! 285

RUSSIAN HYMN 11. 10. 11. 9.
Henry F. Chorley, 1842
John Ellerton, 1870; Alt.
Alexis Lwoff, 1833
1. God the Om - nip - o - tent! King, who or - dain - est
2. God the All - mer - ci - ful! earth hath for - sak - en
3. God the All - right - eous One! man hath de - fied Thee;
4. God the All - wise! by the fire of Thy chas - tening
5. So shall Thy peo - ple, with thank - ful de - vo - tion,
Thun - der Thy clar - ion, the light - ning Thy sword;
Thy ways all - ho - ly, and slight - ed Thy word;
Yet to e - ter - ni - ty stand - eth Thy word;
Earth shall to free - dom and truth be re - stored;
Praise Him who saved them from per - il and sword,
Show forth Thy pit - y on high where Thou reign - est;
Let not Thy wrath in its ter - rors a - wak - en;
False - hood and wrong shall not tar - ry be - side Thee;
Through the thick dark - ness Thy King - dom is has - tening;
Sing - ing in cho - rus from o - cean to o - cean
Give to us peace in our time, O Lord.
Give to us peace in our time, O Lord.
Give to us peace in our time, O Lord.
Thou wilt give peace in Thy time, O Lord.
Peace to the na - tions, and praise to the Lord.
A-MEN.

286 Study War No More

STUDY WAR NO MORE Irregular

Negro Spiritual
Harmonized by Lawrence Curry, 1941

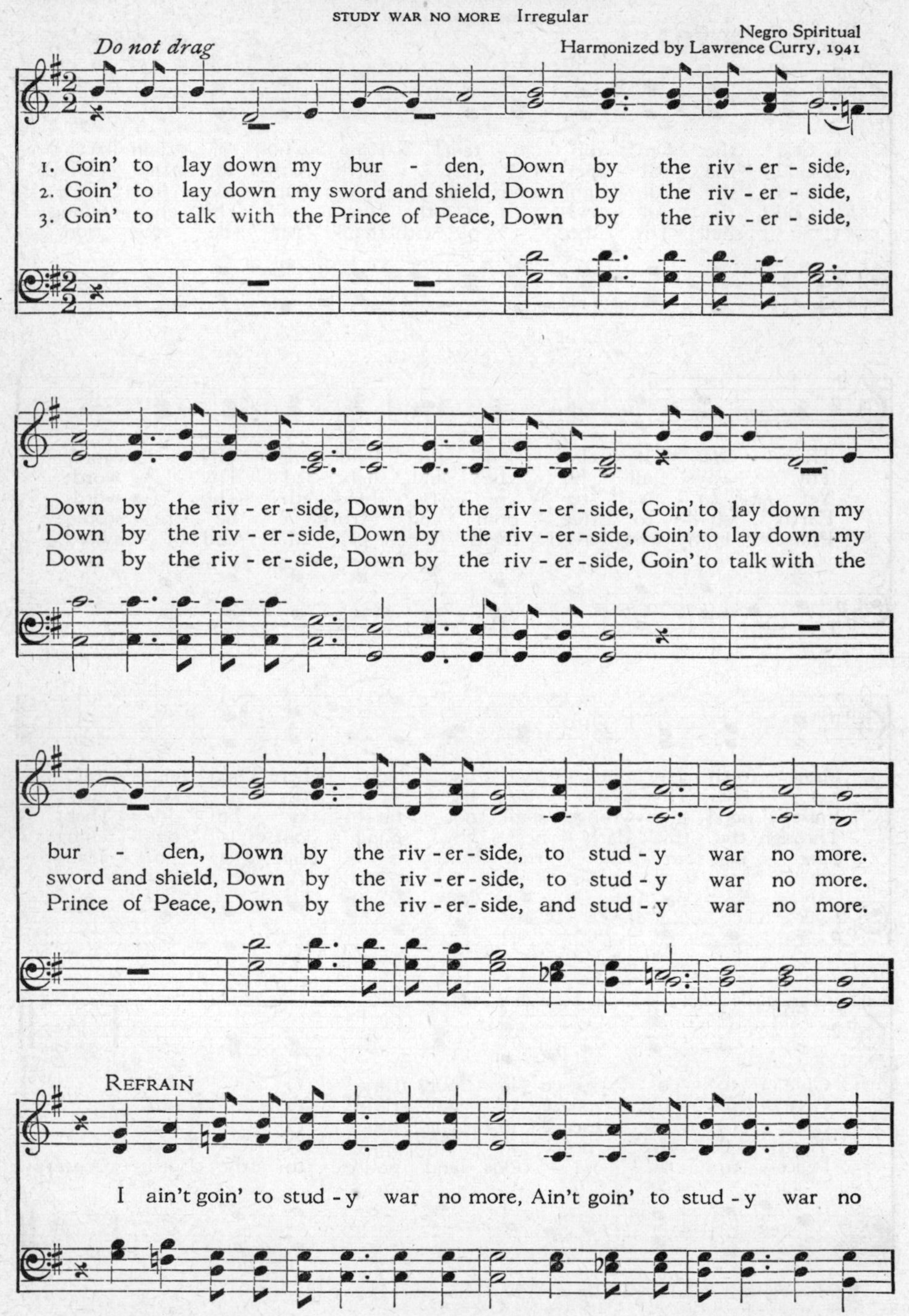
Do not drag
1. Goin' to lay down my bur - den, Down by the riv - er - side,
2. Goin' to lay down my sword and shield, Down by the riv - er - side,
3. Goin' to talk with the Prince of Peace, Down by the riv - er - side,
Down by the riv - er - side, Down by the riv - er - side, Goin' to lay down my
Down by the riv - er - side, Down by the riv - er - side, Goin' to lay down my
Down by the riv - er - side, Down by the riv - er - side, Goin' to talk with the
bur - den, Down by the riv - er - side, to stud - y war no more.
sword and shield, Down by the riv - er - side, to stud - y war no more.
Prince of Peace, Down by the riv - er - side, and stud - y war no more.
Refrain
I ain't goin' to stud - y war no more, Ain't goin' to stud - y war no

Study War No More (Concluded)

more, Ain't goin' to stud-y war no more; I ain't goin' to stud-y war no
stud-y war no more
more, Ain't goin' to stud-y war no more, Ain't goin' to stud-y war no more.

Dear Father, Whom We Cannot See 287

LLEWELLYN 8.6.8.8.6.

Roderic Dunkerley — Stanley L. Osborne, 1939

1. Dear Fa-ther, whom we can-not see, We know that Thou art near; With long-ing hearts we turn to Thee, And ask that Thou wilt set us free From war and hate and fear.
2. Dear Fa-ther, King of love and peace, We know that Thou art strong; Make con-flicts ev-ery-where to cease, Let mer-cy ev-ery-where in-crease, And kind-ness con-quer wrong.
3. Dear Fa-ther, Lord of sea and land, We know that Thou art wise; O make the na-tions un-der-stand That on-ly by Thy guid-ing hand Can last-ing peace a-rise.
A-MEN.

288 At Length There Dawns the Glorious Day

ALL SAINTS NEW C. M. D.

Ozora Stearns Davis, 1909

Henry S. Cutler, 1872

1. At length there dawns the glo-rious day By proph-ets long fore-told,
2. For what are sun-dering strains of blood, Or an-cient caste and creed?
3. One com-mon faith u-nites us all, We seek one com-mon goal;
At length the cho-rus clear-er grows That shep-herds heard of old.
One claim u-nites all men in God To serve each hu-man need.
One ten-der com-fort broods up-on The strug-gling hu-man soul.
The day of dawn-ing broth-er-hood Breaks on our ea-ger eyes,
Then here to-geth-er, broth-er men, We pledge the Lord a-new
To this clear call of broth-er-hood Our hearts re-spon-sive ring;
And hu-man ha-treds flee be-fore The ra-diant east-ern skies.
Our loy-al love, our stal-wart faith, Our serv-ice strong and true.
We join the glo-rious new cru-sade Of our great Lord and King.
A-MEN.

Hark! Hark, My Soul!

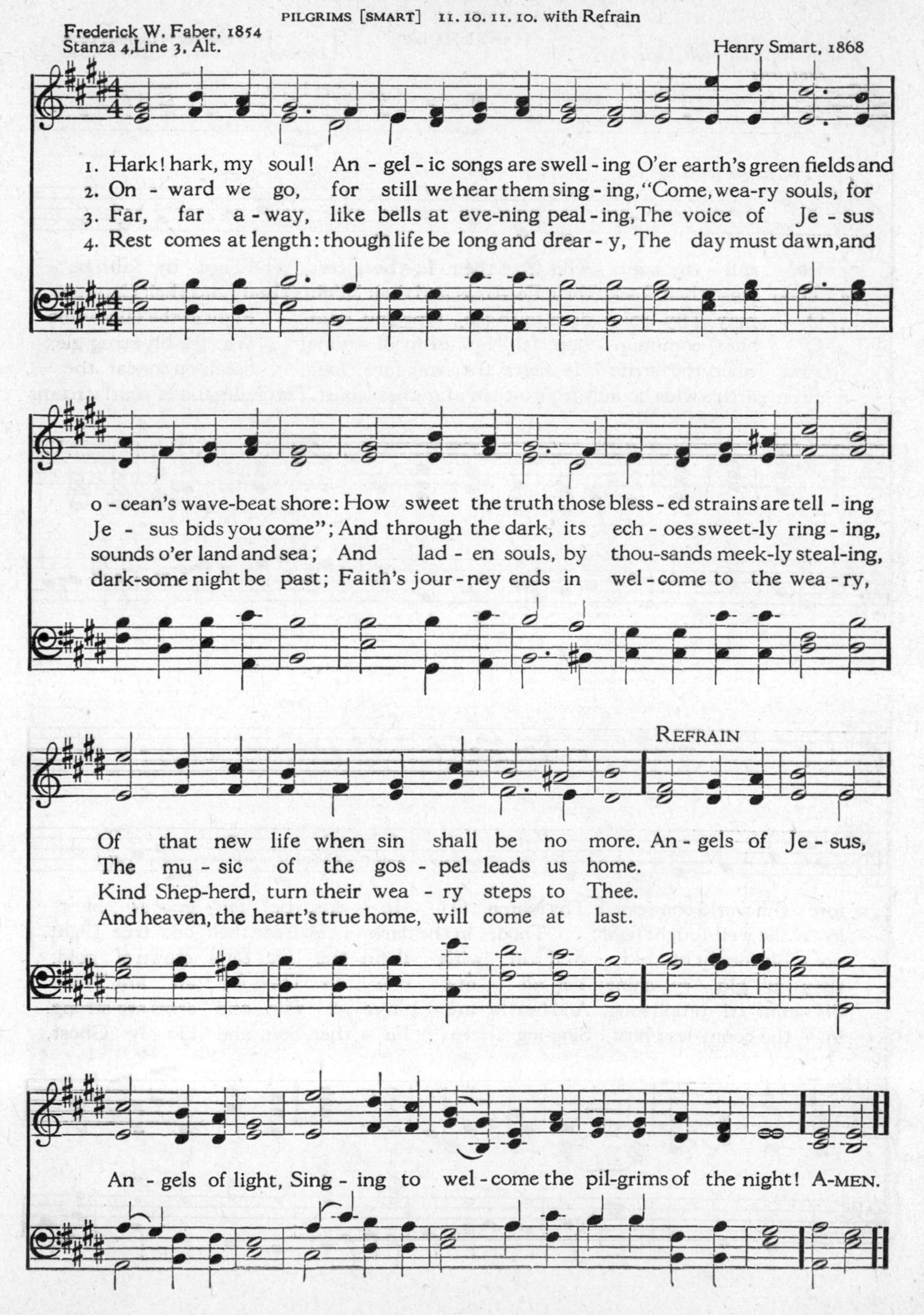
PILGRIMS [SMART] 11. 10. 11. 10. with Refrain
Frederick W. Faber, 1854
Stanza 4, Line 3, Alt.
Henry Smart, 1868
1. Hark! hark, my soul! An - gel - ic songs are swell - ing O'er earth's green fields and o - cean's wave-beat shore: How sweet the truth those bless - ed strains are tell - ing Of that new life when sin shall be no more.
2. On - ward we go, for still we hear them sing - ing, "Come, wea-ry souls, for Je - sus bids you come"; And through the dark, its ech - oes sweet-ly ring - ing, The mu - sic of the gos - pel leads us home.
3. Far, far a - way, like bells at eve-ning peal - ing, The voice of Je - sus sounds o'er land and sea; And lad - en souls, by thou-sands meek-ly steal-ing, Kind Shep-herd, turn their wea - ry steps to Thee.
4. Rest comes at length: though life be long and drear - y, The day must dawn, and dark-some night be past; Faith's jour - ney ends in wel - come to the wea - ry, And heaven, the heart's true home, will come at last.
REFRAIN
An - gels of Je - sus, An - gels of light, Sing - ing to wel - come the pil-grims of the night! A-MEN.

290 For All the Saints Who from Their Labors Rest

SINE NOMINE 10. 10. 10. 4.

(FIRST TUNE)

William Walsham How, 1864, 1875

R. Vaughan Williams, 1906
Descant by Lawrence Curry, 1940

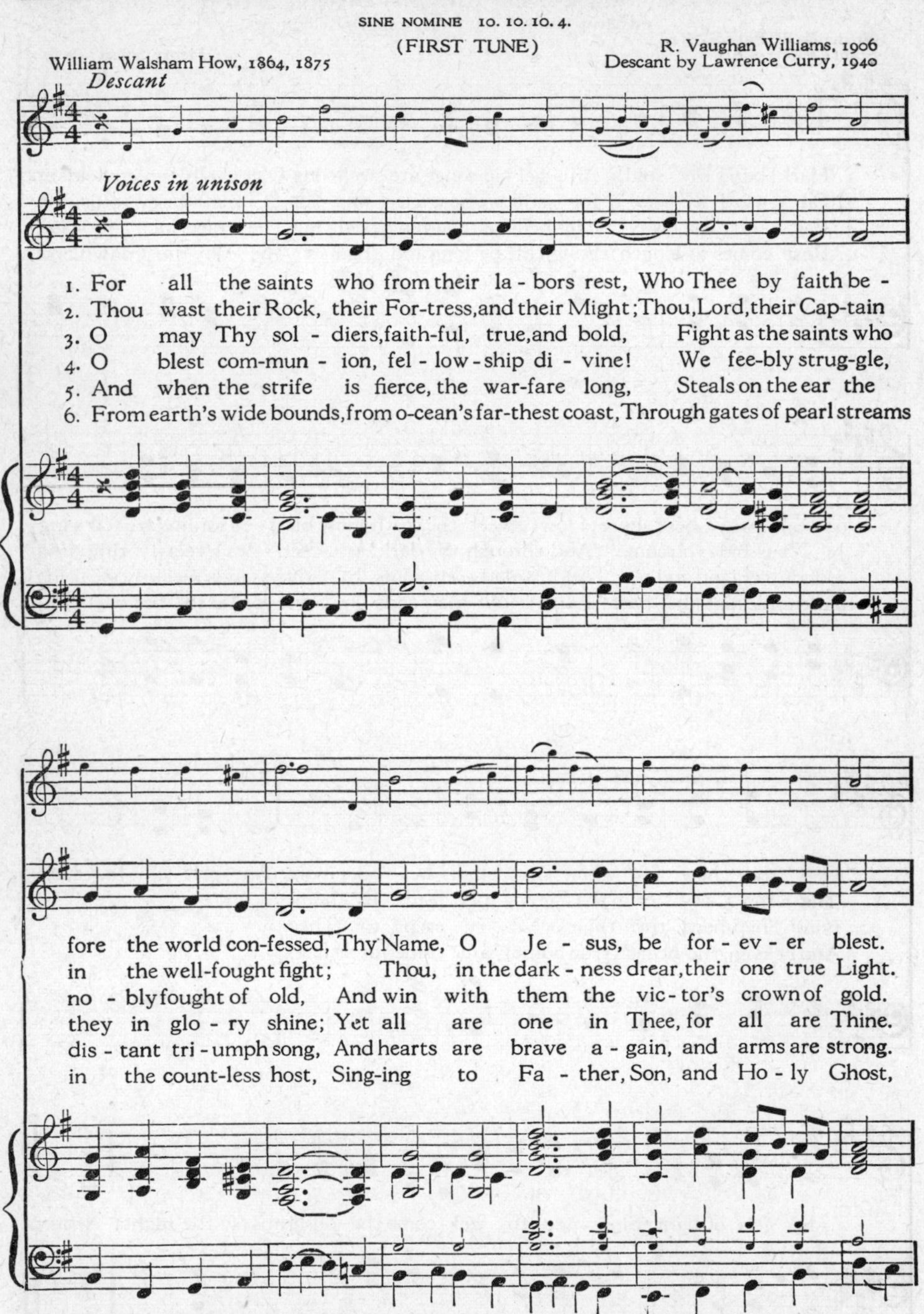
Descant
Voices in unison
1. For all the saints who from their la - bors rest, Who Thee by faith be - fore the world con-fessed, Thy Name, O Je - sus, be for - ev - er blest.
2. Thou wast their Rock, their For-tress, and their Might; Thou, Lord, their Cap-tain in the well-fought fight; Thou, in the dark - ness drear, their one true Light.
3. O may Thy sol - diers, faith-ful, true, and bold, Fight as the saints who no - bly fought of old, And win with them the vic - tor's crown of gold.
4. O blest com-mun - ion, fel - low - ship di - vine! We fee-bly strug-gle, they in glo - ry shine; Yet all are one in Thee, for all are Thine.
5. And when the strife is fierce, the war-fare long, Steals on the ear the dis - tant tri - umph song, And hearts are brave a - gain, and arms are strong.
6. From earth's wide bounds, from o-cean's far-thest coast, Through gates of pearl streams in the count-less host, Sing-ing to Fa - ther, Son, and Ho - ly Ghost,

For All the Saints Who from Their Labors Rest (Concluded)

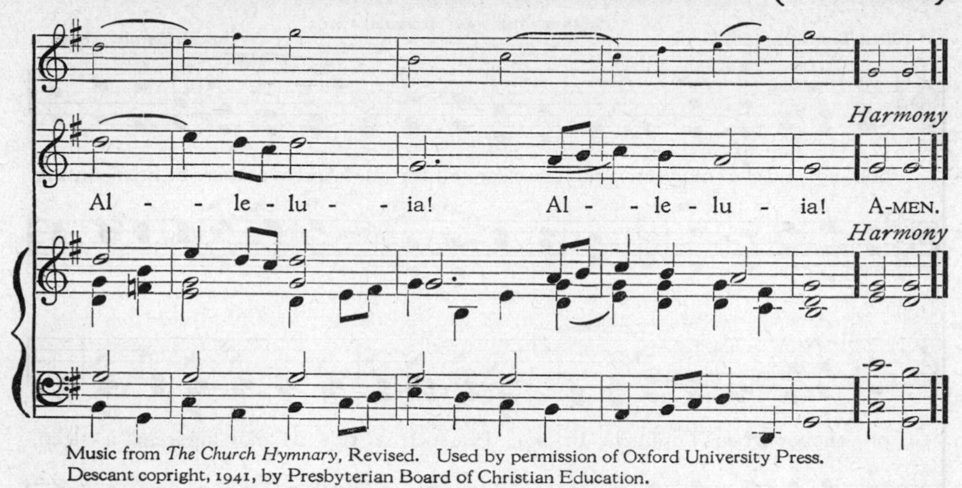
Harmony
Al - - le - lu - - ia! Al - - le - lu - ia! A-MEN.
Harmony

Music from *The Church Hymnary*, Revised. Used by permission of Oxford University Press.

For All the Saints Who from Their Labors Rest 290

SARUM 10. 10. 10. 4.
(SECOND TUNE)

William Walsham How, 1864, 1875

Joseph Barnby, 1869

1. For all the saints who from their la - bors rest, Who Thee by
faith be - fore the world con - fessed, Thy Name, O Je - sus,
f
f
be for - ev - er blest. Al - le - lu - ia! Al - le - lu - ia! A-MEN.

See opposite page for words of other stanzas.

291 Sunset and Evening Star

CROSSING THE BAR Irregular

Alfred Tennyson, 1889

Joseph Barnby, 1893

Sun - set and eve - ning star, And one clear call for me! And may there be no moan-ing
of the bar When I put out to sea, But such a tide as mov-ing seems a - sleep,
Too full for sound and foam, When that which drew from out the bound-less deep
Sempre p
Turns a - gain home. Twi - light and eve - ning bell, And aft - er
home. Twi - - - light and eve - ning bell,
that the dark! And may there be no sad - ness of fare-well When I em - bark;

Sunset and Evening Star (Concluded)

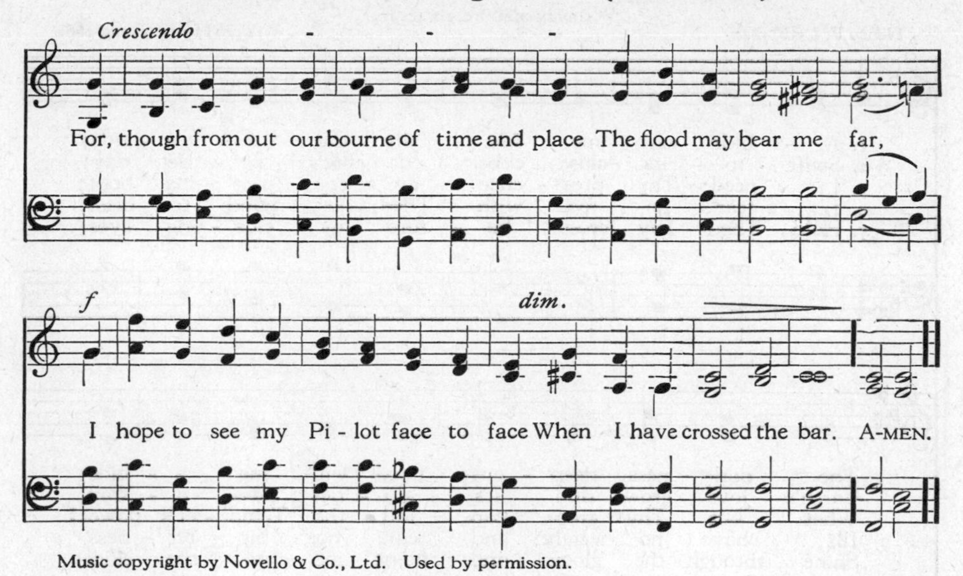
Crescendo
For, though from out our bourne of time and place The flood may bear me far,
f
dim.
I hope to see my Pi - lot face to face When I have crossed the bar. A-MEN.

Jesus, I Live to Thee 292

LAKE ENON (MERCERSBURG) S. M.

Henry Harbaugh, c. 1861 Isaac B. Woodbury (1819–1858)

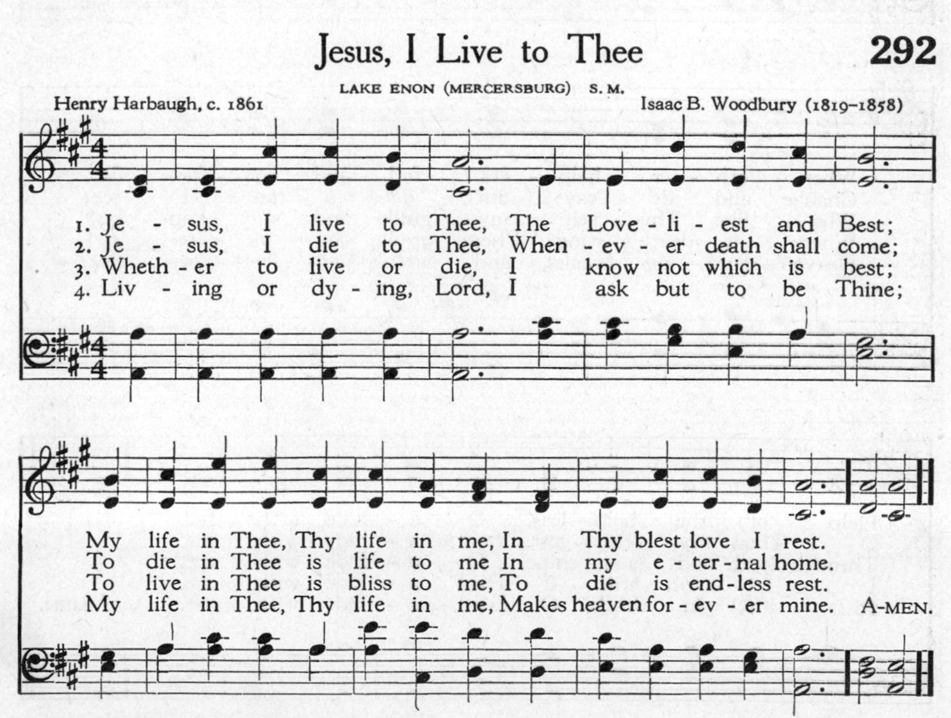
1. Je - sus, I live to Thee, The Love - li - est and Best;
2. Je - sus, I die to Thee, When - ev - er death shall come;
3. Wheth - er to live or die, I know not which is best;
4. Liv - ing or dy - ing, Lord, I ask but to be Thine;
My life in Thee, Thy life in me, In Thy blest love I rest.
To die in Thee is life to me In my e - ter - nal home.
To live in Thee is bliss to me, To die is end-less rest.
My life in Thee, Thy life in me, Makes heaven for - ev - er mine. A-MEN.

Alternative tune, "Trentham," number 265.

293 Abide with Me: Fast Falls the Eventide

EVENTIDE 10. 10. 10. 10.

Henry F. Lyte, 1847

William Henry Monk, 1861

1. A - bide with me: fast falls the e - ven - tide;
2. Swift to its close ebbs out life's lit - tle day;
3. I need Thy pres - ence ev - ery pass - ing hour;
4. I fear no foe, with Thee at hand to bless:
5. Hold Thou Thy cross be - fore my clos - ing eyes;
The dark - ness deep - ens; Lord, with me a - bide:
Earth's joys grow dim, its glo - ries pass a - way;
What but Thy grace can foil the Tempt - er's power?
Ills have no weight, and tears no bit - ter - ness.
Shine through the gloom, and point me to the skies:
When oth - er help - ers fail, and com - forts flee,
Change and de - cay in all a - round I see;
Who like Thy - self my guide and stay can be?
Where is death's sting? Where, grave, thy vic - to - ry?
Heaven's morn - ing breaks, and earth's vain shad - ows flee:
Help of the help - less, O a - bide with me.
O Thou who chan - gest not, a - bide with me.
Through cloud and sun - shine, O a - bide with me.
I tri - umph still, if Thou a - bide with me.
In life, in death, O Lord, a - bide with me.
A-MEN.

CHANTS AND RESPONSES

Call to Worship 294

Isaiah 55: 6 — Calvin W. Laufer, 1926

Seek ye the Lord while He may be found;
Call ye upon Him while He is near.

Music copyright, 1927, by Calvin W. Laufer. Used by permission.

Call to Worship 295

Psalm 100: 4 — Traditional Serbian Melody (Adapted)

mf *crescendo* *f*

En-ter in-to His gates with thanks-giv-ing, And in-to His courts with praise.

f *rall. e dim.* *mf* *p*

En-ter in-to His gates with thanks-giv-ing, And in-to His courts with praise.

296
Introit
PICARDY 8. 7. 8. 7. 8. 7.
Liturgy of St. James
Trans. by Gerard Moultrie (1829-1885)
French Traditional Carol
Unison
Let all mor-tal flesh keep si - lence, And with fear and trem - bling stand;
Pon - der noth - ing earth - ly mind - ed, For with bless-ing in His hand,
God with-in His tem - ple dwell - eth, Our full hom-age doth de - mand.
297
Introit
Habakkuk 2: 20
Calvin W. Laufer, 1926
The Lord is in His ho - ly tem - ple: Let all the earth keep si - lence be-
fore Him; Keep si - lence, keep si - lence, keep si - lence be - fore Him.

Prayer Response

298

Psalm 19: 14 — H. C. Macdougall

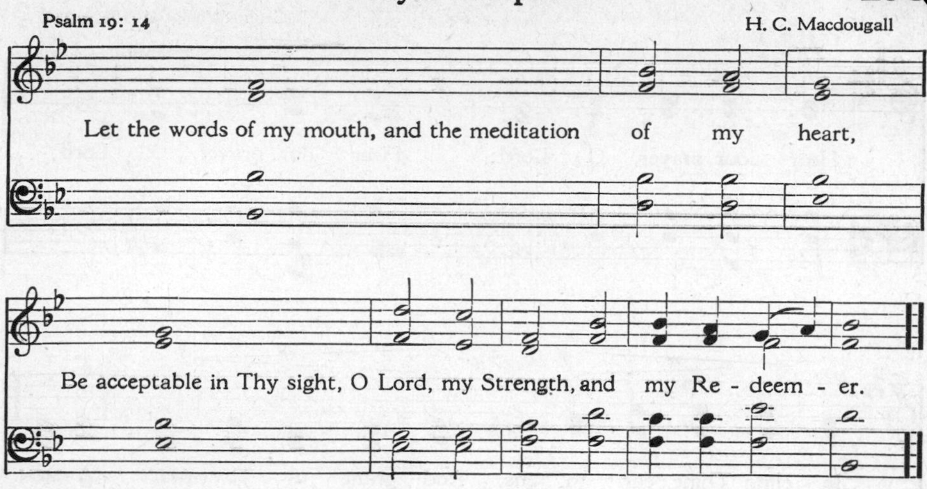
Let the words of my mouth, and the meditation of my heart,
Be acceptable in Thy sight, O Lord, my Strength, and my Re - deem - er.

Prayer Response

299

MORECAMBE 10. 10. 10. 10.

Frederick C. Atkinson, c. 1870

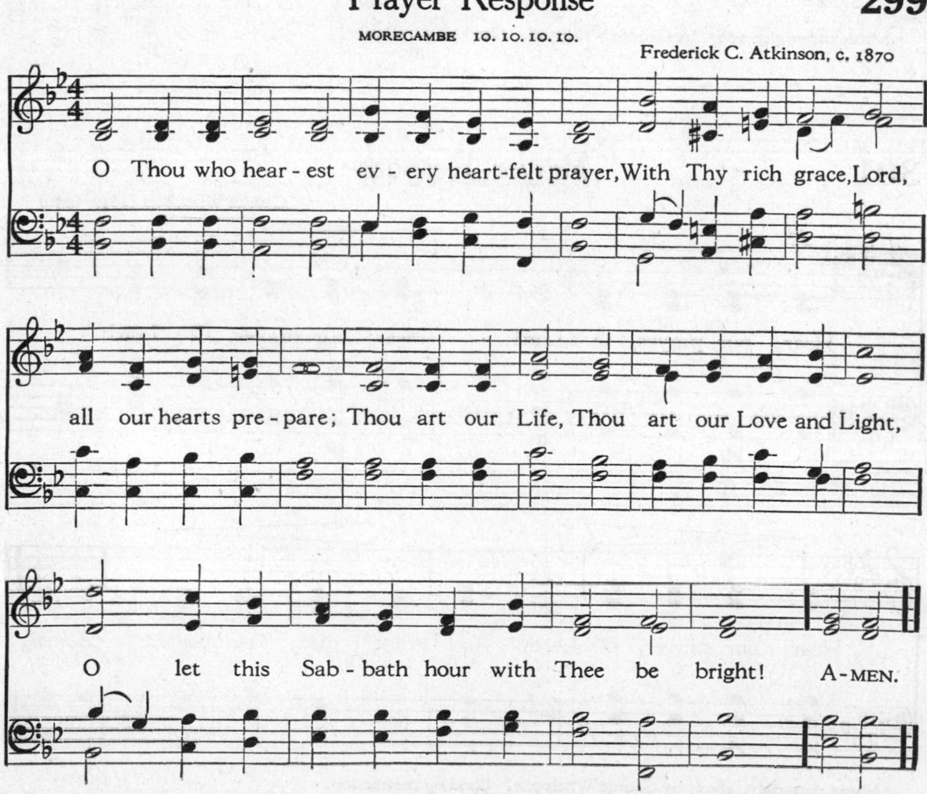
O Thou who hear - est ev - ery heart-felt prayer, With Thy rich grace, Lord,
all our hearts pre - pare; Thou art our Life, Thou art our Love and Light,
O let this Sab - bath hour with Thee be bright! A - MEN.

Prayer Response

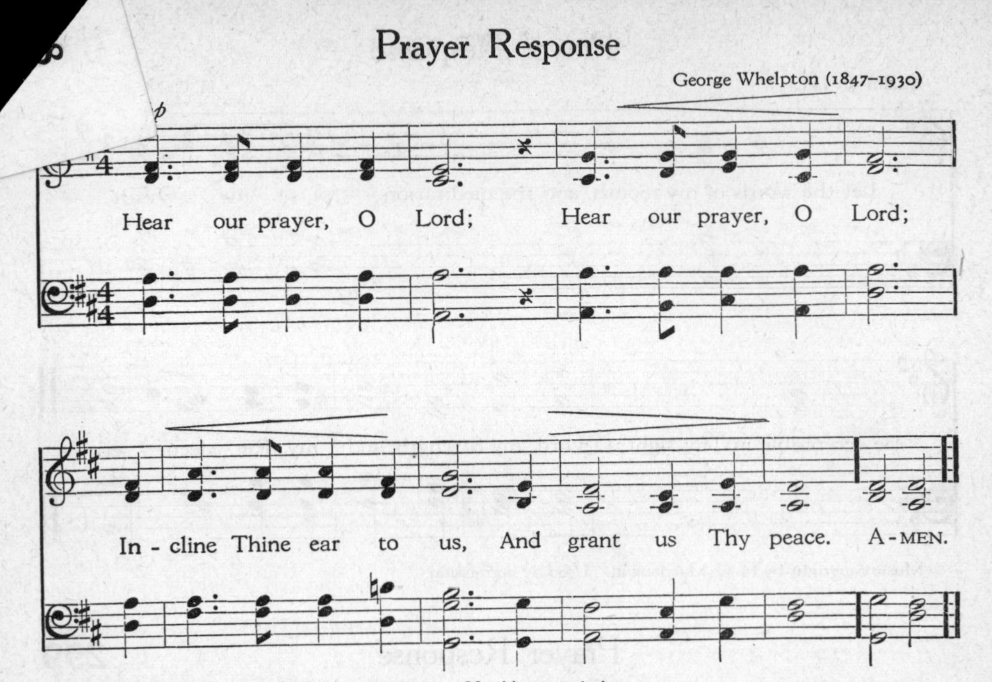
George Whelpton (1847–1930)
pp
Hear our prayer, O Lord; Hear our prayer, O Lord;
In - cline Thine ear to us, And grant us Thy peace. A-MEN.

301 Prayer Response

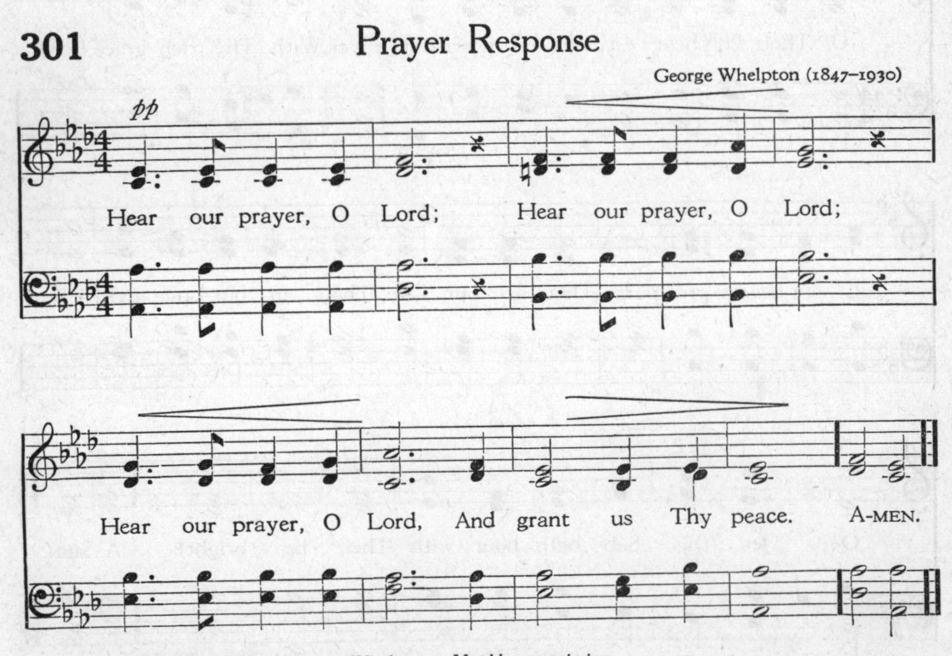
George Whelpton (1847–1930)
pp
Hear our prayer, O Lord; Hear our prayer, O Lord;
Hear our prayer, O Lord, And grant us Thy peace. A-MEN.

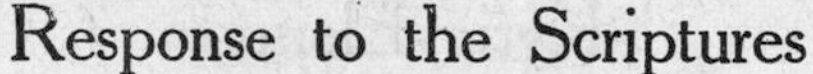

Response to the Scriptures

302

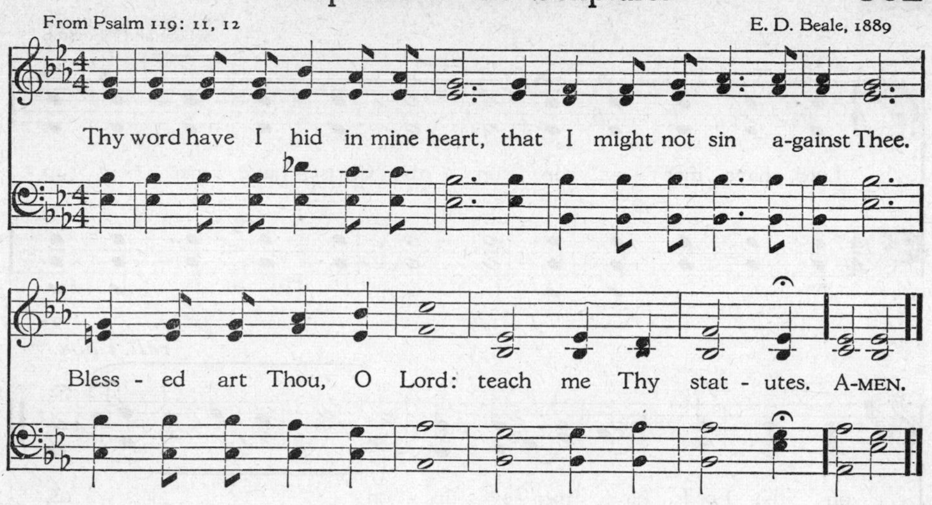
From Psalm 119: 11, 12
E. D. Beale, 1889
Thy word have I hid in mine heart, that I might not sin a-gainst Thee.
Bless - ed art Thou, O Lord: teach me Thy stat - utes. A-MEN.

Responses to the Commandments

303

(Kyrie Eleison)

George J. Elvey (1816–1893)

After each Commandment, except the Tenth
Lord, have mer - cy, have mer - cy up - on us, and in - cline our hearts to
keep this law.
After the Tenth
Lord, have mer - cy, have mer - cy up - on us, and write all
these Thy laws in our hearts, Thy laws in our hearts, we be - seech Thee.

304 Kyrie Eleison

From Serbian Liturgy
Sebastian Dabovitch
p
Lord, have mer - cy up - on us; Christ, have mer - cy up -
mf
rall. e dim.
on us; Lord, have mer - cy up - on us.
305 Sanctus
Isaiah 6: 3
Arr. from Gaul's "The Holy City"
Ho - ly, ho - ly, ho - ly, Lord of Hosts: Ho - ly,
ho - ly, ho - ly is the Lord of Hosts. A-MEN.

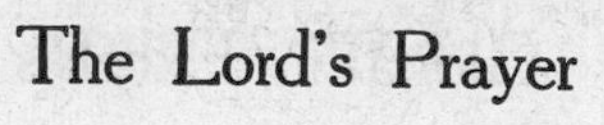
The Lord's Prayer

306
Matthew 6: 9-13
Gregorian Chant
1. Our Father which art in heaven, Hal - lowed be Thy Name.
2. Give us this day our dai - ly bread.
3. And lead us not into temptation, but deliver us from e - vil:
Thy Kingdom come. Thy will be done in earth, as it is in heav - en.
And forgive us our debts, as we for - - - - give our debt - ors.
For Thine is the Kingdom, and the power, and the glory, for ev - er. A - men.
Gloria Patri
307
From the Greek
Henry W. Greatorex, 1851
Glo-ry be to the Fa-ther, and to the Son, and to the Ho-ly Ghost; As it
was in the be-gin-ning, is now, and ev-er shall be, world without end. A-men, A - men.
Gloria Patri
308
From the Greek
Old Scottish Chant
Glory be to the Father, and to the Son, and to the Ho - ly
As it was in the beginning, is now, and ever shall be, world with-out end.

309 Gloria in Excelsis

From the Greek

Old Scottish Chant

1. Glory be to God on high: and on earth peace, good will toward men.
2. {We praise Thee, we bless Thee, we} wor-ship Thee: {we glorify Thee, we give thanks to Thee for} Thy great glo - ry.
3. O Lord God, heaven-ly King: God the Fa - ther Al - might - y.
4. {O Lord, the only begotten Son,} Je - sus Christ: {O Lord God, Lamb of God,} Son of the Fa - ther,
3
5. That takest away the sins of the world: have mer-cy up - on us.
6. Thou that takest away the sins of the world: have mer-cy up - on us.
7. Thou that takest away the sins of the world: re - ceive our prayer.
8. {Thou that sittest at the right hand of God the} Fa - ther: have mer-cy up - on us.
9. For Thou only art ho - ly: Thou on - ly art the Lord.
10. {Thou only, O Christ, with the} Ho - ly Ghost: {art most high in the glory of} God the Fa - ther. A-MEN.

God Be in My Head

GOD BE IN MY HEAD Irregular
Sarum Primer, 1558
H. Walford Davies, 1910
p Unison or harmony
God be in my head, And in my un - der - stand - ing;
God be in mine eyes, And in my look - ing; God be in my mouth,
crescendo
And in my speak - ing; God be in my heart, And in my think-ing;
f
p dim. e rall.
pp
God be at mine end, And at my de - part - ing. A - MEN.

311 Offertory Response

CANONBURY L. M.

Samuel Longfellow, 1886 — Arr. from Robert A. Schumann, 1839

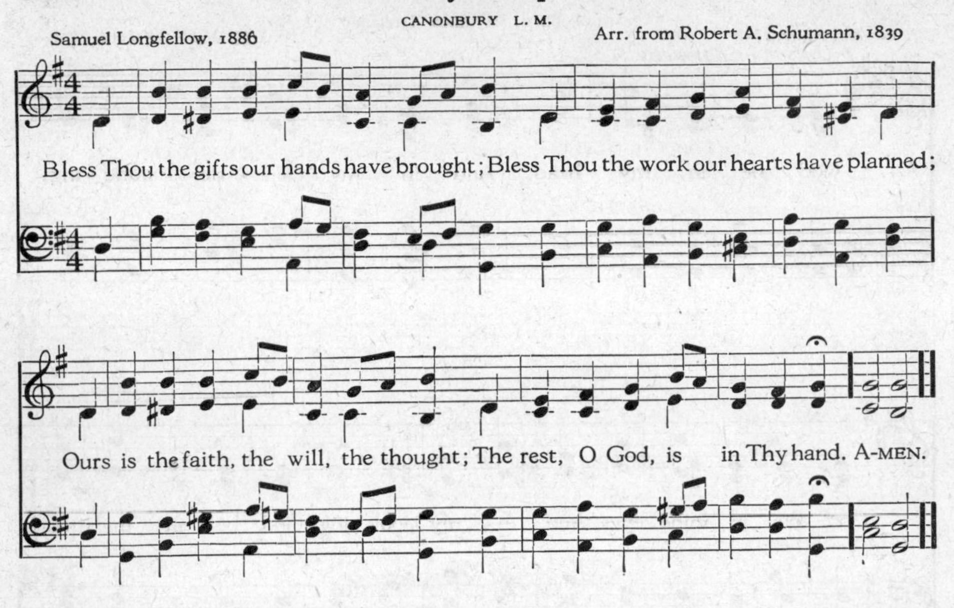
Bless Thou the gifts our hands have brought; Bless Thou the work our hearts have planned;
Ours is the faith, the will, the thought; The rest, O God, is in Thy hand. A-MEN.

312 Offertory Response

MANOAH C. M.

Calvin W. Laufer, 1926 — Arr. by Henry W. Greatorex, 1851

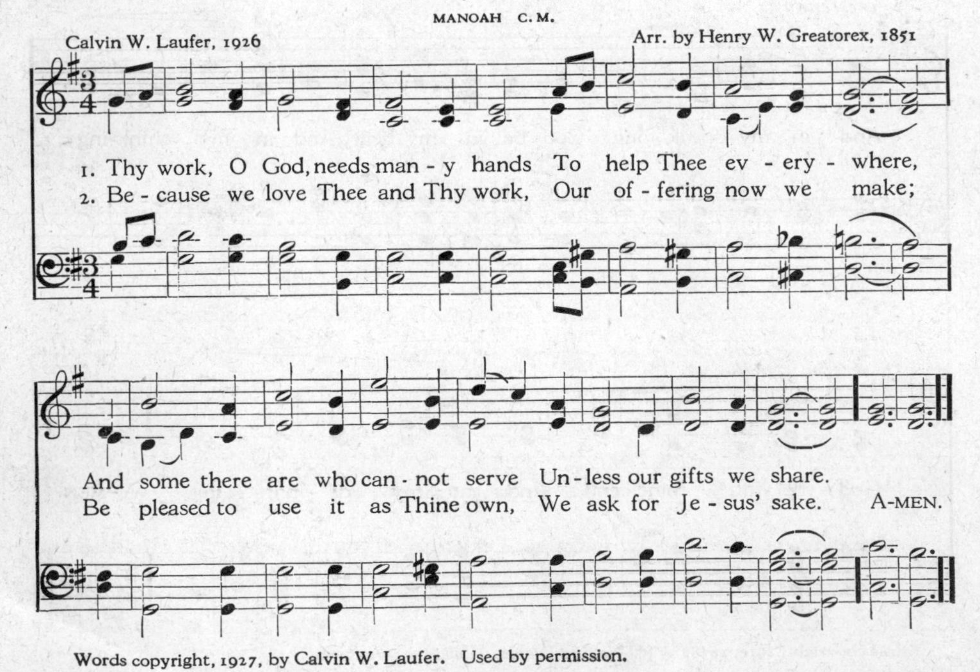
1. Thy work, O God, needs man - y hands To help Thee ev - ery - where,
2. Be - cause we love Thee and Thy work, Our of - fering now we make;
And some there are who can - not serve Un - less our gifts we share.
Be pleased to use it as Thine own, We ask for Je - sus' sake. A-MEN.

Offertory Response 313

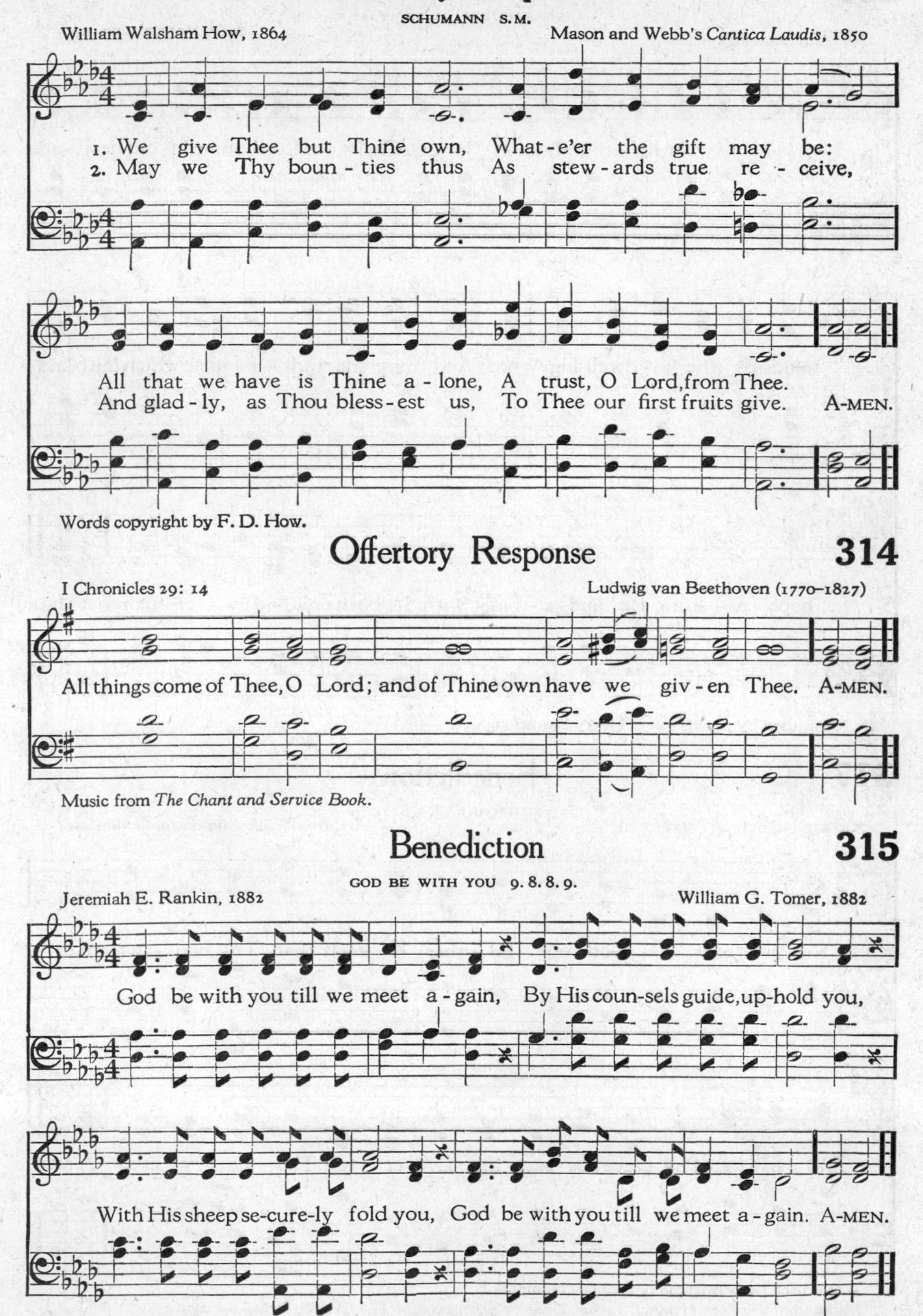
SCHUMANN S.M.
William Walsham How, 1864
Mason and Webb's Cantica Laudis, 1850
1. We give Thee but Thine own, What-e'er the gift may be:
2. May we Thy boun-ties thus As stew-ards true re-ceive,
All that we have is Thine a-lone, A trust, O Lord, from Thee.
And glad-ly, as Thou bless-est us, To Thee our first fruits give. A-MEN.
Words copyright by F. D. How.
Offertory Response
314
I Chronicles 29: 14
Ludwig van Beethoven (1770-1827)
All things come of Thee, O Lord; and of Thine own have we giv-en Thee. A-MEN.
Music from The Chant and Service Book.
Benediction
315
GOD BE WITH YOU 9. 8. 8. 9.
Jeremiah E. Rankin, 1882
William G. Tomer, 1882
God be with you till we meet a-gain, By His coun-sels guide, up-hold you,
With His sheep se-cure-ly fold you, God be with you till we meet a-gain. A-MEN.

16 Benediction

BENEDICTION 12. 12. 12. 12.

Anon. Henry Barraclough, 1932

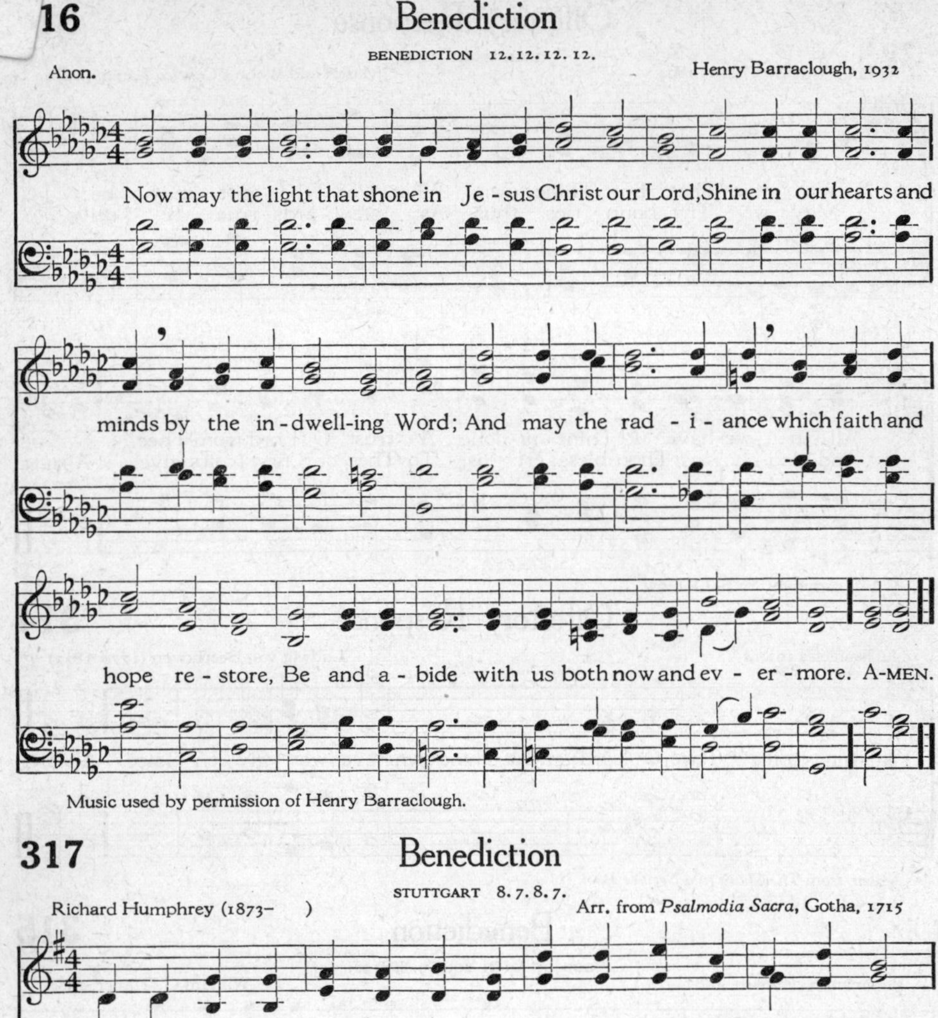
Now may the light that shone in Je - sus Christ our Lord, Shine in our hearts and
minds by the in - dwell - ing Word; And may the rad - i - ance which faith and
hope re - store, Be and a - bide with us both now and ev - er - more. A-MEN.

Music used by permission of Henry Barraclough.

317 Benediction

STUTTGART 8. 7. 8. 7.

Richard Humphrey (1873-) Arr. from *Psalmodia Sacra*, Gotha, 1715

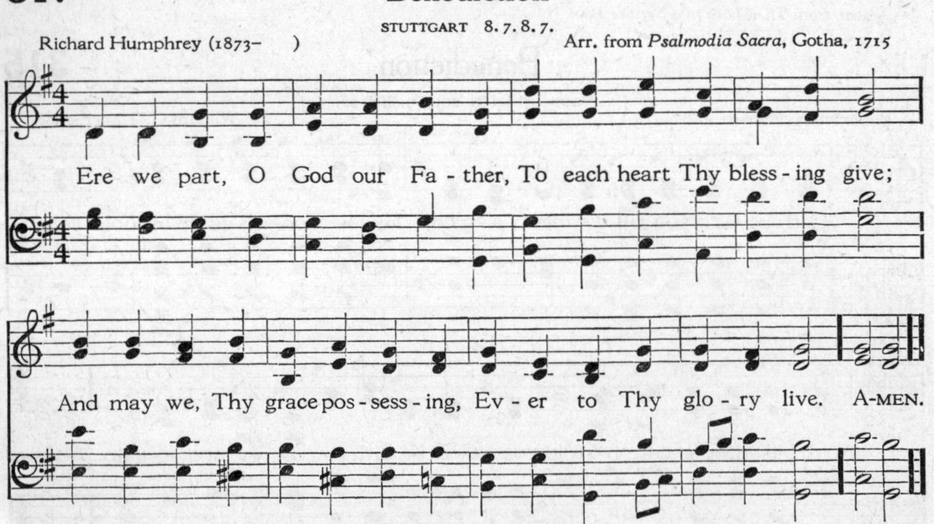
Ere we part, O God our Fa - ther, To each heart Thy bless - ing give;
And may we, Thy grace pos - sess - ing, Ev - er to Thy glo - ry live. A-MEN.

Words used by permission of Richard Humphrey.
Music from *The New Hymnal*, 1916. Used by permission of The Church Pension Fund.

Amens

318
TWOFOLD AMEN
Greek Liturgy
pp
A - - men, A - men.
319
THREEFOLD AMEN
Traditional
pp
A - - men, A-men, A - men.
320
THREEFOLD AMEN
Danish
mf
dim.
pp
A-men, A-men, A - men.
321
DRESDEN AMEN
Traditional
pp
A - men, A - - - men.
322
SEVENFOLD AMEN
John Stainer
pp
crescendo
A - men, A - - - - - - men,
f
A - men, A - men, A - - men, A - - - men, A -
A - - - men, A - - men,
pp A - - - men,
ppp slower
- - - - - men, A - - - - men, A - men.
f A - - - - men,
Music copyright by Novello & Co., Ltd. Used by permission.
323
THREEFOLD AMEN
Lawrence Curry, 1940
A - men, A - - - - men, A - - men.

INSTRUMENTAL MUSIC

324

Frederic Chopin
From "Nocturne," Op. 15, No. 3

In a devotional manner
p legato
Ped.
f
p
1st ending
2d ending

Ludwig van Beethoven
Theme from the Adagio, "Concerto for Piano, No. 5," Op. 73
Slow and sustained
mf
Ped.
cresc.
f
p

Johannes Brahms
Principal Theme of the Last Movement,
"Symphony No. 1," Op. 68

With a firm, sure touch. Do not drag.
f
Ped.
mp
f
poco rit.
a tempo
e
sempre f
Ped.
Ped.
Ped.

mp
Ped.
ff
Ped.
rit.
Ped.
Ped.

327

Franz Schubert
Transposed from "Impromptu in A Flat," Op. 142

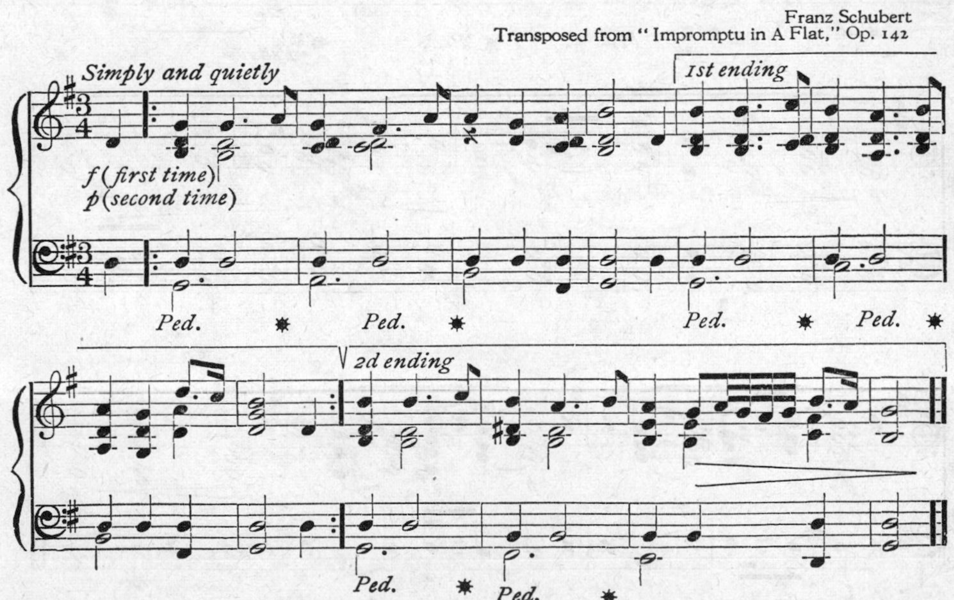
Simply and quietly
1st ending
f (first time)
p (second time)
Ped.
2d ending
Ped.

Robert Schumann
Arr. from "The Poet Speaks,"
"Kinderscenen," Op. 15

Slow and with expression
p
Ped.
Ped.
Ped.
Ped.
Ped.
rit.
Ped.
p
f
p
pp

Frederic Chopin
From "Nocturne," Op. 37, No. 1
Slowly and with reverence
(Repeat)
mf
p
dim. e rit.

Felix Mendelssohn–Bartholdy
Arr. from Adagio, "Sonata No. 1
for Organ," Op. 65

Simply and reverently
mp
Ped.
Ped.
Ped.
Ped.
mf
pp
mf

pp
Ped.

331
Richard Wagner
From Prelude to "Parsifal"
Slowly, prayerfully
mf
rall.
3
p a tempo
Ped. Ped. Ped. Ped.
cresc.
Ped. Ped. Ped. Ped.
f
dim.

In quiet, expressive style
Felix Mendelssohn-Bartholdy
Theme from "Andante con Variazioni," Op. 82
mf
p
cresc.
f
dim. e rit.
p
a tempo
rit.

Ludwig van Beethoven
Theme from Andante con Moto,
"Appassionata Sonata," Op. 57
Slowly and with sonorous tone
p
mf
Ped.
subito p
Ped.
Ped.
Ped.
Ped.
f
Ped.
p

Johann Sebastian Bach (Harmonizer)
"Nun Ruhen Alle Wälder" (Innsbruck)
In meditative style. Smoothly
p
cresc.
broadly
f
gradual diminuendo
pp

Charles Gounod
From "Marche Romaine"

With marked rhythm
f
(Repeat)
mf
ff
Ped.

Giuseppe Verdi
From Triumphal March,
"Aida"

In stately rhythm
f
Ped.
Ped.
Ped.
Ped.
Ped.
Fine
1st ending
2d ending
mf
Ped.
Ped.
Ped.
Ped.
Ped.
Ped.
Ped.
Ped.

D.C. al Fine
Ped.
Ped.
Ped.

Careful attention has been given to the selection of the material in the instrumental section. The music included is useful for preludes, interludes, offertories, postludes, or musical meditations. The selections are of such character that they could well be used as background to the reading of sacred poetry or in conjunction with a dramatic presentation. Numbers 335 and 336 are particularly suitable where marches are needed.

There may arise some occasions when a short line or two of music would suffice. In most of the compositions a natural cadence will be found at the end of four or eight measures. For instance, the following excerpts could be used to good effect: Chopin, Number 329, first four measures; Chopin, Number 324, first eight measures; Beethoven, Number 333, first eight measures; Mendelssohn, Number 332, first eight measures.

The reader will notice that the musical phrasing has been consistently marked throughout the section. Attention to this phase of playing by the pianist or organist will greatly enhance the style and character of the music.

The pedaling has been marked throughout. The duration of the stroke of the pedal has been indicated by the sign Ped. * The sign has been employed only where there is more than one chord in a sustained harmony. Its omission does not necessarily mean that the player should refrain from using the unison pedal but rather that each chord or change of harmony should be accompanied by a stroke of the pedal. Be careful not to overuse the unison pedal. Blurred and indistinct effects will thus be avoided. The quality of the worshipful atmosphere is greatly enriched by smooth, well-phrased playing. This can be achieved only by attention to the musical details of the execution of the piece. The musician should prepare the preludes, interludes, and postludes as carefully as the leader prepares the prayers, the lesson, or any other service part.

The following hymns are suitable for instrumental use: Numbers 6, 9, 12(march), 13, 16, 24, 35, 49, 53, 59, 63, 93, 99, 100, 101, 114, 117, 124(march), 150, 151(first tune), 168, 185, 203, 204, 205, 209, 217, 219, 231(march), 235(march), 251(march), 284(march), 286, 310, 316. This list will be found to be useful when supplementary material is desired.

WORSHIP MATERIALS

SUGGESTIONS FOR WORSHIP

FROM the beginning of time man has felt a desire to worship his Creator. In ways as varied as the individual worshiper, he has made an effort to make contact with his God.

For the Christian, worship is primarily communion with God, but it includes Christian fellowship with other worshipers. Even in private worship one is conscious of those in the scattered parts of the world who also worship. In group worship one receives the inspiration of praising and praying with others who have come together out of a workaday world for a common purpose.

Preparing for Worship

Some worship may be impromptu and instantaneous, but as a rule effective worship comes only as the result of careful planning. Here are five simple rules that have been tested by experience and that may be followed in the preparation for group worship:

1. Prepare in advance. Leaders have been known to spend from one to three hours getting ready for a twenty-minute worship service. Certainly a few minutes is not enough. Advance preparation helps the leader to be in a worshipful mood, and this in turn helps others to worship.

2. Have a purpose for each program. It may be desirable to emphasize some Christian attitude such as reverence, love, praise, adoration, gratitude, loyalty, aspiration, good will, courage, faith, repentance, humility. Usually only one attitude or part of one attitude will serve as a purpose for a single service.

3. Choose a theme for each service. The theme indicates how the purpose is to be developed and achieved. It is the dominant note which runs through the entire program and usually is suggestive of action or desired accomplishment. For example, "Gratitude" may be the desired purpose, and "Thanking God for Friends" may be the theme.

4. Strive for unity in every service. Each part of the program should be in keeping with the theme, and the service should move smoothly from one part to another. For example, a stirring marchlike tune may not be so good a preparation for a period of prayer as soft music or the reading of Scripture.

5. Secure participation of everyone. Most people participate in the singing of hymns. It is also possible to enlist the participation of all the worshipers in the Scripture-reading, prayer, meditation, and other parts of the service. Perhaps a study of worship will be necessary in order to discover the variety of methods which may be used to secure participation.

Planning the Program

The five worship programs that follow are merely suggestive. They show how programs may be planned on various themes and how different worship materials may be used. All the materials suggested in these five programs, except pictures and talks, are found in this book. With these programs as patterns, other selections of hymns, responsive readings, Scripture passages, prayers, poetry, responses, and instrumental numbers may be made, and a wide variety may be secured. In some instances the leader may ask the audience to follow the program as printed, in which case he will need to indicate the particular choice that has been made in each part of the service. Preferably the leader may use one of these programs as a guide, building his own order of service. Each part of the program may be announced for the guidance of the worshipers, or the program may be printed or mimeographed so that the service may proceed without announcement.

Leaders of worship should endeavor to become familiar with the wealth of worship material contained in this hymnal and with its convenient arrangement. The hymns are arranged by subjects, and in addition a topical index makes it possible to find hymns appropriate to almost any theme. If a more formal or liturgical type of service is desired, the chants, responses, and litanies will be found useful. Prayers suitable for many types of service are provided. Appropriate responsive readings or Scripture selections may be chosen easily because of the arrangement under particular topics. Although the selection of poetry is not extensive, the quotations cover a wide variety of subjects and themes.

To the One Who Leads

It is wise to focus the attention of the worshipers on some central object while the worship service is in progress. To this end a "worship center" may be used, such as a well-chosen picture large enough to be seen from anywhere in the room, lighted candles, a cross, an open Bible, flowers, or other decorations. It is conducive to worship to have the whole room in order and made as attractive as possible. All who participate in the leadership of a worship service should stand at approximately the same place. Appropriate comments may be used to introduce different parts of the service, but all distracting announcements and remarks should be avoided. The attitude of the leader should be worshipful. All speaking and reading should be in well-modulated tones, yet clear and loud enough to be easily heard. If the leader keeps in mind the purpose and theme of the service, both he and the worshipers will be conscious of "that filial relationship with God and . . . Christlike fellowship" among themselves which will result in a sharing of God's spirit and purpose and the development of strength for Christian living.

ADORATION AND PRAISE

Possible Themes

Praise to Our God
How Great Is Our God!
Come, Let Us Worship
Rejoicing in God

CALL TO WORSHIP: Come ye, and let us walk in the light of the Lord. He will teach us of His ways, and we will walk in His paths. The hour cometh, and now is, when the true worshipers shall worship the Father in spirit and in truth: for the Father seeketh such to worship Him.

For other Calls to Worship, see page 341.

INVOCATION HYMN (*choose one*):
"Breathe on Me, Breath of God," Hymn 130.
"Spirit of God, Descend Upon My Heart," Hymn 127.
"Holy Spirit, Truth Divine," Hymn 128.

INVOCATION PRAYER: For suggestions, see page 342.

RESPONSIVE READING (*choose one*):
"Adoration," Number 1.
"Adoration and Praise," Number 2.
"The Character of God," Number 11, a unison reading.

THE LORD'S PRAYER (*unison*).

HYMN OF AFFIRMATION (*choose one*):
"Faith of Our Fathers! Living Still," Hymn 224.
"Ye Servants of God, Your Master Proclaim," Hymn 125.
"Rejoice, the Lord Is King," Hymn 123.
"All Hail the Power of Jesus' Name!" Hymn 122.
"We Praise Thee, O God," Hymn 4.

MESSAGES FROM SCRIPTURE (*choose one*):
Ps. 34:1–8 — "O taste and see that the Lord is good."
Psalm 63 — "My soul thirsteth for thee."
Psalm 98 — "O sing unto the Lord a new song."
Ps. 107:1–8 — "O give thanks unto the Lord, for he is good."

A MESSAGE FROM POETRY (*choose one*):
"Credo," page 366.
"All I Need to Know," page 367.
"We Tread Upon Thy Carpets," page 363.

SUGGESTIONS FOR WORSHIP

HYMN (*choose one*):

"I Know Not How That Bethlehem's Babe," Hymn 213.
"Strong Son of God, Immortal Love," Hymn 212.
"Jesus, the Very Thought of Thee," Hymn 194.
"When the Golden Evening Gathered," Hymn 86.
"By Roads That Wound Uphill and Down," Hymn 88.
"Praise to the Lord," Hymn 9.

THE APOSTLES' CREED (*all standing*).

BENEDICTION.

CONSECRATION

Possible Themes

"Here Am I; Send Me"
"I Must Be About My Father's Business"
"Make of Your Heart a Highway"

Suggested Pictures for the Center of Worship

The Appeal to the Great Spirit, by Dallin
The Vigil, by Pettie
Light of the World, by Holman Hunt
"*Go Ye Into All the World*," by Burnand

INSTRUMENTAL PRELUDE:

Use an appropriate selection from the instrumental section, Numbers 324–336; or such hymns as:

"I Want to Be a Christian," Hymn 217;
"My Jesus, as Thou Wilt!" Hymn 172;
"Spirit of God, Descend Upon My Heart," Hymn 127.

CALL TO WORSHIP: "The Ways," page 380; or "Seek Ye the Lord," Number 296, sung by the choir.

OPENING HYMN: "Lead On, O King Eternal," Hymn 226; or "Ancient of Days, Who Sittest Throned in Glory," Hymn 34.

INVOCATION: We have come to this service seeking to know Thy will for our lives, O Lord. Open our hearts to the message of this hour. Help us to pray with true sincerity the prayer which Jesus taught to His disciples, "Our Father, which art in heaven [et cetera]."

SCRIPTURE (*choose one*):

Matt. 25:14–28 — The parable of the Talents.
John 15:7–17 — "If ye abide in me." [over]

Matt. 5:13–16 — "Ye are the salt of the earth."
John 12:24–26 — "If any man serve me."
Matt. 9:35–38 — "The harvest indeed is plenteous."
Isa., ch. 6 — The vision of Isaiah.

RESPONSE: Following the Scripture reading, the leader may say, "May these words from God's Book have a new meaning for us today"; or a choral response, such as "Thy Word Have I Hid in My Heart," Number 302, may be used.

PRAYER: The Litany of Dedication, page 354; or a prayer by the leader or several members of the group, including such thoughts as these:

That we may become sensitive to human needs;
That we may use our talents to lead men to a more abundant life;
That all our living may become a sacrament of holiness.

THE OFFERING:

Offertory — Use an appropriate selection from the instrumental section, Numbers 324–336.

Offertory Response — One of the offertory prayers, page 343; or one of the choral responses, Numbers 311–314.

INTERPRETATION OF THEME (*by talk or story or picture interpretation*): This part of the program may be based on the central idea in the Scripture, on one of the hymns, on the picture used as a worship center, or on the general idea of the need for Christians living in all walks of life.

HYMN OF CONSECRATION (*choose one*):

"Take My Life, and Let It Be," Hymn 175.
"Jesus Calls Us: O'er the Tumult," Hymn 198.
"Christ of the Upward Way," Hymn 230.
"We Thank Thee, Lord, Thy Paths of Service Lead," Hymn 203.
"Now in the Days of Youth," Hymn 169.
"O Master, Let Me Walk with Thee," Hymn 166.

BENEDICTION: "Ere We Part, O God Our Father," Number 317; or the last stanza of "O Master Workman of the Race," Hymn 85:

"O Thou who dost the vision send
And givest each his task,
And with the task sufficient strength,
Show us Thy will, we ask;
Give us a conscience bold and good,
Give us a purpose true,
That it may be our highest joy
Our Father's work to do." Amen.

LIVING COURAGEOUSLY

MUSICAL PRELUDE: Make a selection from the instrumental section, Numbers 324–336.

OPENING HYMN (*choose one*):

"Onward, Christian Soldiers," Hymn 231.
"March On, O Soul, with Strength!" Hymn 234.
"All Glory, Laud, and Honor," Hymn 90.

INVOCATION: O Lord and Master, who courageously lived amid friend and foe, fill us with Thy spirit. Help us to think great thoughts. Mark out for us the path in which we should go. May the desire to know and do our Father's will overcome the inclination to seek temporary security and comfort. May we hear the same compelling call heard by the disciples to follow Thee, and may we with glad devotion yield ourselves to Thy victorious leadership. In Thy Name we pray. Amen.

RESPONSE (*by choir or congregation*): "Jesus Calls Us: O'er the Tumult," Hymn 198, first and last stanzas.

FIRST SCRIPTURE (*choose one*):

Josh. 1:5–9 — "Be strong and of a good courage."
Deut. 31:7, 8 — "Fear not, neither be dismayed."
Ps. 27:1, 8–14 — "Wait on the Lord: be of good courage."
Isa. 12:1–6 — "Behold, God is my salvation."

HYMN (*choose one*):

"Be Strong!" Hymn 229.
"I Bind My Heart This Tide," Hymn 205.
"Now in the Days of Youth," Hymn 169.

SECOND SCRIPTURE (*choose one*):

Matt. 10:5–20 — Jesus' commission to His disciples.
Matt. 10:28–39 — "Who shall confess me before men."
I Tim. 4:11–16 — "Be thou an example."
Eph. 6:10–18 — "Be strong in the Lord."

HYMN (*choose one*):

"O Jesus, I Have Promised," Hymn 174.
"Open My Eyes, that I May See," Hymn 189.
"Lord, Speak to Me," Hymn 196.

SHORT TALK OR STORY. Possible themes:

Courage to Live as a Christian.
Courage to Do Hard Tasks for God.
Courage to Lead in Opposing Social Ills.

[over]

The Spirit of Christ Makes One Courageous.
The Decision to Be Courageous.

RESPONSIVE READING: "Courage," Number 16.

PRAYER (*by the leader or by the group in unison; choose one*):
For Godliness, number 1, page 349.
For Personal Integrity, number 1, page 351.
For Faith and Courage, numbers 1, 2, pages 352, 353.

CLOSING HYMN (*choose one*):
"Faith of Our Fathers! Living Still," Hymn 224.
"Soldiers of Christ, Arise," Hymn 220.
"Lead On, O King Eternal," Hymn 226.
"Fight the Good Fight with All Thy Might," Hymn 228.
"Christ of the Upward Way," Hymn 230.

CLOSING ASCRIPTION: Now unto Him who is able to keep us from falling, and to present us faultless before the presence of His glory with exceeding joy; to the only wise God our Saviour, be glory and majesty, dominion and power, both now and ever. Amen.

THE KINGDOM OF GOD ON EARTH (MISSIONARY)

Possible Themes

Christ of the East and West
All Sheep of One Shepherd
Our Great Commission
Ambassadors for Christ

Suggested Worship Center

A globe circled by short candles. Each candle might represent the countries where the denomination is at work, or the missionaries spoken about in the talk.

INSTRUMENTAL PRELUDE: Select an appropriate number from the instrumental section, Numbers 324–336; or use the music of the opening hymn.

CALL TO WORSHIP:
Ps. 133:1 — How pleasant it is to dwell in unity!
Ps. 95:1–3 — "Great King above all gods."
Isa. 52:7 — "How beautiful upon the mountains."
Ps. 96:1–3 — "Sing unto the Lord, all the earth."

OPENING HYMN (*choose one*):

"O Zion, Haste, Thy Mission High Fulfilling," Hymn 240.
"We've a Story to Tell to the Nations," Hymn 238.
"In Christ There Is No East or West," Hymn 243.
"Our God, Our Help in Ages Past," Hymn 40.
"The Morning Light Is Breaking," Hymn 239.

INVOCATION (*asking God to open our hearts to the needs of men everywhere who long to know a better way of life*).

SCRIPTURE (*choose one*):

Matt. 28:19, 20 — The Great Commission.
Acts 8:26–40 — Philip and the Ethiopian.
John 10:14–16 — "Other sheep I have."
Acts 10:34–48 — Peter's Defense of the Gentiles.
Isa. 60:1–3 — "Arise, shine; for thy light is come."
Isa. 61:1–3 — "The Spirit of the Lord God is upon me."
Isa. 35:1–10 — The wilderness shall be glad.

RESPONSIVE READING: "Peace Among the Nations," Number 22.

PRAYER: The prayers on pages 357–360 may be used; or there may be a directed meditation, using such suggestions as the following (read slowly, with occasional pause for meditation): People have ever sought to know a better way of life. . . . There has always been a mystery of life which can only find its answer in God. . . . We have been given help in finding God through our parents, through the prophets of old and prophets of today, but most of all through Jesus. . . . In acknowledgment of this Gift of God we must share with those who have not known Him. . . . Let us remember those in our own neighborhood who have not known the full joy of fellowship with Him . . . and those far away who long to know Him but have no one to teach them. . . . Let us dedicate ourselves to the furtherance of His Kingdom.

PRAYER RESPONSE: "Let the Words of My Mouth," Number 298, sung by the entire group, the choir, or a soloist.

THE OFFERING:

Offertory — Choose one of the selections from the instrumental section, Numbers 324–336.

Offertory Prayer — All that we have is Thine, O Lord. In recognition of Thy goodness to us we have set apart this portion. May it be used to extend Thy Kingdom throughout the world. Amen. (One of the responses, Numbers 311–314, may also be used.)

INTERPRETATION OF THEME: A story may be told about the work of the missionary supported by the local church, or about some of the missionary accomplishments of the denomination, or about an incident in the life of some well-known missionary.

CLOSING HYMN: "Thy Kingdom Come, O Lord," Hymn 280; or "Fling Out the Banner! Let It Float," Hymn 246.

BENEDICTION: So may Thy Kingdom come, O God, in our own lives, and to all who seek Thee, until the nations shall dwell together in peace through their love for Thee. Dismiss us with Thy blessing. Amen. (Or, one of the benedictions, pages 348, 349, may be used.)

CHRISTIAN PATRIOTISM

INSTRUMENTAL MUSIC: Select an appropriate number from the instrumental section, Numbers 324–336.

CALL TO WORSHIP: The choir may sing, "Enter Into His Gates with Thanksgiving," Number 297; or these sentences may be used:

Leader — Be still, and know that I am God:
I will be exalted among the nations, I will be exalted in the earth.
Response — The Lord of hosts is with us;
The God of Jacob is our refuge.
Leader — They that trust in the Lord
Shall be as mount Zion, which cannot be moved, but abideth for ever.

Response — As the mountains are round about Jerusalem,
So the Lord is round about His people
From this time forth and for evermore.

HYMNS (*choose one*):
"God of Our Fathers, Known of Old," Hymn 270.
"Now to Heaven Our Prayer Ascending," Hymn 159.
"God of Our Fathers, Whose Almighty Hand," Hymn 271.

INVOCATION: Help us, O God, to love our country. Grant us grace to cherish the ideals which made it possible and have given it eminence among the nations. May the faith of our fathers be our faith. Forgive us our personal and national sins, and endow us with the patriotism that reveals a likeness to Thee in love and righteousness. We ask it in Jesus' Name. Amen.

INTERPRETATION OF THEME:

First Reader — A Scriptural Call to Christian Citizenship, *Rom. 13:1, 7, 10–14.*

Hymn Response by the Choir (choose one):

"Once to Every Man and Nation," Hymn 221.

"Dare to Be Brave, Dare to Be True," Hymn 223.

"I Would Be True," Hymn 180.

Second Reader — Calls from Great National Leaders:

George Washington said, "Let us, then, as a nation be just — observe good faith toward all nations, cultivate peace and harmony with all, and give to mankind the example of a people always guided by an exalted justice and benevolence."

Abraham Lincoln said, "With malice toward none, with charity for all, with firmness in the right as God gives us to see the right; let us strive on to finish the work we are in . . . to do all which may achieve and cherish a just and lasting peace among ourselves and with all nations."

Woodrow Wilson said: "Our civilization cannot serve materially unless it be redeemed spiritually. It can be saved only by becoming permeated with the spirit of Christ, and being made free and happy by the practices which spring out of that spirit."

Hymn Response by the Congregation (choose one):

"O Son of Man, Thou Madest Known," Hymn 197.

"Lead On, O King Eternal," Hymn 226.

"Who Is on the Lord's Side?" Hymn 222.

Third Reader — Spiritual Qualities of Patriotism, *Ps. 33:11–22.*

A Unison Response in Prayer — Almighty and eternal Father, who hast made of one blood all nations and hast determined the bounds of their habitations, we beseech Thee to bless the peoples whom Thou hast created. Grant that the families of the earth may live together in the spirit of brotherhood. We pray for those who rule over us and guide our policies. May they lead us in the paths of peace and justice. Fill our hearts with the love of God and with understanding sympathy for all mankind. May we as a nation be ambitious to practice peace and good will. Teach us to walk in the paths of service and of sacrifice with patience and humility. We ask it in the Name and for the sake of the Saviour of men. Amen.

SILENT MEDITATION: A full minute of silence when all may consider the implications of Christian patriotism for them as individuals, ending with the choir singing a prayer response. (See Numbers 298–301.)

HYMN (*choose one*):

"America the Beautiful," Hymn 272.

"God Save America!" Hymn 273.

"My Country, 'Tis of Thee," Hymn 267.

BENEDICTION.

READINGS FROM SCRIPTURE

ADORATION AND PRAISE

NO.		PAGE
1.	Adoration	319
2.	Adoration and Praise	319
3.	Assurance and Confidence	320
4.	Awe and Reverence	320
5.	God in Nature	321
6.	God of the Past and the Future	322
7.	Gratitude and Thanksgiving	323
8.	Joy	323
9.	Love for God	324
10.	Praise	325
11.	The Character of God	325
12.	The Presence of God	326

CHRISTIAN EXPERIENCE

13.	Brotherhood	327
14.	Children of God	327
15.	Confidence	328
16.	Courage	328
17.	Dependence on God	329
18.	Desire for God's Truth	329
19.	Fellowship and Good Will	331
20.	Hope	331
21.	Jesus, Son of God (Christmas)	332
22.	Peace Among the Nations	332
23.	Prayer	333
24.	Prayer for Forgiveness	334
25.	Repentance	335
26.	Self-Control	335
27.	Taking Up the Cross	336
28.	The Risen Christ (Easter)	336
29.	Trust in God	337

Additional Scripture References 339

READINGS FROM SCRIPTURE

ADORATION AND PRAISE

1. ADORATION

LEADER: Holy, holy, holy, is the Lord of hosts: the whole earth is full of his glory. *Isa. 6:3.*

RESPONSE: **Exalt ye the Lord our God,**
And worship at his holy hill;
For the Lord our God is holy. *Ps. 99: 9.*

LEADER: Honor and majesty are before him:
Strength and gladness are in his place. *I Chron. 16: 27*

RESPONSE: **Glory ye in his holy name:**
Let the heart of them rejoice that seek the Lord. *Ps. 105: 3.*

LEADER: Ascribe unto the Lord the glory due unto his name: . . .
Worship the Lord in holy array. *I Chron. 16: 29.*

RESPONSE: **Oh magnify the Lord with me,**
And let us exalt his name together. *Ps. 34: 3.*

LEADER: Great and marvellous are thy works, O Lord God, the Almighty; righteous and true are thy ways, thou King of the ages.

RESPONSE: **Who shall not fear, O Lord, and glorify thy name? for thou only art holy; for all the nations shall come and worship before thee; for thy righteous acts have been made manifest.** *Rev. 15: 3, 4.*

LEADER: O give thanks unto the Lord; for he is good;
For his lovingkindness endureth for ever. *I Chron. 16: 34.*

RESPONSE: **Let the heavens be glad, and let the earth rejoice;**
And let them say among the nations, The Lord reigneth. *I Chron. 16: 31.*

ALL: Blessing, and glory, and wisdom, and thanksgiving, and honor, and power, and might, be unto our God for ever and ever. Amen. *Rev. 7: 12.*

2. ADORATION AND PRAISE

LEADER: Make a joyful noise unto the Lord, all ye lands.

RESPONSE: **Serve the Lord with gladness:**
Come before his presence with singing.

LEADER: Know ye that the Lord, he is God:
It is he that hath made us, and we are his;

RESPONSE: **We are his people, and the sheep of his pasture.**
Enter into his gates with thanksgiving,
And into his courts with praise:

LEADER: Give thanks unto him, and bless his name.

For the Lord is good; his lovingkindness endureth for ever,

And his faithfulness unto all generations. *Psalm 100.*

RESPONSE: **Oh sing unto the Lord a new song:**

Sing unto the Lord, all the earth.

LEADER: Sing unto the Lord, bless his name;

Show forth his salvation from day to day.

RESPONSE: **Let the heavens be glad, and let the earth rejoice;**

Let the sea roar, and the fulness thereof;

LEADER: Let the field exult, and all that is therein;

Then shall all the trees of the wood sing for joy

RESPONSE: **Before the Lord; for he cometh,**

For he cometh to judge the earth:

He will judge the world with righteousness,

And the peoples with his truth.

Ps. 96: 1, 2, 11–13.

3. ASSURANCE AND CONFIDENCE

LEADER: I will hear what God the Lord will speak;

For he will speak peace unto his people, and to his saints *Ps. 85: 8.*

RESPONSE: **Show us thy lovingkindness, O Lord,**

And grant us thy salvation.

Ps. 85: 7.

LEADER: In the fear of the Lord is strong confidence:

And his children shall have a place of refuge. *Prov. 14: 26.*

RESPONSE: **He only is my rock and my salvation:**

He is my high tower; I shall not be greatly moved. *Ps. 62: 2.*

LEADER: Be not afraid of sudden fear,

Neither of the desolation of the wicked, when it cometh:

For the Lord will be thy confidence,

And will keep thy foot from being taken. *Prov. 3: 25, 26.*

RESPONSE: **How precious is thy lovingkindness, O God!**

And the children of men take refuge under the shadow of thy wings. *Ps. 36: 7.*

LEADER: He that dwelleth in the secret place of the Most High

Shall abide under the shadow of the Almighty.

RESPONSE: **I will say of the Lord, He is my refuge and my fortress;**

My God, in whom I trust.

Ps. 91: 1, 2.

LEADER: The eternal God is thy dwelling-place,

And underneath are the everlasting arms. *Deut. 33: 27.*

RESPONSE: **Oh give thanks unto the Lord; for he is good;**

For his lovingkindness endureth for ever. *Ps. 118: 29.*

4. AWE AND REVERENCE

LEADER: O Lord God of hosts,

Who is a mighty one, like unto thee, O Lord?

And thy faithfulness is round about thee. *Ps. 89: 8.*

RESPONSE: **Guide me in thy truth, and teach me;**

For thou art the God of my salvation;

For thee do I wait all the day.
Ps. 25: 5.

LEADER: Delight thyself also in the Lord;

And he will give thee the desires of thy heart. *Ps. 37: 4.*

RESPONSE: **Unto thee, O Lord, do I lift up my soul.** *Ps. 25: 1.*

LEADER: Let all the earth fear the Lord:

Let all the inhabitants of the world stand in awe of him. *Ps. 33: 8.*

RESPONSE: **Teach me thy way, O Lord; I will walk in thy truth:**

Unite my heart to fear thy name.
Ps. 86: 11.

LEADER: Holy, holy, holy, is the Lord God, the Almighty, who was and who is and who is to come. *Rev. 4: 8.*

RESPONSE: **I will praise thee, O Lord my God, with my whole heart;**

And I will glorify thy name for evermore. *Ps. 86: 12.*

LEADER: Worthy art thou, our Lord and our God, to receive the glory and the honor and the power: for thou didst create all things, and because of thy will they were, and were created. *Rev. 4: 11.*

RESPONSE: **O Lord, how manifold are thy works!**

In wisdom hast thou made them all:

The earth is full of thy riches.
Ps. 104: 24.

ALL: Blessed be the Lord for evermore. Amen, and Amen. *Ps. 89: 52.*

5. GOD IN NATURE

LEADER: Oh come, let us sing unto the Lord;

Let us make a joyful noise to the rock of our salvation.

Let us come before his presence with thanksgiving;

Let us make a joyful noise unto him with psalms.

RESPONSE: **For the Lord is a great God,**

And a great King above all gods.

In his hand are the deep places of the earth;

The heights of the mountains are his also.

The sea is his, and he made it;

And his hands formed the dry land.

LEADER: Oh come, let us worship and bow down;

Let us kneel before the Lord our Maker:

RESPONSE: **For he is our God,**

And we are the people of his pasture, and the sheep of his hand.
Ps. 95: 1–7.

LEADER: Praise ye the Lord.

Praise ye the Lord from the heavens:

Praise him in the heights.

RESPONSE: **Praise ye him, all his angels:**

Praise ye him, all his host.

LEADER: Praise ye him, sun and moon:

Praise him, all ye stars of light.

Praise him, ye heavens of heavens,

And ye waters that are above the heavens.

RESPONSE: **Let them praise the name of the Lord;**

For he commanded, and they were created.

He hath also established them for ever and ever:

He hath made a decree which shall not pass away.

LEADER: Praise the Lord from the earth,

Ye sea-monsters, and all deeps;

RESPONSE: **Fire and hail, snow and vapor;**

Stormy wind, fulfilling his word;

LEADER: Mountains and all hills;

Fruitful trees and all cedars;

RESPONSE: **Beasts and all cattle;**

Creeping things and flying birds;

LEADER: Kings of the earth and all peoples;

Princes and all judges of the earth;

Both young men and virgins;

Old men and children:

RESPONSE: **Let them praise the name of the Lord;**

For his name alone is exalted;

His glory is above the earth and the heavens. *Ps. 148: 1–13.*

6. GOD OF THE PAST AND THE FUTURE

LEADER: Thou shalt love the Lord thy God with all thy heart, and with all thy soul, and with all thy mind.

Thou shalt love thy neighbor as thyself. *Matt. 22: 37, 39.*

RESPONSE: **Deliver me from all my transgressions.** *Ps. 39: 8.*

LEADER: No man, having put his hand to the plow, and looking back, is fit for the kingdom of God. *Luke 9: 62.*

RESPONSE: **Increase our faith.** *Luke 17: 5.*

LEADER: Be strong and of good courage; for thou shalt cause this people to inherit the land which I sware unto their fathers to give them. Only be strong and very courageous, to observe to do according to all the law, which Moses my servant commanded thee: turn not from it to the right hand or to the left, that thou mayest have good success whithersoever thou goest. This book of the law shall not depart out of thy mouth, but thou shalt meditate thereon day and night, that thou mayest observe to do according to all that is written therein: for then thou shalt make thy way prosperous, and then thou shalt have good success. Have not I commanded thee? Be strong and of good courage; be not affrighted, neither be thou dismayed: for the Lord thy God is with thee whithersoever thou goest. *Josh. 1: 6–9.*

RESPONSE: **Not that I have already obtained, or am already made perfect: but I press on, if so be that I may lay hold on that for which also I was laid hold on by Christ Jesus. Brethren, I count not myself yet to have laid hold: but one thing I do, forgetting the things which are behind, and stretching forward to the things which are before, I press on toward the goal unto the prize of the high calling of God in Christ Jesus.** *Phil. 3: 12–14.*

7. GRATITUDE AND THANKSGIVING

LEADER: Oh give thanks unto the Lord, call upon his name;

Make known among the peoples his doings.

Sing unto him, sing praises unto him;

Talk ye of all his marvellous works.

Glory ye in his holy name:

Let the heart of them rejoice that seek the Lord.

Seek ye the Lord and his strength;

Seek his face evermore. *Ps. 105: 1–4.*

FIRST GROUP: He sendeth forth springs into the valleys;

They run among the mountains;

SECOND GROUP: **They give drink to every beast of the field;**

The wild asses quench their thirst.

FIRST GROUP: By them the birds of the heavens have their habitation;

They sing among the branches.

SECOND GROUP: **He watereth the mountains from his chambers:**

The earth is filled with the fruit of thy works.

FIRST GROUP: He causeth the grass to grow for the cattle,

And herb for the service of man;

That he may bring forth food out of the earth.

SECOND GROUP: **O Lord, how manifold are thy works!**

In wisdom hast thou made them all:

The earth is full of thy riches.

Ps. 104: 10–14, 24.

UNISON: Oh praise the Lord, all ye nations;

Laud him, all ye peoples.

For his lovingkindness is great toward us;

And the truth of the Lord endureth for ever.

Praise ye the Lord. *Psalm 117.*

8. JOY

FIRST GROUP: Oh come, let us sing unto the Lord;

Let us make a joyful noise to the rock of our salvation.

SECOND GROUP: **Let us come before his presence with thanksgiving;**

Let us make a joyful noise unto him with psalms. *Ps. 95: 1, 2.*

FIRST GROUP: Sing praises to the Lord, who dwelleth in Zion:

Declare among the people his doings. *Ps. 9: 11.*

SECOND GROUP: **The Lord reigneth; let the earth rejoice;**

Let the multitude of isles be glad.

Ps. 97: 1.

FIRST GROUP: Make a joyful noise unto God, all the earth:

Sing forth the glory of his name:

SECOND GROUP: **All the earth shall worship thee,**

And shall sing unto thee.

Ps. 66: 1, 2, 4.

FIRST GROUP: Sing aloud unto God our strength:

Make a joyful noise unto the God of Jacob. *Ps. 81: 1.*

SECOND GROUP: **Rejoice in the Lord, O ye righteous:**

Praise is comely for the upright.

FIRST GROUP: Give thanks unto the Lord with the harp:
Sing praises unto him with the psaltery of ten strings.

SECOND GROUP: **Sing unto him a new song;**
Play skilfully with a loud noise.

FIRST GROUP: For the word of the Lord is right;
And all his work is done in faithfulness. *Ps. 33: 1–4.*

SECOND GROUP: **Sing praise unto the Lord, O ye saints of his,**
And give thanks to his holy memorial name.

FIRST GROUP: For his anger is but for a moment;
His favor is for a life-time:

SECOND GROUP: **Weeping may tarry for the night,**
But joy cometh in the morning. *Ps. 30: 4, 5.*

FIRST GROUP: I will bless the Lord at all times:
His praise shall continually be in my mouth.

SECOND GROUP: **My soul shall make her boast in the Lord:**
The meek shall hear thereof, and be glad.

FIRST GROUP: Oh magnify the Lord with me,
And let us exalt his name together. *Ps. 34: 1–3.*

SECOND GROUP: **I will give thanks unto the Lord with my whole heart;**
I will show forth all thy marvellous works.

FIRST GROUP: I will be glad and exult in thee;
I will sing praise to thy name, O thou Most High. *Ps. 9: 1, 2.*

UNISON: Oh satisfy us in the morning with thy lovingkindness,
That we may rejoice and be glad all our days. *Ps. 90: 14.*

9. LOVE FOR GOD

LEADER: Thou shalt love the Lord thy God with all thy heart, and with all thy soul, and with all thy mind. *Matt. 22: 37.*

RESPONSE: **I love thee, O Lord, my strength.** *Ps. 18: 1.*

LEADER: Oh love the Lord, all ye his saints:
The Lord preserveth the faithful. *Ps. 31: 23.*

RESPONSE: **I love the Lord, because he heareth**
My voice and my supplications. *Ps. 116: 1.*

LEADER: He that loveth not knoweth not God; for God is love.

RESPONSE: **Herein was the love of God manifested in us, that God hath sent his only begotten Son into the world that we might live through him.**

LEADER: Beloved, if God so loved us, we also ought to love one another.

RESPONSE: **If we love one another, God abideth in us, and his love is perfected in us.**

LEADER: God is love; and he that abideth in love abideth in God, and God abideth in him. *I John 4: 8, 9, 11, 12, 16.*

RESPONSE: **Herein is love, not that we loved God, but that he loved us, and sent his Son to be the propitiation for our sins.**

LEADER: Whosoever shall confess that Jesus is the Son of God, God abideth in him, and he in God.

I John 4: 10, 15.

RESPONSE: **Finally, brethren, . . . be perfected; be comforted; be of the same mind; live in peace: and the God of love and peace shall be with you.** *II Cor. 13: 11.*

LEADER: We love, because he first loved us. *I John 4: 19.*

10. PRAISE

LEADER: Oh sing unto the Lord a new song;

For he hath done marvellous things:

His right hand, and his holy arm, hath wrought salvation for him.

RESPONSE: **The Lord hath made known his salvation:**

His righteousness hath he openly showed in the sight of the nations.

LEADER: He hath remembered his lovingkindness and his faithfulness toward the house of Israel:

All the ends of the earth have seen the salvation of our God.

RESPONSE: **Make a joyful noise unto the Lord, all the earth:**

Break forth and sing for joy, yea, sing praises.

LEADER: Sing praises unto the Lord with the harp;

With the harp and the voice of melody.

RESPONSE: **With trumpets and sound of cornet**

Make a joyful noise before the King, the Lord.

LEADER: Let the sea roar, and the fulness thereof;

The world, and they that dwell therein;

RESPONSE: **Let the floods clap their hands;**

Let the hills sing for joy together

Before the Lord; for he cometh to judge the earth:

He will judge the world with righteousness,

And the peoples with equity.

Psalm 98.

LEADER: Oh that men would praise the Lord for his lovingkindness,

And for his wonderful works to the children of men!

RESPONSE: **For he satisfieth the longing soul,**

And the hungry soul he filleth with good. *Ps. 107: 8, 9.*

11. THE CHARACTER OF GOD

UNISON: Oh come, let us worship and bow down;

Let us kneel before the Lord our Maker:

For he is our God,

And we are the people of his pasture, and the sheep of his hand.

Ps. 95: 6, 7.

The heavens declare the glory of God;

And the firmament showeth his handiwork.

Day unto day uttereth speech,

And night unto night showeth knowledge. *Ps. 19: 1, 2.*

O Lord, our Lord,
How excellent is thy name in all the earth,
Who hast set thy glory upon the heavens! *Ps. 8: 1.*

O Lord, how manifold are thy works!
In wisdom hast thou made them all:
The earth is full of thy riches. *Ps. 104: 24.*

So the nations shall fear the name of the Lord,
And all the kings of the earth thy glory. *Ps. 102: 15.*

For the Lord is righteous; he loveth righteousness:
The upright shall behold his face. *Ps. 11: 7.*

The words of the Lord are pure words;
As silver tried in a furnace on the earth,
Purified seven times. *Ps. 12: 6.*

For though the Lord is high, yet hath he respect unto the lowly;
But the haughty he knoweth from afar. *Ps. 138: 6.*

For thou, Lord, art good, and ready to forgive,
And abundant in lovingkindness unto all them that call upon thee. *Ps. 86: 5.*

The friendship of the Lord is with them that fear him;
And he will show them his covenant. *Ps. 25: 14.*

My soul shall be joyful in the Lord:
It shall rejoice in his salvation. *Ps. 35: 9.*

12. THE PRESENCE OF GOD

LEADER: Holy, holy, holy, is the Lord of hosts: the whole earth is full of his glory. *Isa. 6: 3.*

UNISON: Whither shall I go from thy Spirit?
Or whither shall I flee from thy presence?
If I ascend up into heaven, thou art there:
If I make my bed in Sheol, behold, thou art there.
If I take the wings of the morning,
And dwell in the uttermost parts of the sea;
Even there shall thy hand lead me,
And thy right hand shall hold me.
If I say, Surely the darkness shall overwhelm me,
And the light about me shall be night;
Even the darkness hideth not from thee,
But the night shineth as the day:
The darkness and the light are both alike to thee. *Ps. 139: 7–12.*

Lord, I love the habitation of thy house,
And the place where thy glory dwelleth. *Ps. 26: 8.*

LEADER: Honor and majesty are before him:
Strength and gladness are in his place.
Ascribe unto Jehovah, ye kindreds of the peoples,
Ascribe unto Jehovah glory and strength;
Ascribe unto Jehovah the glory due unto his name:
Bring an offering, and come before him;
Worship Jehovah in holy array. *I Chron. 16: 27–29.*

CHRISTIAN EXPERIENCE

13. BROTHERHOOD

LEADER: The God that made the world and all things therein . . . made of one every nation of men to dwell on all the face of the earth, having determined their appointed seasons, and the bounds of their habitation; . . . for in him we live, and move, and have our being.
Acts 17: 24, 26, 28.

RESPONSE: **He that saith he is in the light and hateth his brother, is in the darkness even until now. He that loveth his brother abideth in the light, and there is no occasion of stumbling in him.** *I John 2: 9, 10.*

LEADER: He that loveth not his brother whom he hath seen, cannot love God whom he hath not seen. And this commandment have we from him, that he who loveth God love his brother also. *I John 4: 20, 21.*

RESPONSE: **If therefore thou art offering thy gift at the altar, and there rememberest that thy brother hath aught against thee, leave there thy gift before the altar, and go thy way, first be reconciled to thy brother, and then come and offer thy gift.**

LEADER: Ye have heard that it was said, Thou shalt love thy neighbor, and hate thine enemy: but I say unto you, Love your enemies, and pray for them that persecute you; that ye may be sons of your Father who is in heaven: for he maketh his sun to rise on the evil and the good, and sendeth rain on the just and the unjust.

RESPONSE: **For if ye love them that love you, what reward have ye? do not even the publicans the same? And if ye salute your brethren only, what do ye more than others?**
Matt. 5: 23, 24, 43–47.

LEADER: He hath showed thee, O man, what is good; and what doth the Lord require of thee, but to do justly, and to love kindness, and to walk humbly with thy God?
Micah 6: 8.

14. CHILDREN OF GOD

LEADER: Thou, O Lord, art our Father; our Redeemer from everlasting is thy name. *Isa. 63: 16.*

RESPONSE: **Behold what manner of love the Father hath bestowed upon us, that we should be called children of God.** *I John 3: 1.*

LEADER: And because ye are sons, God sent forth the Spirit of his Son into our hearts, crying, Abba, Father. So that thou art no longer a bondservant, but a son; and if a son, then an heir through God.
Gal. 4: 6, 7.

RESPONSE: **Beloved, now are we children of God, and it is not yet made manifest what we shall be.**

LEADER: We know that, if he shall be manifested, we shall be like him; for we shall see him even as he is.

RESPONSE: **And every one that hath this hope set on him purifieth himself, even as he is pure.** *I John 3: 2, 3.*

LEADER: As many as are led by the Spirit of God, these are sons of God.

RESPONSE: **The Spirit himself beareth witness with our spirit, that we are children of God.**

LEADER: I am persuaded, that neither death, nor life, nor angels, nor principalities, nor things present, nor things to come, nor powers, nor height, nor depth, nor any other creature, shall be able to separate us from the love of God, which is in Christ Jesus our Lord.
Rom. 8: 14, 16, 38, 39.

RESPONSE: **Now unto our God and Father be the glory for ever and ever. Amen.** *Phil. 4: 20.*

15. CONFIDENCE

LEADER: Trust ye in the Lord for ever; for in the Lord, even the Lord, is an everlasting rock. *Isa. 26: 4.*

RESPONSE: **Thou wilt keep him in perfect peace, whose mind is stayed on thee; because he trusteth in thee.** *Isa. 26: 3.*

LEADER: Fear not; for thou shalt not be ashamed: neither be thou confounded; for thou shalt not be put to shame.

RESPONSE: **And all thy children shall be taught of the Lord; and great shall be the peace of thy children.**

LEADER: In righteousness shalt thou be established: thou shalt be far from oppression, for thou shalt not fear; and from terror, for it shall not come near thee. *Isa. 54: 4, 13, 14.*

RESPONSE: **And the work of righteousness shall be peace; and the effect of righteousness, quietness and confidence for ever.**

LEADER: And my people shall abide in a peaceable habitation, and in safe dwellings, and in quiet resting-places. *Isa. 32: 17, 18.*

RESPONSE: **Fear not, for I have redeemed thee; I have called thee by thy name, thou art mine.**

LEADER: When thou passest through the waters, I will be with thee; and through the rivers, they shall not overflow thee: when thou walkest through the fire, thou shalt not be burned, neither shall the flame kindle upon thee. *Isa. 43: 1, 2.*

UNISON: Peace I leave with you; my peace I give unto you: not as the world giveth, give I unto you. Let not your heart be troubled, neither let it be fearful. *John 14: 27.*

16. COURAGE

LEADER: Be strong and of good courage, fear not, nor be affrighted at them: for the Lord thy God, he it is that doth go with thee; he will not fail thee, nor forsake thee.
Deut. 31: 6.

RESPONSE: **The Lord is my strength and my shield;**
My heart hath trusted in him, and I am helped:
Therefore my heart greatly rejoiceth;
And with my song will I praise him. *Ps. 28: 7.*

LEADER: Watch ye, stand fast in the faith, quit you like men, be strong.
I Cor. 16: 13.

RESPONSE: **The Lord God will help me; therefore have I not been confounded: therefore have I set my face like a flint, and I know that I shall not be put to shame.** *Isa. 50: 7.*

LEADER: Hast thou not known? hast thou not heard? The everlasting God, the Lord, the Creator of the ends of the earth, fainteth not, neither is weary. . . . He giveth power to the faint; and to him that hath no might he increaseth strength. *Isa. 40: 28, 29.*

RESPONSE: **The Lord is my strength and song;**
And he is become my salvation. *Ps. 118: 14.*

LEADER: Even the youths shall faint and be weary, and the young men shall utterly fall: but they that wait for the Lord shall renew their strength; they shall mount up with wings as eagles; they shall run, and not be weary; they shall walk, and not faint. *Isa. 40: 30, 31.*

RESPONSE: **Therefore, will we be strong and of good courage:**
The Lord of hosts is with us:
Blessed be his holy name.

17. DEPENDENCE ON GOD

LEADER: I will lift up mine eyes unto the mountains:
From whence shall my help come?
My help cometh from the Lord,
Who made heaven and earth.

RESPONSE: **He will not suffer thy foot to be moved:**
He that keepeth thee will not slumber.

LEADER: Behold, he that keepeth Israel
Will neither slumber nor sleep.

RESPONSE: **The Lord is thy keeper:**
The Lord is thy shade upon thy right hand.

LEADER: The sun shall not smite thee by day,
Nor the moon by night.

RESPONSE: **The Lord will keep thee from all evil;**
He will keep thy soul.

LEADER: The Lord will keep thy going out and thy coming in
From this time forth and for evermore. *Psalm 121.*

RESPONSE: **My soul, wait thou in silence for God only;**
For my expectation is from him.

LEADER: He only is my rock and my salvation:
He is my high tower; I shall not be moved.

RESPONSE: **With God is my salvation and my glory:**
The rock of my strength, and my refuge, is in God. *Ps. 62: 5–7.*

UNISON: O Lord my God, I will give thanks unto thee for ever. *Ps. 30: 12.*
For thou art my stronghold. *Ps. 31: 4.*

18. DESIRE FOR GOD'S TRUTH

LEADER: Good and upright is the Lord:
Therefore will he instruct sinners in the way.
The meek will he guide in justice;
And the meek will he teach his way.

All the paths of the Lord are lovingkindness and truth
Unto such as keep his covenant and his testimonies. *Ps. 25: 8-10.*

RESPONSE: **Show me thy ways, O Lord;**
Teach me thy paths.
Guide me in thy truth, and teach me;
For thou art the God of my salvation;
For thee do I wait all the day.
Ps. 25: 4, 5.

LEADER: Wherewith shall a young man cleanse his way?
By taking heed thereto according to thy word.

RESPONSE: **With my whole heart have I sought thee:**
Oh let me not wander from thy commandments.
Thy word have I laid up in my heart,
That I might not sin against thee.
Blessed art thou, O Lord:
Teach me thy statutes.
Ps. 119: 9-12.

LEADER: Blessed are they that keep his testimonies,
That seek him with the whole heart.
Yea, they do no unrighteousness;
They walk in his ways. *Ps. 119: 2, 3.*

RESPONSE: **Teach me thy way, O Lord; I will walk in thy truth:**
Unite my heart to fear thy name.
I will praise thee, O Lord my God, with my whole heart;
And I will glorify thy name for evermore. *Ps. 86: 11, 12.*

LEADER: I will instruct thee and teach thee in the way which thou shalt go:
I will counsel thee with mine eye upon thee. *Ps. 32: 8.*

My son, forget not my law;
But let thy heart keep my commandments:
For length of days, and years of life,
And peace, will they add to thee.
Let not kindness and truth forsake thee:
Bind them about thy neck;
Write them upon the tablet of thy heart. *Prov. 3: 1-3.*

RESPONSE: **Thy hands have made me and fashioned me:**
Give me understanding, that I may learn thy commandments.
Ps. 119: 73.

LEADER: What man is he that feareth the Lord?
Him shall he instruct in the way that he shall choose. *Ps. 25: 12.*

RESPONSE: **Blessed is the man whom thou chastenest, O Lord,**
And teachest out of thy law.
Ps. 94: 12.

Teach me thy statutes.
Make me to understand the way of thy precepts:
So shall I meditate on thy wondrous works. *Ps. 119: 26, 27.*

Open thou mine eyes, that I may behold
Wondrous things out of thy law.
Ps. 119: 18.

UNISON: Show us thy lovingkindness, O Lord,
And grant us thy salvation.
Ps. 85: 7.

19. FELLOWSHIP AND GOOD WILL

LEADER: Behold, how good and how pleasant it is
For brethren to dwell together in unity! *Ps. 133: 1.*

UNISON: Beloved, let us love one another: for love is of God; and every one that loveth is begotten of God, and knoweth God. He that loveth not knoweth not God; for God is love. Herein was the love of God manifested in us, that God hath sent his only begotten Son into the world that we might live through him. Herein is love, not that we loved God, but that he loved us, and sent his Son to be the propitiation for our sins. Beloved, if God so loved us, we also ought to love one another. *I John 4: 7–11.*

LEADER: Put on therefore, as God's elect, holy and beloved, a heart of compassion, kindness, lowliness, meekness, longsuffering; forbearing one another, and forgiving each other, if any man have a complaint against any; even as the Lord forgave you, so also do ye: and above all these things put on love, which is the bond of perfectness. *Col. 3: 12–14.*

UNISON: Whosoever believeth that Jesus is the Christ is begotten of God: and whosoever loveth him that begat loveth him also that is begotten of him. Hereby we know that we love the children of God, when we love God and do his commandments. . . . And his commandments are not grievous. For whatsoever is begotten of God overcometh the world: and this is the victory that hath overcome the world, even our faith. And who is he that overcometh the world, but he that believeth that Jesus is the Son of God? *I John 5: 1–5.*

LEADER: Let the peace of Christ rule in your hearts, to the which also ye were called in one body; and be ye thankful. . . . Be perfected; be comforted; be of the same mind; live in peace: and the God of love and peace shall be with you. *Col. 3: 15; II Cor. 13: 11.*

20. HOPE

LEADER: O Israel, hope in the Lord;
For with the Lord there is lovingkindness,
And with him is plenteous redemption. *Ps. 130: 7.*

RESPONSE: **I wait for the Lord, my soul doth wait,**
And in his word do I hope.
My soul waiteth for the Lord
More than watchmen wait for the morning;
Yea, more than watchmen for the morning. *Ps. 130: 5, 6.*

LEADER: The angel of the Lord encampeth round about them that fear him,
And delivereth them.
Oh taste and see that the Lord is good:
Blessed is the man that taketh refuge in him.
Oh fear the Lord, ye his saints;
For there is no want to them that fear him. *Ps. 34: 7–9.*

RESPONSE: **Why art thou cast down, O my soul?**
And why art thou disquieted within me?
Hope thou in God; for I shall yet praise him
For the help of his countenance.
Ps. 42: 5

LEADER: Happy is he that hath the God of Jacob for his help,
Whose hope is in the Lord his God. *Ps. 146: 5*

RESPONSE: **I have set the Lord always before me:**
Because he is at my right hand, I shall not be moved.
Thou art my hope, O Lord God:
Thou art my trust from my youth.
Ps. 16: 8; Ps. 71: 5.

21. JESUS, SON OF GOD

LEADER: Oh clap your hands, all ye peoples;
Shout unto God with the voice of triumph. . .
He is a great King over all the earth. *Ps. 47: 1, 2.*

RESPONSE: **For unto us a child is born, unto us a son is given; and the government shall be upon his shoulder: and his name shall be called Wonderful, Counsellor, Mighty God, Everlasting Father, Prince of Peace.**

LEADER: Of the increase of his government and of peace there shall be no end, upon the throne of David, and upon his kingdom, to establish it, and to uphold it with justice and with righteousness from henceforth even for ever. *Isa. 9: 6, 7.*

RESPONSE: **Sing unto the Lord; for he hath done excellent things: let this be known in all the earth. Cry aloud and shout, thou inhabitant of Zion; for great in the midst of thee is the Holy One of Israel.**
Isa. 12: 5, 6.

LEADER: Behold, a king shall reign in righteousness, and princes shall rule in justice. *Isa. 32: 1.*

RESPONSE: **Blessed be the Lord, the God of Israel;**
For he hath visited and wrought redemption for his people. . . .
To shine upon them that sit in darkness and the shadow of death;
To guide our feet into the way of peace. *Luke 1: 68, 79.*

LEADER: Be not afraid; for behold, I bring you good tidings of great joy which shall be to all the people.

RESPONSE: **For there is born to you this day in the city of David a Saviour, who is Christ the Lord.**

UNISON: Glory to God in the highest,
And on earth peace among men in whom he is well pleased.
Luke 2: 10, 11, 14.

22. PEACE AMONG THE NATIONS

LEADER: How beautiful upon the mountains are the feet of him that bringeth good tidings, that publisheth peace, that bringeth good tidings of good, that publisheth salvation, that saith unto Zion, Thy God reigneth! *Isa. 52: 7.*

RESPONSE: **Rejoice greatly, O daughter of Zion; shout, O daughter of Jerusalem: behold, thy king cometh unto thee; he is just, and having salvation; lowly, and riding upon an ass, even upon a colt the foal of an ass.** *Zech. 9: 9.*

LEADER: And the Spirit of the Lord shall rest upon him, the spirit of wisdom and understanding, the spirit of counsel and might, the spirit of knowledge and of the fear of the Lord.

RESPONSE: **And his delight shall be in the fear of the Lord; and he shall not judge after the sight of his eyes, neither decide after the hearing of his ears; but with righteousness shall he judge the poor, and decide with equity for the meek of the earth; and he shall smite the earth with the rod of his mouth; and with the breath of his lips shall he slay the wicked.**

LEADER: And righteousness shall be the girdle of his waist, and faithfulness the girdle of his loins.

RESPONSE: **And the wolf shall dwell with the lamb, and the leopard shall lie down with the kid; and the calf and the young lion and the fatling together; and a little child shall lead them.**

LEADER: They shall not hurt nor destroy in all my holy mountain; for the earth shall be full of the knowledge of the Lord, as the waters cover the sea. *Isa. 11: 2–6, 9.*

UNISON: And he will judge between many peoples, and will decide concerning strong nations afar off: and they shall beat their swords into plowshares, and their spears into pruning-hooks; nation shall not lift up sword against nation, neither shall they learn war any more. *Micah 4: 3.*

23. PRAYER

UNISON: O thou that hearest prayer,
Unto thee shall all flesh come. *Ps. 65: 2.*

Hear, O Lord, when I cry with my voice:
Have mercy also upon me, and answer me.
When thou saidst, Seek ye my face; my heart said unto thee,
Thy face, Lord, will I seek. *Ps. 27: 7, 8.*

Give ear, O Lord, unto my prayer;
And hearken unto the voice of my supplications.
In the day of my trouble I will call upon thee;
For thou wilt answer me. *Ps. 86: 6, 7.*

Give ear to my words, O Lord,
Consider my meditation.
Hearken unto the voice of my cry, my King, and my God;
For unto thee do I pray.
O Lord, in the morning shalt thou hear my voice;
In the morning will I order my prayer unto thee, and will keep watch. *Ps. 5: 1–3*

Let my prayer enter into thy presence;
Incline thine ear unto my cry.
For my soul is full of troubles.
Ps. 88: 2, 3.

Hear the voice of my supplications, when I cry unto thee.
Ps. 28: 2

For thy name's sake, O Lord,
Pardon mine iniquity, for it is great.
Ps. 25: 11.

Make thy face to shine upon thy servant:
Save me in thy lovingkindness.
Ps. 31: 16.

Arise, O Lord; O God, lift up thy hand:
Forget not the poor.
Ps. 10: 12.

The Lord hath heard my supplication;
The Lord will receive my prayer.
Ps. 6: 9.

24. PRAYER FOR FORGIVENESS

LEADER: Have mercy upon me, O God, according to thy lovingkindness:
According to the multitude of thy tender mercies blot out my transgressions.

RESPONSE: **Wash me thoroughly from mine iniquity,**
And cleanse me from my sin.

LEADER: Against thee, thee only, have I sinned,
And done that which is evil in thy sight;
That thou mayest be justified when thou speakest,
And be clear when thou judgest.

RESPONSE: **Purify me with hyssop, and I shall be clean:**
Wash me, and I shall be whiter than snow.

LEADER: Make me to hear joy and gladness,
That the bones which thou hast broken may rejoice.

RESPONSE: **Hide thy face from my sins,**
And blot out all mine iniquities.

LEADER: Create in me a clean heart, O God;
And renew a right spirit within me.

RESPONSE: **Cast me not away from thy presence;**
And take not thy holy Spirit from me.

LEADER: Restore unto me the joy of thy salvation;
And uphold me with a willing spirit.
Ps. 51: 1, 2, 4, 7–12.

RESPONSE: **Give ear, O Lord, unto my prayer;**
And hearken unto the voice of my supplications.

UNISON: Rejoice the soul of thy servant;
For unto thee, O Lord, do I lift up my soul.
For thou, Lord, art good, and ready to forgive,
And abundant in lovingkindness unto all them that call upon thee.
Ps. 86: 6, 4, 5.

25. REPENTANCE

LEADER: Out of the depths have I cried unto thee, O Lord.
Lord, hear my voice:
Let thine ears be attentive
To the voice of my supplications.

RESPONSE: **If thou, Lord, shouldest mark iniquities,**
O Lord, who could stand?
But there is forgiveness with thee,
That thou mayest be feared.
Ps. 130: 1–4.

LEADER: Hear my cry, O God;
Attend unto my prayer.
From the end of the earth will I call unto thee, when my heart is overwhelmed:
Lead me to the rock that is higher than I.

RESPONSE: **For thou hast been a refuge for me,**
A strong tower from the enemy.
I will dwell in thy tabernacle for ever:
I will take refuge in the covert of thy wings. *Ps. 61: 1–4.*

LEADER: Give ear to my prayer, O God;
And hide not thyself from my supplication.
Attend unto me, and answer me.
Ps. 55: 1, 2.

RESPONSE: **Make haste to answer me, O Lord; my spirit faileth:**
Hide not thy face from me,
Lest I become like them that go down into the pit. *Ps. 143: 7.*

LEADER: Out of my distress I called upon the Lord:
The Lord answered me and set me in a large place. *Ps. 118: 5.*

RESPONSE: **Blessed be God,**
Who hath not turned away my prayer,
Nor his lovingkindness from me.
Ps. 66: 20.

26. SELF-CONTROL

LEADER: He that is slow to anger is better than the mighty;
And he that ruleth his spirit, than he that taketh a city.
Prov. 16: 32.

RESPONSE: **Teach me to do thy will;**
For thou art my God:
Thy Spirit is good;
Lead me in the land of uprightness. *Ps. 143: 10.*

LEADER: Keep thy heart with all diligence;
For out of it are the issues of life.
Prov. 4: 23.

RESPONSE: **Incline not my heart to any evil thing,**
To practise deeds of wickedness
With men that work iniquity.
Ps. 141: 4.

LEADER: Put away from thee a wayward mouth,
And perverse lips put far from thee. *Prov. 4: 24.*

RESPONSE: **Set a watch, O Lord, before my mouth;**
Keep the door of my lips.
Ps. 141: 3.

LEADER: My son, attend to my words;
Incline thine ear unto my sayings.
Let them not depart from thine eyes;
Keep them in the midst of thy heart.
For they are life unto those that find them,
And health to all their flesh.
Prov. 4: 20–22.

RESPONSE: **Teach me, O Lord, the way of thy statutes;**
And I shall keep it unto the end.
Give me understanding, and I shall keep thy law;
Yea, I shall observe it with my whole heart. *Ps. 119: 33, 34.*

LEADER: Let thine eyes look right on,
And let thine eyelids look straight before thee. *Prov. 4: 25.*

RESPONSE: **But as for me, I will walk in mine integrity:**
Redeem me, and be merciful unto me.
My foot standeth in an even place:
In the congregations will I bless the Lord. *Ps. 26: 11, 12.*

27. TAKING UP THE CROSS

LEADER: Then said Jesus unto his disciples, If any man would come after me, let him deny himself, and take up his cross, and follow me. For whosoever would save his life shall lose it: and whosoever shall lose his life for my sake shall find it. *Matt. 16: 24, 25.*

RESPONSE: **What things were gain to me, these have I counted loss for Christ. Yea verily, and I count all things to be loss for the excellency of the knowledge of Christ Jesus my Lord: for whom I suffered the loss of all things, and do count them but refuse, that I may gain Christ, and be found in him, not having a righteousness of mine own, even that which is of the law, but that which is through faith in Christ, the righteousness which is from God by faith: that I may know him, and the power of his resurrection, and the fellowship of his sufferings, becoming conformed unto his death; if by any means I may attain unto the resurrection from the dead.** *Phil. 3: 7–11.*

LEADER: Have this mind in you, which was also in Christ Jesus: who, existing in the form of God, counted not the being on an equality with God a thing to be grasped, but emptied himself, taking the form of a servant, being made in the likeness of men; and being found in fashion as a man, he humbled himself, becoming obedient even unto death, yea, the death of the cross. Wherefore also God highly exalted him. *Phil. 2: 5–9.*

RESPONSE: **The Spirit himself beareth witness with our spirit, that we are children of God: and if children, then heirs; heirs of God, and joint-heirs with Christ; if so be that we suffer with him, that we may be also glorified with him.** *Rom. 8: 16, 17.*

LEADER: Be not fashioned according to this world: but be ye transformed by the renewing of your mind, that ye may prove what is the good and acceptable and perfect will of God. *Rom. 12: 2.*

28. THE RISEN CHRIST

LEADER: Jesus . . . said unto them, Destroy this temple, and in three days I will raise it up. The Jews therefore said, Forty and six years was this temple in building, and wilt thou raise it up in three days? But he spake of the temple of his body. When therefore he was raised from the dead, his disciples remembered that he spake this; and they believed the scripture, and the word which Jesus had said. *John 2: 19–22.*

RESPONSE: **Now late on the sabbath day, as it began to dawn toward the first day of the week, came Mary Magdalene and the other Mary to see the sepulchre.**

LEADER: And behold, there was a great earthquake; for an angel of the Lord descended from heaven, and came and rolled away the stone, and sat upon it. His appearance was as lightning, and his raiment white as snow: and for fear of him the watchers did quake, and became as dead men.

RESPONSE: **And the angel answered and said unto the women, Fear not ye; for I know that ye seek Jesus, who hath been crucified. He is not here; for he is risen, even as he said. Come, see the place where the Lord lay.**

LEADER: And go quickly, and tell his disciples, He is risen from the dead; and lo, he goeth before you into Galilee; there shall ye see him: lo, I have told you.

RESPONSE: **And they departed quickly from the tomb with fear and great joy, and ran to bring his disciples word.** *Matt. 28: 1–8.*

LEADER: Now hath Christ been raised from the dead, the firstfruits of them that are asleep. For since by man came death, by man came also the resurrection of the dead.

RESPONSE: **O death, where is thy victory? O death, where is thy sting?**

LEADER: Thanks be to God, who giveth us the victory through our Lord Jesus Christ.

I Cor. 15: 20, 21, 55, 57.

RESPONSE: **Glory be to the Father, and to the Son: and to the Holy Ghost;**

As it was in the beginning, is now, and ever shall be: world without end. Amen.

29. TRUST IN GOD

LEADER: God is our refuge and strength,
A very present help in trouble.

RESPONSE: **Therefore will we not fear, though the earth do change,**
And though the mountains be shaken into the heart of the seas;
Though the waters thereof roar and be troubled,
Though the mountains tremble with the swelling thereof. *Ps. 46: 1–3.*

LEADER: The Lord is my light and my salvation;
Whom shall I fear?

RESPONSE: **The Lord is the strength of my life;**
Of whom shall I be afraid?

LEADER: Though a host should encamp against me,
My heart shall not fear:

RESPONSE: **Though war should rise against me,**
Even then will I be confident.

LEADER: One thing have I asked of the Lord, that will I seek after:
That I may dwell in the house of the Lord all the days of my life,
To behold the beauty of the Lord, And to inquire in his temple.

Ps. 27: 1, 3, 4.

RESPONSE: **Trust in the Lord with all thy heart,**
And lean not upon thine own understanding:
In all thy ways acknowledge him,
And he will direct thy paths.

Prov. 3: 5, 6.

LEADER: For as many as are led by the Spirit of God, these are sons of God. For ye received not the spirit of bondage again unto fear; but ye received the spirit of adoption, whereby we cry, Abba, Father.

RESPONSE: **The Spirit himself beareth witness with our spirit, that we are children of God: and if children, then heirs; heirs of God, and joint-heirs with Christ; if so be that we suffer with him, that we may be also glorified with him.**

LEADER: What then shall we say to these things? If God is for us, who is against us? He that spared not his own Son, but delivered him up for us all, how shall he not also with him freely give us all things?

RESPONSE: **Nay, in all these things we are more than conquerors through him that loved us. For I am persuaded that neither death, nor life, nor angels, nor principalities, nor things present, nor things to come, nor powers, nor height, nor depth, nor any other creature, shall be able to separate us from the love of God, which is in Christ Jesus our Lord.**

Rom. 8: 14–17, 31, 32, 37–39.

ADDITIONAL SCRIPTURE REFERENCES

Christmas

Isaiah 9: 2–7
Isaiah 11: 1–12
Isaiah 40: 1–11
Micah 5: 2–4
Matthew 1: 18–25
Matthew 2: 1–12
Matthew 3: 1–4
Luke 1: 46–55
Luke 1: 67–79
Luke 2: 1–20
John 1: 1–18
Philippians 2: 5–11

Easter

Job 19: 23-27
Psalm 32
Psalm 34
Psalm 51
Isaiah, ch. 53
Matthew 28: 1–15
Mark 16: 1–15
Luke 24: 1–43
John 20: 1–18
Romans 6: 1–13
I Corinthians, ch. 15

The Holy Spirit

Psalm 139: 1–10
Joel 2: 28, 29
Matthew 3: 11–17
Mark 13: 9–11
Luke 24: 49; Acts 2: 1–18
John, ch. 14
I Corinthians 12: 1–11
I John 5: 1–7

Eternal Life

Job 19: 25–27
John 3: 14–17
John 14: 1–7
I Corinthians, ch. 15
I Thessalonians 4: 13–18
I John 5: 1–13

Loving as Jesus Loved

Micah 6: 8
Matthew, chs. 5; 6; 7 (select appropriate passages)
Matthew, ch. 10
Matthew 25: 34–40
Luke 10: 25–37
John, ch. 15
I Corinthians, ch. 13
I Peter 3: 9–17
I John 4: 7–21

God in Nature

Job, ch. 28
Job, ch. 38
Psalm 8
Psalm 19
Psalm 104
Psalm 148
Isaiah 40: 9–25

Missions, World Fellowship

Psalm 67
Psalm 72
Isaiah 2: 1–5
Isaiah 49: 1–13
Isaiah, ch. 61
Matthew 28: 16–20
John 4: 1–14
John, ch. 17
Acts 1: 1–8
Acts, ch. 10
Acts 16: 6–40
Acts 17: 16–28
Romans 10: 1–15

Loyalty, Courage, Christian Living

Joshua 1: 1–9
I Samuel 17: 32–50
I Kings 18: 17–24, 36–39
Proverbs, ch. 28
Isaiah 40: 28–31
Matthew 3: 1–12
Matthew 4: 1–11
Matthew 10: 5–10, 32, 33
Matthew 25: 1–13
Matthew 25: 14–30
Matthew 25: 31-46
Acts 4: 13-21
Ephesians, ch. 3
I Timothy, ch. 4
Hebrews 10: 19–25
Hebrews 13: 1–21

New Year's Day

Genesis 1: 1–5
Deuteronomy, ch. 8
Psalm 90
Psalm 91
Ecclesiastes 12: 1–7
Isaiah, ch. 40
Matthew 25: 1–13
Revelation, ch. 22

Thanksgiving

Deuteronomy 26: 1–11
Psalm 65
Psalm 92
Psalm 103
Psalm 116
Psalm 147
Isaiah, ch. 61
I Corinthians 15: 57, 58

Patriotic and National Occasions

Deuteronomy 26: 1–11
Psalm 47
Psalm 137: 1–6
Psalm 145
Micah 4: 1–5
Matthew 5: 43–48
Romans, ch. 13
Ephesians 6: 1–18
Hebrews 11: 1 to 12: 2

PRAYERS AND COLLECTS

PAGE

I. WORSHIP AND PRAISE . . . 341
1. Calls to Worship . . . 341
2. Invocations — Prayers of Adoration and Praise . . . 342
3. Offertory Prayers . . . 343
4. Prayers of Confession . . . 343
5. Prayers of Thanksgiving . . . 345
6. Prayers of Intercession . . . 348
7. Benedictions . . . 348

II. GENERAL PRAYERS . . . 349
For Godliness . . . 349
For Loyalty to the Highest . . . 350
For Daring to Use All Our Resources . . . 350
For Personal Integrity . . . 351
A Young Person's Prayer . . . 352
For Faith and Courage . . . 352
For a Christian Attitude Toward Others . . . 353
For Making Right Choices . . . 353
Prayer of Dedication (Easter) . . . 354
Litany of Dedication . . . 354
For the Church . . . 355
Guidance for Prayer on the Work Problem . . . 355
Prayer of an Unemployed Man . . . 356
For Schools and Colleges . . . 356
For Christian Brotherhood . . . 357
For a Christian Nation . . . 358
For the Kingdom of God . . . 359
For This Universe . . . 360

PRAYERS AND COLLECTS

I. WORSHIP AND PRAISE

1. Calls to Worship

The Lord is in His holy temple: let all the earth keep silence before Him.

O worship the Lord in the beauty of holiness: fear before Him, all the earth.

Oh come, let us sing unto the Lord;
Let us make a joyful noise to the rock of our salvation.
Let us come before His presence with thanksgiving;
Let us make a joyful noise unto Him with psalms.

Come ye, and let us walk in the light of the Lord. He will teach us of His ways, and we will walk in His paths.

The hour cometh, and now is, when the true worshippers shall worship the Father in spirit and in truth: for the Father seeketh such to worship Him. God is a Spirit: and they that worship Him must worship Him in spirit and in truth.

Seek ye the Lord while He may be found; call ye upon Him while He is near: let the wicked forsake his way, and the unrighteous man his thoughts; and let him return unto the Lord, and He will have mercy upon him; and to our God, for He will abundantly pardon.

LEADER: God is Spirit. Let us worship the God who is Spirit.

RESPONSE: "They that worship him must worship him in spirit and in truth."

LEADER: God is Light. Let us worship the God who is Light.

RESPONSE: "If we walk in the light as he is in the light, we have fellowship one with another, and truly our fellowship in the spirit is with the Father, and his Son Jesus Christ."

LEADER: God is Love. Let us worship the God who is Love.

RESPONSE: "Everyone that loveth is born of God and knoweth God; and we know that we have passed from death unto life because we love."

LEADER: God is Power. Let us worship the God who is Power.

RESPONSE: "They that wait upon the Lord shall renew their strength. They shall mount up with wings as eagles. They shall run and not be weary. They shall walk and not faint."

— Wade Crawford Barclay, in *Challenge and Power*.

O come, let us worship and bow down;
Let us kneel before the Lord our Maker.
Know ye that the Lord, He is God:
It is He that hath made us, and we are His;
We are His people, and the sheep of His pasture.

2. Invocations — Prayers of Adoration and Praise

Almighty God, unto whom all hearts are open, all desires known, and from whom no secrets are hid; cleanse the thoughts of our hearts by the inspiration of Thy Holy Spirit, that we may perfectly love Thee, and worthily magnify Thy holy Name; through Christ our Lord. Amen.

— From *The Book of Common Worship*, Revised.

Holy, Holy, Holy! Lord God Almighty, who hast set Thy glory above the heavens, praise waiteth for Thee in Zion, and unto Thee shall the vow be performed; Receive the adoration of Thy people, we beseech Thee, and let the words of our mouth and the meditation of our heart be acceptable in Thy sight, O Lord our Strength and our Redeemer. Amen.

— From *The Book of Common Worship*, Revised.

O God, whose being and perfections are infinite, eternal, and unchangeable, the same yesterday, today, and forever: Thou art glorious in holiness, full of love and compassion, abundant in grace and truth. All Thy works praise Thee in all places of Thy dominion: and Thy Son hath glorified Thee upon earth. Therefore we bow down and adore Thee, Father, Son, and Holy Ghost, one God, blessed forevermore. Amen.

— From *The Book of Common Worship*.

Our heavenly Father, we would always be conscious of Thy loving care and presence. We are glad that Thou art our Father, and that we may have fellowship with Thee. Grant that in this service we may come close to Thee, and that we may always have a deep sense of Thy nearness. We are glad that we know about that One who first taught men to call Thee "Our Father." With hearts open to Thee, we unite in the prayer which He taught to His disciples: (The Lord's Prayer).

Our Father, we thank Thee for the joy that Thou hast given Thy people through Thy marvelous works. Most of all we thank Thee for Jesus Christ, the Gift of Thy love to us. Grant us Thy Spirit to guide our thoughts that we may see Jesus with clear vision. Cleanse us from all sin that we may have room in our hearts to receive Him. We ask it in Jesus' Name. Amen.

To Thee, O Lord, we come, with a desire to know Thee better. As we worship Thee may we be conscious of Thy nearness and of Thy love. Help us to love Thee, and loving Thee to serve Thee. Give us, we pray, a clearer idea of what Thou dost expect of us, and may none of us ever disappoint Thee. Hear our prayer and bless us, for Jesus' sake. Amen.

3. Offertory Prayers

Humbly do we lay our gifts before Thee, O God, who hast given unto us the priceless Gift of Thy Son, Jesus Christ. May these offerings be accompanied by the consecration of our wills and by an increased desire to see Thy Kingdom come. Help us always to know that not what we get but what we give measures our devotion to Thee and our right to receive additional gifts from Thee. Amen.

Our heavenly Father, in this offering we consecrate ourselves to Thee. We will be friendly to others and we will help and serve Thee in every possible way. And because we show ourselves friendly, grant that we may have Jesus Christ for our great Friend, in whose Name we make this offering of our money and ourselves. Amen.

4. Prayers of Confession

Almighty and most merciful Father; We have erred and strayed from Thy ways like lost sheep. We have followed too much the devices and desires of our own hearts. We have offended against Thy holy laws. We have left undone those things which we ought to have done; And we have done those things which we ought not to have done; And there is no health in us. But Thou, O Lord, have mercy upon us, miserable offenders. Spare Thou those, O God, who confess their faults. Restore Thou those who are penitent; According to Thy promises declared unto mankind in Christ Jesus our Lord. And grant, O most merciful Father, for His sake; That we may hereafter live a godly, righteous, and sober life, To the glory of Thy holy Name. Amen.

— From *The Book of Common Worship*, Revised

O Thou whose chosen dwelling is the heart that longs for Thy presence and humbly seeks Thy love: We come to Thee to acknowledge and to confess that we have sinned in thought and word and deed; we have not loved Thee with all our heart and soul, with all our mind and strength; we have not enough loved our neighbor as ourselves. Deepen within us our sorrow for the wrong we may have done, or for the good we may have left undone. But Thou, O Lord, art full of compassion and gracious, slow to anger and plenteous in mercy; there is forgiveness with Thee. Restore to us the joy of Thy salvation; bind up that which is broken, give light to our minds, strength to our wills, and rest to our souls. Speak to each of us the word that we need, and let Thy word abide with us till it has wrought in us Thy holy will. Amen.

— From *Devotional Services*, compiled by John Hunter. Used by permission of E. P. Dutton & Co., Inc., publishers.

O God our Father, we want to remember Jesus. Especially we want to remember how He went into a quiet place to think and pray and choose what He would do. Help us to bring our minds and hearts, as He brought His, for You to see. We are not like Him, who had nothing to be ashamed of; but we want to be like Him, as much as we can. We are sorry for anything in us that is wrong, and we pray for a blessing on everything in us that is good; for Jesus' sake. Amen.

If we are to do better today and tomorrow, we need to be forgiven for the blunders we have already made.

And so, for all our faults we know of, and for the mistakes we made because we did not know,

We ask forgiveness.

For greediness or laziness, and for anything that has kept our bodies from being at their best,

Forgive us, O God.

For not trying hard enough to find out what was right, and for cowardice in standing up for what we knew was right and true,

Forgive us.

For thinking so much about ourselves that we did not think of others and of what we might do for them,

Forgive us.

For trying to get the best things for ourselves instead of being quick to see that others had their share,

Forgive us.

For the times when we have hurt anybody, and for the times when we have been too careless to be kind,

Forgive us.

For the hasty words our tongues have spoken, and for the helpful words we did not have the sense to say,

Forgive us.

For any unclean speech or cruel gossip, and for ever forgetting to repeat the lovely things which would have made somebody glad,

Forgive us.

For any lies we may have told, and for the other lies we helped to spread by keeping silence when the truth was twisted,

Forgive us.

For ever having bullied those who are not as big as we, or having part in making any boy or girl unhappy,

Forgive us.

For bad temper and gloominess, and for nursing our grievances when we ought to have gone ahead with cheerfulness again,

Forgive us.

For cheating or crookedness in work or play or sport, and for cutting corners to get the things we wanted,

Forgive us.

For the little rudenesses which have disappointed those who loved us, and for every chance we have lost to be courteous and kind,

Forgive us.

But we do not ask, dear God, to be forgiven only. We want to be better than we have been before.

We remember Jesus, who gave His body, mind, and soul for God to use.

Help us to try to be like Him.

By His shining goodness, He can make us glad in being good.

Help us to follow Him.

By His strength He can make us strong.

Help us to follow Him.

By His bravery He can make us brave.

Help us to follow Him.

By His truth He can keep us true.

Help us to follow Him.

And so, our Father, as we have asked for blessing in our worship, we ask again for blessing as we go away. Help us to remember all that we have prayed for, and to trust in You to answer all our prayers; for Jesus' sake. Amen.

— From *Lift Up Your Hearts*, by Walter Russell Bowie. Used by permission of The Macmillan Company, publishers.

5. Prayers of Thanksgiving

Almighty God, Father of all mercies; We Thine unworthy servants; Do give Thee most humble and hearty thanks; For all Thy goodness and loving-kindness to us and to all men. We bless Thee for our creation, preservation, and all the blessings of this life; But above all for Thine inestimable love in the redemption of the world by our Lord Jesus Christ; For the means of grace, and for the hope of glory. And, we beseech Thee, give us that due sense of all Thy mercies; That our hearts may be unfeignedly thankful; And that we show forth Thy praise, not only with our lips, but in our lives; By giving up ourselves to Thy service, And by walking before Thee in holiness and righteousness all our days; Through Jesus Christ our Lord; To whom with Thee and the Holy Spirit, be all honor and glory, World without end. Amen.

— From *The Book of Common Worship*, Revised.

O God, Father of mercies, from whom cometh every good gift and every perfect gift, we thank Thee.

We thank Thee for Thy gifts in creation: for light and eyes to behold all its beauties; for sound and ears to hear its music; for taste and the flavor of fruit and grain; for hunger and food to strengthen us. We thank Thee that Thou hast made us for achievement and given us the day for work, and the night for rest; that Thou hast endowed us with minds that may think Thy thoughts, and hearts that may feel Thy love, and wills that may grow strong for the right.

We thank Thee for the blessings of Thy providence: for Thy protecting care from infancy until now; for the love of parents who have watched over us in Thy Name; for teachers who have sought to prepare us for fuller living; for our land with its privileges. [over]

We thank Thee for the gifts of Thy grace: for the Church with its ordinances; for Thy Word with its revelation of Thy will; for Jesus Christ, Thy Son, our Saviour; for the work of Thy Holy Spirit in our hearts.

Forgive us for our ingratitude, and, through a new appreciation of Thy goodness, help us to render to Thee not only the thanksgiving of our lips but the gratitude of our hearts, and enable us to express our praise in joyful devotion to Thy service. We pray in the Name of Him who is Thy greatest Gift to us. Amen.

LITANY:

For the love of home and the counsel and sacrificial care of parents in childhood and youth,

We thank Thee, O God.

For the understanding and sympathy of friends, and for the strength that flows daily out of their lives into our own,

We thank Thee, O God.

For tasks that are sometimes hard, whose problems baffle us, and yet summon us to our best,

We give Thee thanks, O God.

For the strengthening of purpose and quickening of effort that even failure may bring, and for the joy and encouragement of success,

We give Thee thanks, O God.

For the conviction and vision of a divine purpose at the heart of the universe with which we may ally ourselves and for Thy promise of daily strength and wisdom in seeking to fulfill it,

We give Thee thanks, O God.

For all those who before us have caught some glimpse of that purpose, in its pursuit have lived, and have gone on before,

We give Thee thanks, O God.

— Wade Crawford Barclay, in *Challenge and Power*. Copyright, 1936.
Used by permission of Abingdon-Cokesbury Press.

Master divine,
We thank Thee for all new beginnings,
For this new day
With its new opportunities of service for Thee and communion with Thee.
We thank Thee for landmarks passed
And new vistas opening ahead;
For new hope and new inspiration,
New national awakening, and new desire to serve our time and our country.

We thank Thee that, to those who love Thee,
The best is ever yet to be:
That, if we abide in Thee, we can never grow old,
For Thou, our Master, art eternally young,
Eternally radiant with the joyful energy, the freshness and buoyancy of youth.

We thank Thee for the sacred elixir of Thy Spirit,
Which wardeth forever from those who love Thee
All weariness of soul, all carking anxiety,
All discouragement in failure,
All old age of the soul.

— J. S. Hoyland, in *A Book of Prayers for Youth.*
Used by permission of Association Press.

LITANY:

With hearts responsive
And enfranchised eyes,
We thank Thee, Lord, —
For all things beautiful and good, and true;
For all things that seemed not good yet turned to good;
For all the sweet compulsions of Thy will
That chased, and tried, and wrought us to Thy shape;
For things unnumbered that we take of right,
And value first when first they are withheld;
For light and air, sweet sense of sound and smell;
For ears to hear the heavenly harmonies;
For eyes to see the unseen in the seen;
For vision of The Worker in the work;
For hearts to apprehend Thee everywhere; —
We thank Thee, Lord!

— John Oxenham, in *The Te Deums and the Sacraments.* Used by permission.

LITANY:

O Thou who givest to all liberally and upbraidest not, we call to remembrance Thy lovingkindness and Thy tender mercies which have been ever of old, and with grateful hearts we lift to Thee the voice of our thanksgiving. For the life Thou hast given us, and the world in which we live,

We praise Thee, O God.

For the order and constancy of nature, for the beauty of earth and sea and racing cloud; for the bounty of fruitful fields,

We praise Thee, O God.

For all home blessings, for friends, and for all the pure pleasures of life together; for the love, sympathy, and good will of men,

We praise Thee, O God.

For the zest of sport, and the sting of the wind, and sun upon our faces,

We praise Thee, O God.

For that provision which sendeth seedtime and harvest, which scattereth the hoarfrost like ashes and setteth the fountains of the deep, which clotheth the mountains with forest and maketh fertile the spreading plain,

We praise Thee, O God.

[over]

For the sheer joy of life and the pulsing energy within our bodies,

We praise Thee, O God.

For the gift of Thy Son, Jesus Christ, and all the helps and hopes which are ours as His disciples; for the presence and inspiration of Thy Holy Spirit, and for all the ministers of Thy truth and grace;

We praise Thee, O God.

In Unison: And now, O Lord, having praised Thee with our lips; grant that we may also praise Thee in consecrated and faithful lives, through Jesus Christ our Lord. Amen.

— George Stewart, in *The Sanctuary*. Used by permission of Association Press.

6. Prayers of Intercession

O God, the Creator and Preserver of all mankind, we humbly beseech Thee for all sorts and conditions of men; that Thou wouldest be pleased to make Thy ways known unto them, Thy saving health unto all nations. More especially, we pray for Thy holy Church universal; that it may be so guided and governed by Thy good Spirit that all who profess and call themselves Christians may be led into the way of truth, and hold the faith in unity of spirit, in the bond of peace, and in righteousness of life. Finally, we commend to Thy fatherly goodness all those who are any ways afflicted or distressed in mind, body, or estate (and especially those for whom our prayers are asked at this time); that it may please Thee to comfort and relieve them according to their several necessities; giving them patience under their sufferings, and a happy issue out of all their afflictions. And this we beg for Jesus Christ's sake. Amen.

— From *The Book of Common Worship*, Revised.

O God, let us not be lovers of our own selves, but make us to love our neighbor as ourself.

We beseech Thee to hear us, O Lord.

May Christ, who pleased not Himself, make us strong to bear the infirmities of the weak, and not seek to please ourselves.

We beseech Thee to hear us, O Lord.

May the love of Christ constrain us, that we may not henceforth live unto ourselves alone.

We beseech Thee to hear us, O Lord.

—From *A Service Book for Youth*, by S. M. E. Trood. Published by the Society for Promoting Christian Knowledge.

7. Benedictions

May the grace of the Lord Jesus Christ, and the love of God, and the communion of the Holy Spirit, be with us all. Amen.

The Lord bless us, and keep us: the Lord make His face to shine upon us, and be gracious unto us: the Lord lift up His countenance upon us and give us peace. Amen.

May the peace of God, which passeth all understanding, guard our hearts and our thoughts in Christ Jesus. Amen.

Now unto Him that is able to keep us from falling, and to present us faultless before the presence of His glory with exceeding joy, to the only wise God our Saviour, be glory and majesty, dominion and power, both now and ever. And may grace, mercy, and peace, from God the Father, Son, and Holy Spirit be with us all forevermore. Amen.

Now may the light that shone in Jesus Christ our Lord,
Shine in our hearts and minds by the indwelling Word;
And may the radiance which faith and hope restore,
Be and abide with us both now and evermore. Amen.

II. GENERAL PRAYERS

For Godliness

Lord of life and death,
Save us from contentment with things that perish;
Save us from entanglement in delusion and desire.

Make us pure with Thy purity,
Hating, as Thou hatest, sin and oppression,
Seeing with Thine eyes the fatal tragedy of self-indulgence,
Hungering and thirsting after Thy righteousness.

Make us humble and obedient to Thy voice;
Teach us to find our life by losing it;
Give us the will to follow Thy guidance
Wherever it may lead us, in loneliness, in pain, and in grief.

Form in us Thine own likeness, the image of Thyself;
May we be clothed continually with Thy nature of love.
Vouchsafe unto us the perpetual sacrament of Thy grace;
The perpetual sharing of Thine own redemptive purposes.

If we sleep, awake us mercilessly from our lethargy;
Stir us to desperate faith,
Drive us to the undertaking of impossible tasks for Thee;
Use us this day and every day for the salvation of Thy world.

— J. S. Hoyland, in *A Book of Prayers for Youth.* Used by permission of Association Press.

O God, Light of the minds that see Thee, Life of the souls that love Thee, and Strength of the thoughts that seek Thee, enlarge our minds and raise the vision of our hearts, that with swift wings of thought our spirits may reach Thee, the eternal Wisdom, who art from everlasting to everlasting; through Jesus Christ, our Lord. Amen.

— Saint Augustine

Grant me, O God, Thy merciful protection;
And, in protection, give me strength, I pray;
And, in my strength, O grant me wise discretion;
And, in discretion, make me ever just;
And, with my justice, may I mingle love,
And, with my love, O God, the love of Thee;
And, with the love of Thee, the love of all.

— "Talhairn's Prayer," from the Welsh

For Loyalty to the Highest

Lord of truth and purity,
We beseech Thee to build up in us Thine own nature.

Found our souls upon the rock,
That we may be content with no transient happiness
Bought at the cost of compromise and unfaithfulness.

Teach us the bitterness of forsaking noble ideals;
Teach us the glory and warmth of the loneliness and pain
That come from fearless following of the highest that we know.

Give us Thine own vision of the eternal values,
Thine own resolute disregard of the second best,
Thine own unflinching loyalty to duty and honor.

— J. S. Hoyland, in *A Book of Prayers for Youth.* Used by permission of Association Press.

God, help us in this day's duties, and in its pleasures also, to be Thy good and obedient servants: help us to be faithful over a few things, that we may prove worthy to be rulers over many things. When we are tempted to do wrong, remind us of Thy presence: if still we fall into evil, forgive us once more and help us to start afresh. And because Thou lovest all of us, help us to be kind to one another. We ask it for Christ's sake, our Saviour and our Elder Brother. Amen.

— Louis F. Benson, in *Christian Song.* Copyright, 1926.

For Daring to Use All Our Resources

We come to Thee, almost empty-handed
Because we have not dared to use what Thou hast given to us.
Like him who laid his talent in the earth to molder there unused,
We have held back words which could have meant life
To many a hard-pressed neighbor.
The thick mantle of self-love
Has promised comfort,
But has frozen our souls.

We have cherished to ourselves gifts of music and of Sacred Writ;
We have taken for our own the worship our fathers gave us,
The beauty and the help entrusted to Thy Church.
Help us, O Lord,
To share all gifts within our keeping
As widely as the needs of men.
Aid us to present Thy Son, our Lord,
In all His strength and beauty.
Feeble though we be,
Remind us that even as the boy with loaves and fishes
Under Thy hands the weak are able;
Through Jesus Christ, our Lord.

— George Stewart, in *A Face to the Sky*. Used by permission of Association Press

For Personal Integrity

O God, cultivate within us the spirit of righteousness, and build Thy Kingdom there. We would manifest the spirit of our Lord in every act and thought, and bring Thy message unto our fellow men. Make us pure within, where no one can see. Help us not to develop virtues merely that they may be seen of men, and help us to remain faithful to our own testimony of Thee, and not try to take over the experience of others which is not ours. Inspire us to acquire purity of mind, strength of will, and beauty of spirit, that our inmost souls may be temples in which Thou wouldst dwell. Help us to seek character and spiritual power without thought of reward or praise. Keep us from the error of thinking that we have done our best when we have merely refrained from breaking the laws and have never been publicly condemned for unworthiness. Help us to keep faith with ourselves, and to respect the value of our own personalities. May we live as if Thy Son lived every minute of every day within us, and may the radiance of our faces be the indication of the fires of hope and faith and love within us. In Jesus' Name we pray. Amen.

— Richard K. Morton, in *A Book of Prayers for Young People*. Copyright, 1935. Used by permission of Abingdon-Cokesbury Press

Almighty God, who seest that we have no power of ourselves to help ourselves; keep us both outwardly in our bodies and inwardly in our souls, that we may be defended from all adversities which may happen to the body, and from all evil thoughts which may assault and hurt the soul; through Jesus Christ our Lord. Amen.

From *The Book of Common Worship*, Revised.

Almighty God, we thank Thee for rest and health; for work to do, and strength to do it; and for all the surroundings of our life that make it desirable and enjoyable. Do Thou raise our thoughts, and purify our aspirations. Strengthen our wills, we beseech Thee, on the side of what is right and good, and against what is wrong and evil, through Jesus Christ our Lord. Amen.

— From *Prayers Ancient and Modern*. Copyright, 1897, by Mary Wilder Tileston

A Young Person's Prayer

O God of all wisdom, thrust Thou me into a lifelong quest of great ideas.
Save me from easy contentment with small thoughts that cost little and whose rewards are slight.
Stir within me some inward and holy passion for the mighty thoughts that, costing all, reward the soul with all.
Quicken me with the growing pains of the mind that come from the great books.
Teach me the thrill and the enlargement that are found in keeping pace with the great minds of the ages.
Grant me the divine grace of being able to ask questions — sharp questions that cut deep and divide truth from error.
Spare me the inner defeat of easy answers.
Enlarge me by the wisdom that has come down from my fathers, but grant me the courage to outgrow it as they outgrew what had come down to them.
Cleanse me of small spites, purge my soul of puny hatreds, sweep my heart of paralyzing bitterness — through the ennobling power of great ideas.
In the Name of Him who is the Truth. Amen.

— P. R. Hayward. Used by permission.

Father, as a new day comes to bring its unmarred opportunity, help me to use it better than I used yesterday. While yet there is time, I would remember the special temptations which have overcome me before, and can overcome me again unless I am better armed against them. I have been ashamed too late of the failures against which I ought to have been on guard. I have spoken harshly when I should have put a bit upon a hasty and bitter tongue; I have been so intent on my own way that I have turned others aside from the ways in which they might have walked more happily; I have been too preoccupied to be understanding and to be kind. I do not ask that these faults may be forgiven now. I would not have the sharpness of my remembrance of them dulled. I ask rather that I may be made more thoughtful and more vigilant, so that when this day ends there may be less for which I need to be forgiven and more for which I may be glad, because I shall have tried to let the goodness of God express itself through my obedient mind and heart and will. Amen.

— Walter Russell Bowie, in *Lift Up Your Hearts*. Used by permission of The Macmillan Company, publishers.

For Faith and Courage

O Thou who art our Refuge and Strength, who dost say unto us, "It is I, be not afraid," enable us to abide in Thee, and so to gain the courage we need. Increase our faith in Thee, who lovest us and whom we love. Teach us that there is no fear in love. Thou hast said, "Let not your hearts be troubled."

So we look to Thee as we face the duties and the problems of today. We rejoice that we can see Thee, our Help, our Shield, and our Salvation as we become acquainted with Jesus Christ, Thy Son, our Lord. Amen.

O God, whose power is made perfect in weakness, we would find our strength in Thee. Through right thought of Thee, give firmness to our thinking. Impart courage to our hearts because we hear Thy call coming to us with no uncertain sound. Kindle within us that flame of holy love which burns out all that is wrong and base. Strengthen our wills, that undiscouraged we may face duty as high privilege. Grant us the confidence of Jesus who set His face steadfastly to do Thy will. In His Name we pray. Amen.

Our Father, we thank Thee for Jesus Christ our Saviour and Friend, through whom Thou hast revealed the strength and beauty of faith. We thank Thee for His life of prayer and trust, of courage without thought of self, of fearless devotion to duty. Grant unto us, we beseech Thee, such a faith that trusting in Thee we may cast out every fear, and overcome selfish desire. Teach us to speak true, live pure, and right the wrong, for Jesus' sake. Amen.

For a Christian Attitude Toward Others

O God of love and mercy, help me to be slow to condemn others for their frailties and swift to recognize and mourn my own. May I never forget the understanding heart of Him who wrote on the ground and gave an erring life another chance. Because I have been forgiven, help me to forgive. Fortify me with strength to lead others nearer Thee, through Jesus Christ the Lord. Amen.

For Making Right Choices

Lord of our inner life, where choices are made, help us to guard the citadel of freedom which Thou hast put in our souls. Keep us from making foolish choices which lead to slavery or to a character which is less than our best. May Christ so dominate our hearts that in our work and recreation and friendship we shall choose to do His will and share His abundant life by joyously living and sacrificing for the common good. Thus may we help in the coming of Thy Kingdom. Amen.

Our Father, guide us by Thy voice within. Often there seems to be no light on the path and we long for Thee, O Light of light. Mistrusting our own powers we crave assurance that Thou canst use us in the service of others, for we accept that as the true way of life. Release us from the bonds of selfishness, free us from fears, and lead us forth to work for the Kingdom of God in the glad and valiant spirit of Jesus, our great Leader. Amen.

Father,
The path ahead is dark,
And we know not where Thou wouldst have us to go.
Give us, oh, give us, Thy gracious guidance
And a tranquil trust in Thy love,
That we may walk forward through the gloom,
Unfaltering, fearless, and confident,
Having within us that divine light
Which maketh clear as day the darkest midnight,
Guiding the traveler who shall trust in Thee
Safe through impenetrable forests and ever trackless mountains.

— J. S. Hoyland, in *A Book of Prayers for Youth.*
Used by permission of Association Press.

Prayer of Dedication (Easter)

O God, help us to walk with Jesus and have His mind. May we follow Him all the way, even unto Calvary. Show us the meaning of the cross, and cast its shadow over our lives. Help us to be courageous enough to face the fate of the cross and to give our lives for the cause He loved. We know that all those who sincerely try to live as He lived and to teach His message will also find a cross atop the hill. Strengthen us, O God, to follow this way with confidence and faith. Grant that through our suffering and sacrifice we may understand the Easter message and claim true discipleship with Him. O may the Easter glory rest upon us today, and may new life be born within us. In the victory of Thy Son we go forward to victory in our own life, and He dwells with us always. May He transform us as He transformed His first disciples, and may we spread His truth abroad today, in His Name. Amen.

— Richard K. Morton, in *A Book of Prayers for Young People.* Copyright, 1935.
Used by permission of Abingdon-Cokesbury Press.

Litany of Dedication

LEADER: O God, who by Thine own will created the world and all that is therein, Thou art working in the world and in the lives of Thy children today, even as in the past.

RESPONSE: Create within us a desire to know Thy will, our Father.

LEADER: Thou has made man after Thine own image and hast breathed into him Thy breath of eternal life, and hast given him the power to think, to will, and to do.

RESPONSE: May our thoughts and our actions be the channels of Thy will, our Father.

LEADER: Truly the fields are white unto harvest and the laborers are too few. In the world, in the Church, and in the daily contacts of life there is need for those who will fulfill Thy purpose and Thy plan.

RESPONSE: May we so live and work that Thy Kingdom shall come and Thy will shall be done, our Father.

LEADER: We have in Thy Son, Jesus Christ, the perfect revelation of Thy will, O God. We hear Him telling us how to live; we see Him in His ministry of love; and in the crisis hour of His life we hear Him say, "Not my will, but thine, be done." Hear us as in the dedication of our lives and wills we pray.

RESPONSE:

"Take Thou ourselves, O Lord, heart, mind, and will;
Through our surrendered souls Thy plans fulfill.
We yield ourselves to Thee — time, talents, all;
We hear, and henceforth heed, Thy sovereign call."

For the Church

On the mountain, by the seashore, in discouraged homes, on the roadside,
Thou didst call the high and the low to enter into life.
No prodigal was too far away,
None too wrapt in self-praise,
None too base,
None too good to miss the invitation.
As in Thine eye all were kin,
All children of earth, and yet, the children of God,
So help us, Thy latter servants,
To uphold the ancient welcome of the Church.
Let the joyous there double their rejoicing;
The deserted find a Friend;
The lonely discover One who sticketh closer than a brother.
Aid us to make Thy Church a praise in the earth,
To keep wide her doors to all questing and wistful spirits,
A refuge for all driven or distressed,
A source of strength for the least, last son of men,
A bringer of salvation to home and nation;
Through Jesus Christ, our Lord.

— George Stewart, in *A Face to the Sky*. Used by permission of Association Press.

Guidance for Prayer on the Work Problem

That we may prepare ourselves as thoroughly as possible for getting work.
That we may share work as we are able.
That we may really sympathize with the unemployed.
That we may inform ourselves about labor conditions and work for the passage of fair labor laws.
That we may avoid the feeling that the world owes us a living.
That we may keep our faith in God even if we cannot find work.

Prayer of an Unemployed Man

Here in the quiet of my room, O God,
I come to Thee for friendship; to feel
That Someone is with me, though unseen.
All day I have seen a multitude of people,
But I am still lonely and hungry for human cheer.

No life has touched mine in understanding;
No hand has clasped mine in friendship;
My heart is empty and my hands are idle.
Help me to feel Thy presence,
So that the disappointment of this day
Shall not overwhelm me.

Keep me from becoming cynical and bitter;
Keep me warm and human, and set a new faith
Before my eyes — a new hope to live by
And a new spirit with which to overcome discouragements.
Guide me to that very necessary thing
Of life — work;
Abide with me and be my Friend.

In the Name of Him who went about
Doing good. Amen.

— W. C. Ackerly.

For Schools and Colleges

Our heavenly Father, Thou hast enriched our lives with the joy and power of learning. From Thy wisdom comes all knowledge.

Wilt Thou grant Thy direction and blessing upon all schools where youth gathers to seek the better way of truth and understanding.

May teachers first find in Christian character the supreme aim of all teaching, and so impart the facts and principles of knowledge that Christ's life may be formed in those they teach.

May science shed more light on the old things of God so that teacher and taught may together walk in that path of learning that shineth more and more unto the perfect day of spiritual understanding. In Christ's Name. Amen.

God of all wisdom, grant us this day knowledge of Thy truth.

Lead us into closer fellowship with Thy Son, Jesus Christ, our Master and Teacher, that we may know the Way, the Truth, and the Life.

Upon schools, colleges, and all institutions where youth is in training, be pleased to bestow the guidance of Thy Holy Spirit.

Give us courage; give us patience; give us joy as we work for Thy Kingdom; forgive every doubt; keep us faithful; and Thine shall be the glory. Amen.

For Christian Brotherhood

O Lord, our Christ, may we have Thy mind and Thy spirit; make us instruments of Thy peace; where there is hatred, let us sow love; where there is injury, pardon; where there is discord, union; where there is doubt, faith; where there is despair, hope; where there is darkness, light; and where there is sadness, joy. O divine Master, grant that we may not so much seek to be consoled as to console; to be understood, as to understand; to be loved, as to love; for it is in giving that we receive, it is in pardoning that we are pardoned, and it is in dying that we are born to eternal life. Amen.

— Saint Francis of Assisi.

LITANY:

For the diversities of gifts which Thou hast given to the races of mankind, with the possibilities which these afford of each making its peculiar contribution to the common wealth of all,

We thank Thee, O Lord.

For the increase of social sympathy, and the swelling tide of indignation against greed and those forces and customs which thwart and oppress and hold in subjection vast multitudes of Thy children,

We thank Thee, O Lord.

That commerce and industry both within our own nation, and between the several nations of the earth, may be so imbued with the spirit of co-operation and service that all may have their fair share of wealth and freedom and thus enter more fully into opportunity for health, happiness, and abundant living,

We beseech Thee, O God.

That the spirit of good will, of tolerance, and of sacrificial service may more and more prevail in our own hearts, and in the hearts of men everywhere, and that the desire and purpose of human brotherhood may more and more dominate the minds and wills of men of all nations and races,

We implore and beseech Thee, O God.

— Wade Crawford Barclay, in *Challenge and Power*. Copyright, 1936.
Used by permission of Abingdon-Cokesbury Press.

O God, Thy love unites men in brotherhood and common purposes. In love for Thee we would draw closer to youth of all races, creeds, and lands, and we would study the problems of life together and jointly seek for truth and light. . . . As we prepare for leadership in the days that are to come, may we do our part to banish war and strife and hate. May we settle our differences with calmness and love, and may we strengthen each other for the tasks that lie ahead. Make us worthy of friendships everywhere, and may these help to make our communities, our state, and our nation better. May this spirit of friendship dominate our churches and societies that we may better serve Thee and hasten the coming of Thy Kingdom for Jesus' sake. Amen.

— Richard K. Morton, in *A Book of Prayers for Young People*. Copyright, 1935.
Used by permission of Abingdon-Cokesbury Press

For a Christian Nation

O God, we thank Thee for the lives, the service, and the sacrifice of those who died for our country. May their memory be precious to us, and may we never forget what they did nor why they did it. They met their test, and gave the last full measure of devotion, and so our country was saved.

Help us in our day, we beseech Thee, to build for them the best kind of memorial in a movement which seeks to remove forever the need of any more sacrifice like that. Help us to build monuments for them in the lives of our generation and those to come. May we remember the needs of the future, as well as the glories of the past. We bless Thee that Thou hast given our country men of consecration, courage, bravery, and unselfishness, and we ask that Thou wilt not fail our country in its need of meeting the greater crises of the present hour. May it be that all these men may not have died in vain because we live to bring about a day of peace and brotherhood and more abundant life, through the influence of the life and teachings of Thy Son, Jesus Christ. Amen.

— Richard K. Morton, in *A Book of Prayers for Young People.* Copyright, 1935.
Used by permission of Abingdon-Cokesbury Press.

O Lord, our God, the strong Father of all nations, make us truly thankful for our country; for the multitude that have lived, sacrificed, and died to make it a "land of the free and the home of the brave"; for the land of opportunity and freedom to worship God as one desires. May we as citizens of this great country so live that those who have gone on before shall not have died in vain. May our country be one great family in the brotherhood of the nations. May peace and good will abide in the hearts of all. Through Jesus Christ, our Lord. Amen.

Almighty and eternal Father, who hast made of one blood all nations and hast determined the bounds of their habitations, we beseech Thee to bless the peoples whom Thou hast created. Grant that the families of the earth may live together in the spirit of brotherhood. We pray for those who rule over us and guide our policies. May they lead us in the paths of peace and justice. Let this great nation, which Thou hast wonderfully blest, take its place among the peoples of the earth as one that serveth. Fill our hearts with the love of God and with understanding sympathy for all mankind. May we as a nation be ambitious to practice peace and good will. Teach us to walk in the paths of service and of sacrifice with patience and humility. We ask it in the Name and for the sake of the Saviour of men, who loved us and gave Himself for us. Amen.

God of all nations,
We beseech Thee to bring that day nearer
When our country shall be truly one,
When every barrier shall be broken down,

When no man shall work for his own selfish good,
When no man shall defraud or oppress his neighbor,
When no man shall reckon his neighbor worse than himself,
When none shall be despised or outcast,
But all shall be free to work in equal manhood for
Thee and their country.

— J. S. Hoyland, in *A Book of Prayers for Youth.* Used by permission of Association Press.

For the Kingdom of God

O Jesus Christ, the Lord of all good life, who hast called us to build the city of God: do Thou give unto us keenness and clarity of spiritual, ethical vision. Help us daily to know more of Thee, and of Thy purpose and will for men. By the power of Thy Spirit help us to show forth Thyself to other men. Make us humble, brave, and loving. Make us ready for adventure. We do not ask that Thou wilt keep us safe, but that Thou wilt keep us loyal. From lack of reverence for truth and beauty; from prejudice and sentimentalism; from being contented with the mean and ugly; from the cowardice that dare not face new truth, the laziness contented with half-truths, and the arrogance that thinks it knows all truths; from the blasphemy of cynicism about our brethren made in the image of God; from all false pride, intolerance, and contempt; from everything in our lives and methods which may hide the true light of Thee, who art the Light of the world; from the disloyalty of being satisfied with things as they are in the Church and in the world; and from failing to share Thy indignation, O Christ, deliver us. Amen.

— Adapted from "The Kingdom, the Power, and the Glory," in *Challenge and Power*, by Wade Crawford Barclay. Copyright, 1936. Used by permission of Abingdon-Cokesbury Press.

Dear heavenly Father, we thank Thee that we are living in a time when we know more about other people than has ever been known before. We thank Thee for Jesus Christ who teaches us that all men everywhere are brothers. Help us to understand what brotherhood really means, and may it become in us all a consuming passion. That Thy purposes for all mankind may be realized, help us to put aside pride and prejudice; deliver us from hatreds that divide; unite us in the holy ministry of friendship and good will. Grant, O God, that through loving service we may take Christ and His abundant life to all. Make us faithful as children in Thy great world family through Jesus Christ our Lord. Amen.

Heavenly Father, guard with Thy care those who devote their lives to Thee in the mission field. Cheer them in loneliness, be near them in fever and sickness, uphold them in temptation, comfort them in sorrow and weariness, and fill them with joy amid all their work; for the sake of Jesus Christ Thy Son, our Lord. Amen.

— *School Worship.*

Lord of the harvest and of the lives of men, according to Thine own word we pray Thee to send forth laborers into the harvest. Long ago Thou sawest it ready for reaping; Thou seest it ready today. Thy Church cannot excuse her delay by the thought that the harvest is not yet ripe. She may not say that there are yet four months and then will come harvest. We hear Thy clear voice speaking still: "Lift up your eyes, and look on the fields, that they are white already unto harvest." Help us to lift up our eyes and look, and then help us to lay down our lives at Thy feet with Isaiah's prayer: "Here am I; send me." In Christ's Name we ask it. Amen.

LEADER: For all who bear the burden of unrequited toil; who labor before the dawn and tarry working till the night is spent,

RESPONSE: We pray in sympathy, O God.

LEADER: For all children who are deprived of the right of play, and for grown men and women who break beneath the load too heavy to be borne,

RESPONSE: We entreat Thy mercy and Thy help, O God.

LEADER: With those who eat their bread in loneliness or sorrow, to whom the days bring bitter grief and unending sorrow,

RESPONSE: We would enter into fellowship, O God.

UNISON: For all who are oppressed by the wrongs or injustice of their fellow men; for all who dwell in darkness and the prisonhouse of sin; for all who for any cause have failed to enter into their heritage of life and light as children of God, we intercede before Thy throne, O God. Give unto us of Thy spirit of love and compassion and in Thy Name may we do our part to undo the bands of the yoke and to let the oppressed go free. In the Name of Christ our Lord. Amen.

— Wade Crawford Barclay, in *Challenge and Power*. Copyright, 1936.
Used by permission of Abingdon-Cokesbury Press.

For This Universe

O God, we thank Thee for this universe, our great home; for its vastness and its riches, and for the manifoldness of the life which teems upon it and of which we are part. We praise Thee for the arching sky and the blessed winds, for the driving clouds and the constellations on high. We praise Thee for the salt sea and the running water, for the everlasting hills, for the trees, and for the grass under our feet. We thank Thee for our senses by which we can see the splendor of the morning, and hear the jubilant songs of love, and smell the breath of the springtime. Grant us, we pray Thee, a heart wide open to all this joy and beauty, and save our souls from being so steeped in care or so darkened by passion that we pass heedless and unseeing when even the thorn-bush by the wayside is aflame with the glory of God.

— Walter Rauschenbusch, in *Prayers of the Social Awakening*. Copyright by The Pilgrim Press. Used by permission.

POETRY AND PROSE FOR WORSHIP

	PAGE
A hungry man is at my door	381
But once I pass this way	371
Draw in the latchstring, lad	375
Dreams are they — but they are God's dreams	371
Earth's crammed with heaven	377
Forgive, O Lord, our severing ways	377
God hath not promised	377
God, I need Thee	378
God — let me be aware	365
He built a house; time laid it in the dust	374
He never spoke a word to me	378
He who has lived each shining day's duration	368
I believe in the wonder of the out-of-doors	370
I dream'd in a dream	376
I know not by what methods rare	380
I paused last eve beside the blacksmith's door	368
I read in a book	380
I sought His love in sun and stars	364
If Jesus Christ is a man	379
If people are more precious than all else	370
If we work upon marble, it will perish	373
In men whom men condemn as ill	379
Is true Freedom but to break	379
Let me but live my life from year to year	369
Let me put by some hour of every day	369
Let us have a Church that dares	377
Life is a great, worthy, holy, and divine thing	372
Lord, what a change within us	365
Make me too brave to lie or be unkind	366
More things are wrought by prayer	372
My God, Thou art a God of strength and beauty	363
No one could tell me what my soul might be	368
Not what, but Whom, I do believe	366
Not what we give, but what we share	381
O God, through all the life that will fill today	378
One ship drives east, another west	378
Our purpose	374
Pray, brothers, pray	377
So many things I do not understand	367
Teach us today	372
The builder who first bridged Niagara's gorge	365
The call of the hour	376
The Eternal is reigning, robed in majesty	362
The spirit of self-sacrifice	378
The world is one; we cannot live apart	375
The world stands out on either side	376
These are the gifts I ask	367
This generation has no alternative to living dangerously	375
Thou must be true thyself	379
Thy Kingdom come	380
Thy Will be done	364
To every man there openeth a Way	380
To man, it seemed that Evil had prevailed	362
Today I have grown taller from walking with the trees	369
Use all your hidden forces	370
We are all blind	379
We tread upon Thy carpets in the meadows	363
When Jesus came to Golgotha	364
Work! Thank God for the might of it	373

POETRY AND PROSE FOR WORSHIP

The Two Views

To man, it seemed that Evil had prevailed,
That His fair life had altogether failed,
And nought was left but what the Cross impaled; —
But God saw otherwise!

They would have hailed Him King, and with acclaim,
Upon the wings of His far-reaching fame,
Have swept the land like a devouring flame;
But God saw otherwise!

It seemed as though His life had gone for nought, —
Nothing to show for that long battle fought,
But a pale prisoner to the gibbet brought; —
But God saw otherwise!

No lasting good seemed ever like to come
Of all His sowing, — neither fruit nor bloom,
Instead — a felon's cross, an alien tomb; —
But God saw otherwise!

We too, at times, come nigh to lose our hope,
When with life's evils we no more can cope,
And in the dark with heavy hearts we grope;
But God saw otherwise!

— John Oxenham, in *"Gentlemen — The King!"* Used by permission.

The Eternal is reigning, robed in majesty;
the Eternal is robed with a girdle of power.
Thou hast steadied and settled the world,
thy throne stands firm from of old,
thou art from all eternity.
The floods may storm, O thou Eternal,
the floods may storm aloud,
the floods may storm and thunder;
but high above the roaring billows,
high above the ocean breakers,
the Eternal stands supreme.

— Ps. 93: 1–4. From *The Bible: A New Translation,* by James Moffatt.
Used by permission of Harper & Brothers, publishers.

We Tread Upon Thy Carpets

We tread upon Thy carpets in the meadows,
We look into Thy mirror by the lakes;
We trace Thy hand above us in the shadows,
We eat the daily bread our Father breaks.

The voices of the waters are Thy singing,
The bending of the grass Thy passing by;
The thunders of the clouds Thy church bells ringing,
The wrappings of the fogs reveal Thee nigh.

The mountains are the gatherings of Thy glory,
The fountains are the flowings of Thy grace;
The ripples in the rock beds tell Thy story,
The settings of the sun reflect Thy face.

We see Thy beauty beaming in the dewdrops,
We mark Thy covenant bow on land and sea.
We hear Thy footsteps moving through the tree tops,
And everywhere Thy voice, "I am with thee."

— Gerrit Verkuyl. Used by permission.

Thanksgiving

My God, Thou art a God of strength and beauty,
Thou art the mighty Keeper of the seas;
Thou givest me my life, my faith, my seeing —
And I, so small — what can I give for these?

Thou givest me the sun, the hills, the rainfall,
Clear eyes to see the daybreak and the night,
A mind to fathom truth and follow straightly —
And I, so small — what can I give of might?

Thou givest me the love of little children,
The quiet shining of the passing day,
The flow of peace within a burning heartache —
And I, so small — what can I give or say?

And then, as though Thou countest not these blessings,
Thou sendest Thine own Son to die for me —
And I, so small — oh, humbly and with gladness,
I give my all — I give my life to Thee!

— *Peter Pan.* Used by permission of *The Chicago Tribune.*

Indifference

When Jesus came to Golgotha they hanged Him on a tree,
They drave great nails through hands and feet, and made a Calvary;
They crowned Him with a crown of thorns, red were His wounds and deep,
For those were crude and cruel days, and human flesh was cheap.

When Jesus came to Birmingham, they simply passed Him by,
They never hurt a hair of Him, they only let Him die;
For men had grown more tender, and they would not give Him pain,
They only just passed down the street, and left Him in the rain.

Still Jesus cried, "Forgive them for they know not what they do,"
And still it rained the winter rain that drenched Him through and through;
The crowds went home and left the streets without a soul to see,
And Jesus crouched against a wall and cried for Calvary.

— G. A. Studdert Kennedy, in *Unutterable Beauty*. Used by permission of Harper & Brothers, publishers.

The Search

I sought His love in sun and stars,
And where the wild seas roll,
And found it not. As mute I stood,
Fear overwhelmed my soul;
But when I gave to one in need,
I found the Lord of Love indeed.

I sought His love in lore of books,
In charts of science' skill;
They left me orphaned as before —
His love eluded still;
Then in despair I breathed a prayer;
The Lord of Love was standing there!

— Thomas Curtis Clark. Used by permission.

Thy Will be done. No greater words than these
Can pass from human lips, than these which rent
Their way through agony and bloody sweat,
And broke the silence of Gethsemane
To save the world from sin.

— G. A. Studdert Kennedy, in *The Wicket Gate*. Used by permission of Harper & Brothers, publishers.

Prayer

Lord, what a change within us one short hour
  Spent in Thy presence will prevail to make!
  What heavy burdens from our bosoms take!
What parchèd grounds refresh as with a shower!
We kneel, and all around us seems to lower;
  We rise, and all, the distant and the near,
  Stands forth in sunny outline, brave and clear;
We kneel, how weak! we rise, how full of power!
  Why, therefore, should we do ourselves this wrong,
  Or others — that we are not always strong —
That we are sometimes overborne with care —
  That we should ever weak or heartless be,
Anxious or troubled — when with us is prayer,
  And joy and strength and courage are with Thee?

— Richard C. Trench.

God — let me be aware.
Stab my soul fiercely with other's pain,
Let me walk seeing horror and stain.
Let my hands, groping, find other hands.
Give me the heart that divines, understands.
Give me the courage, wounded, to fight.
Flood me with knowledge, drench me with light.
Please, keep me eager just to do my share.
God — let me be aware.

— Miriam Teichner.

The builder who first bridged Niagara's gorge,
Before he swung the cable, shore to shore,
Sent out across the gulf his venturing kite,
Bearing a slender cord for unseen hands
To grasp upon the further cliff and draw
A greater cord, and then a greater yet;
Till at last across the chasm swung
The cable — then the mighty bridge in air!

So we may send our little timid thought
Across the void, out to God's reaching hands —
Send out our love and faith to thread the deep,
Thought after thought until the little cord
Has greatened to a chain no chance can break,
And — we are anchored to the Infinite!

— Edwin Markham. Used by permission of Virgil Markham.

Credo

Not what, but Whom, I do believe,
That, in my darkest hour of need,
Hath comfort that no mortal creed
To mortal man may give; —
Not what, but Whom!
For Christ is more than all the creeds,
And His full life of gentle deeds
Shall all the creeds outlive.

Not what I do believe, but Whom!
Who walks beside me in the gloom?
Who shares the burden wearisome?
Who all the dim way doth illume,
And bids me look beyond the tomb
The larger life to live? —
Not what I do believe,
But Whom!
Not what
But Whom!

— John Oxenham, in *Bees in Amber*. Used by permission.

A Prayer

Make me too brave to lie or be unkind.
Make me too understanding, too, to mind
The little hurts companions give, and friends,
The careless hurts that no one quite intends.
Make me too thoughtful to hurt others so.
Help me to know
The inmost hearts of those for whom I care,
Their secret wishes, all the loads they bear,
That I may add my courage to their own.
May I make lonely folks feel less alone
And happy ones a little happier yet.
May I forget
What ought to be forgotten; and recall
Unfailingly, all
That ought to be recalled, each kindly thing,
Forgetting what might sting.
To all upon my way,
Day after day,
Let me be joy, be hope! Let my life sing!

— Mary Carolyn Davies. Used by permission

All I Need to Know

So many things I do not understand —
The throbbing mysteries of infinite creation,
I long to rend the veil that hangs between,
Yet, linger, torn with mingled fear and exultation.

I see the sunrise that proclaims the dawn,
And my being marvels at the sight;
From what wondrous realm beyond our ken
Did God produce the wonder that is light?

I ponder long the velvet, jeweled night,
And, dreaming, speculate upon the stars:
What lies behind their diamond points of light
That beam so kindly on this world of ours?

My heart is thrilled at sight of ocean's roll,
As rhythmic tides clutch wildly at the sand.
What secret torment goads its restless soul,
Or does it come and go when God commands?

Yet, why ponder I the essence of it all,
Or question still the wonders of His hand?
God holds the world secure within His thrall,
That is all I need to know or understand.

— Wilma Dalby, in *Youth*. Used by permission.

These are the gifts I ask
Of Thee, Spirit serene:
Strength for the daily task,
Courage to face the road,
Good cheer to help me bear the traveler's load,
And, for the hours of rest that come between,
An inward joy in all things heard and seen.
These are the sins I fain
Would have Thee take away:
Malice, and cold disdain,
Hot anger, sullen hate,
Scorn of the lowly, envy of the great,
And discontent that casts a shadow gray
On all the brightness of the common day.

— Henry van Dyke. Used by permission of Charles Scribner's Sons, publishers, and Tertius van Dyke.

No one could tell me what my soul might be;
I searched for God, and God eluded me;
I sought my brother out and found all three,
My soul, my God, and all humanity.

— Firdausi.

I paused last eve beside the blacksmith's door,
And heard the anvil ring, the vesper's chime,
And looking in I saw upon the floor
Old hammers, worn with beating years of time.
"How many anvils have you had?" said I,
"To wear and batter all these hammers so?"
"Just one," he answered. Then with twinkling eye:
"The anvil wears the hammers out, you know."
And so, I thought, the anvil of God's Word
For ages skeptics' blows have beat upon,
But though the noise of falling blows was heard
The anvil is unchanged; the hammers gone.

— John Clifford.

Praise

He who has lived each shining day's duration
As best he could,
Who meets the dawn and views it with elation
And finds it good,

Whose eyes are lifted to the high-noon glory
Of sky and sun,
Whose ears are tuned to catch earth's old sweet story
When day is done —

I think his God accepts it as high tribute,
As honest praise,
This sane, light-hearted, trusting way of living
His gift of days.

For being glad is one sure way of praying
As on men trod,
And happiness, a certain way of saying:
"We thank Thee, God."

— Grace Noll Crowell, in *Songs of Faith.* Used by permission of Harper & Brothers, publishers.

Life

Let me but live my life from year to year,
With forward face and unreluctant soul;
Not hurrying to, nor turning from, the goal;
Not mourning for the things that disappear
In the dim past, nor holding back in fear
From what the future veils; but with a whole
And happy heart, that pays its toll
To Youth and Age, and travels on with cheer.

So let the way wind up the hill or down,
O'er rough or smooth, the journey will be joy:
Still seeking what I sought when but a boy,
New friendship, high adventure, and a crown,
My heart will keep the courage of the quest,
And hope the road's last turn will be the best.

— Henry van Dyke. Used by permission of Charles Scribner's Sons, publishers, and Tertius van Dyke.

Let us put by some hour of every day
For holy things — whether it be when dawn
Peers through the window pane, or when noon
Flames, like a burnished topaz, in the vault,
Or when the thrush pours in the ear of eve
Its plaintive melody; some little hour
Wherein to hold rapt converse with the soul,
From sordidness and self a sanctuary,
Swept by the winnowings of unseen things,
And touched by the White Light ineffable!

— Clinton Scollard. Used by permission of Jessie B. Rittenhouse.

Good Company

Today I have grown taller from walking with the trees,
The seven sister poplars who go softly in a line;
And I think my heart is whiter for its parley with a star
That trembled out at nightfall and hung above the pine.

The call note of a red bird from the cedars in the dusk
Woke his happy mate within me to an answer free and fine;
And a sudden angel beckoned from a column of blue smoke —
Lord, who am I that they should stoop — these holy folk of Thine?

— Karle Wilson Baker, in *Blue Smoke*. Used by permission of Yale University Press, publishers.

Attainment

Use all your hidden forces. Do not miss
The purpose of this life, and do not wait
For circumstance to mold or change your fate.
In your own self lies destiny. Let this
Vast truth cast out all fear, all prejudice,
All hesitation. Know that you are great,
Great with divinity. So dominate
Environment, and enter into bliss.
Love largely and hate nothing. Hold no aim
That does not chord with universal good.
Hear what the voices of the silence say,
All joys are yours if you put forth your claim,
Once let the spiritual laws be understood,
Material things must answer and obey.

— Ella Wheeler Wilcox. Used by permission of W. B. Conkey Company, publisher.

I believe in the wonder of the out-of-doors,
in the inspiration of the stars;
I believe in the strength of the hills,
in the silence of the night, and in
the music of the birds and trees;
I believe that my body was made for action,
that my mind was made for thinking, and
that my heart was made for loving.

— R. C. Stoll.

If people are more precious than all else, does that not mean that the secrets of a truly successful use of the gift of life are all bound up in learning how to live our lives in right relationship to the lives of other people? We need not tax our minds or burden our hearts by learning a long list of things which we must or must not do. The *whole* law of life, Jesus tells us, is summed up in the Commandment to love the people who come into our lives: the Great Person, God, and the other persons, our neighbors, who are sharers with us in the gift of life. In other words, if we have learned how to live in rich and glad friendship with God and other people, we have learned Jesus' own rule "for abundant life." For the problem of friendship is the problem of life itself. He who has learned to love — and only he — has learned to live.

— Henry Churchill King.

God's Dreams

Dreams are they — but they are God's dreams!
Shall we decry them and scorn them?
That men shall love one another,
That white shall call black man brother,
That greed shall pass from the market place,
That lust shall yield to love for the race,
That man shall meet with God face to face —
Dreams are they all,
  But shall we despise them —
  God's dreams!

Dreams are they — to become man's dreams!
Can we say nay as they claim us?
That men shall cease from their hating,
That war shall soon be abating,
That the glory of kings and lords shall pale,
That the pride of dominion and power shall fail,
That the love of humanity shall prevail —
Dreams are they all,
  But shall we despise them —
  God's dreams!

— Thomas Curtis Clark. Used by permission.

The Pilgrim Way

But once I pass this way,
And then — no more.
But once — and then, the Silent Door
Swings on its hinges, —
Opens . . . closes, —
And no more
I pass this way.
So while I may,
With all my might,
I will essay
Sweet comfort and delight,
To all I meet upon the Pilgrim Way.
For no man travels twice
The Great Highway,
That climbs through Darkness up to Light, —
Through Night
To Day.

— John Oxenham, in *Bees in Amber*. Used by permission.

Life is a great, worthy, holy, and divine thing. Life is to be used as a sacred trust. Life is to be a cup out of which thirsty men and women are to be given drink. Our lives are bread, by which hungry men and women are to be fed. We are in the world, like our Master, not to be ministered unto, but to minister, and to give our lives as ransoms for many.

— Robert E. Speer.

More things are wrought by prayer
Than this world dreams of. Wherefore, let thy voice
Rise like a fountain for me night and day.
For what are men better than sheep or goats
That nourish a blind life within the brain,
If, knowing God, they lift not hands of prayer
Both for themselves and those who call them friend?
For so the whole round earth is every way
Bound by gold chains about the feet of God.

— Alfred Lord Tennyson.

Self-Control

Teach us today,
O Master,
To rule ourselves,
To be stern, harsh, merciless
To our bodies and minds,
To discipline our lives with an iron hand,
So that no sloth of ours,
No craven despair,
No self-indulgence,
No failure of sympathy and imagination,
May mar the work of Thy Kingdom.
Teach us today,
O Master,
That true self-sacrifice
Which is yet a sacrament of joy,
Which never restrains the rich current of life
With narrow-souled, puritanical barriers,
But guides it, with steadfast purpose,
Into one broad and generous channel —
The channel of that great Will of Thine,
Which is, forever, abundance of life unto men.

— J. S. Hoyland.

Work: A Song of Triumph

Work!
Thank God for the might of it,
The ardor, the urge, the delight of it —
Work that springs from the heart's desire,
Setting the brain and the soul on fire —
Oh, what is so good as the heat of it,
And what is so glad as the beat of it,
And what is so kind as the stern command,
Challenging brain and heart and hand? . . .

Work!
Thank God for the swing of it,
For the clamoring, hammering ring of it,
Passion of labor daily hurled
On the mighty anvils of the world.
Oh, what is so fierce as the flame of it?
And what is so huge as the aim of it?
Thundering on through dearth and doubt,
Calling the plan of the Maker out.
Work, the Titan: Work, the Friend,
Shaping the earth to a glorious end,
Draining the swamps and blasting the hills,
Doing whatever the Spirit wills —
Rending a continent apart,
To answer the dream of the Master heart.
Thank God for a world where none may shirk —
Thank God for the splendor of work!

– Angela Morgan. Used by permission of the publishers,
Dodd, Mead & Company, Inc.

If we work upon marble, it will perish;
If we work upon brass, time will efface it;
If we rear temples, they will crumble into dust;
But, if we work upon immortal souls, if we imbue them with principles, with the just fear of God and the love of fellow man, we engrave on those tablets something which will brighten all eternity.

— Daniel Webster.

Our Purpose

Our purpose
is to become such complete disciples of Christ
that we will discover God's will for our lives
and do it.
Therefore:
We commit ourselves to Christ
and purpose to acquire a dynamic faith
through Christian experience, worship, and study.
We dedicate our lives
to the expression of this faith
by word and deed,
seeking to work with those of like purpose
and inviting others to join with us
in building today
for a Christian world.

— Adopted by the delegates at the Lake Geneva, Wisconsin, Conference on Westminster Fellowship.

The Greatest Work

He built a house; time laid it in the dust;
He wrote a book, its title now forgot;
He ruled a city, but his name is not
On any table graven, or where rust
Can gather from disuse, or marble bust.
He took a child from out a wretched cot,
Who on the state dishonor might have brought,
And reared him to the Christian's hope and trust.
The boy, to manhood grown, became a light
To many souls, and preached for human need
The wondrous love of the Omnipotent.
The work has multiplied like stars at night
When darkness deepens; every noble deed
Lasts longer than a granite monument.

— Author Unknown.

The World Is One

The world is one; we cannot live apart,
To earth's remotest races we are kin;
God made the generations of one blood;
Man's separation is a sign of sin.

What though we solve the secret of the stars,
Or from the vibrant ether pluck a song,
Can this for all man's tyranny atone
While Mercy weeps and waits and suffers long?

Put up the sword, its day of anguish past;
Disarm the forts, and then, the war-flags furled,
Forever keep the air without frontiers,
The great, free, friendly highway of the world.

So that at last to rapture men may come,
And hear again the music of the spheres,
And stand erect, illumined, radiant, free,
The travail and the triumph of the years.

— Hinton White. Used by permission of *Boston Evening Transcript.*

This generation has no alternative to living dangerously. It merely has the choice between various perilous ways. If religious revolutionists are to retain confidence in nonwarlike procedures, and if they are to persevere in their efforts to socialize basic industries, they must store up resources upon which they can draw in hours of crisis. Fortunately, vast reservoirs of power are accessible. Communion with the eternal God and fellowship with comrades in struggle multiply a man's strength by ten or by a hundred or by a thousand.

— Kirby Page. Used by permission.

Draw In the Latchstring, Lad

Draw in the latchstring, lad, and close the door,
Lest those who faint without from toil and pain
Shall rob thee of thine own too meager store.
Can one poor crust sustain those famished forms?
Can one poor shelter save them from the storms?
And surely those who wait and hope in vain
Shall turn and rend thee when thou hast no more,
So — draw the latchstring in and close the door.

Such is the world's advice,
But — there was One who flung it open wide —
And He was crucified.

— Jessica Nelson North, in *A Warning.*

I dream'd in a dream I saw a city invincible to the attacks of the whole of the
rest of the earth,
I dream'd that was the new city of Friends,
Nothing was greater there than the quality of robust love, it led the rest,
It was seen every hour in the actions of the men of that city,
And in all their looks and words.

— Walt Whitman, in *Leaves of Grass*. Copyright, 1934. Used by permission of Doubleday, Doran and Company, Inc., publishers.

The world stands out on either side
No wider than the heart is wide;
Above the world is stretched the sky —
No higher than the soul is high.
The heart can push the sea and land
Farther away on either hand;
The soul can split the sky in two,
And let the face of God shine through.
But East and West will pinch the heart
That cannot keep them pushed apart;
And he whose soul is flat — the sky
Will cave in on him by and by.

— Edna St. Vincent Millay, in *Renascence and Other Poems*. Copyright, 1917, by Edna St. Vincent Millay. Harper & Brothers, publishers.

The Church's Challenge to Youth

The call of the hour is not for lower but for higher standards of Christianity. . . . Lowering the standard spells defeat. The bill of exaction cannot be satisfied by writing in fifty or eighty where the requirement calls for one hundred.

This old world can never be evangelized by Christians who compromise. The cross of Christ was not entwined with flowers. Those who carry that cross will feel its sharp angles and corners. Hooks baited with a soft gospel adapted to the natural senses and tastes will never catch that type of souls of which martyrs are made. Christ is not offering pillows of ease but calling for pillars of power. . . .

To You, O Youth, Christ is throwing this challenge for a great Christian crusade for plainer living, higher thinking, and sacrificial service.

To You, O Youth, Your Church looks for that day when you shall place the supremacy of human values above all other values of life and make Christ the dominating motive although that may involve you in social ostracism, financial hardship, personal sacrifice, and suffering.

"If any man would come after me, let him deny himself, and take up his cross, and follow me."

— John Bunyan Smith. Used by permission.

Forgive, O Lord, our severing ways,
The separate altars that we raise,
The varying tongues that speak thy praise!

Suffice it now. In time to be
Shall one great temple rise to Thee,
Thy church our broad humanity.

White flowers of love its walls shall climb,
Sweet bells of peace shall ring its chime,
Its days shall all be holy time.

The hymn, long sought, shall then be heard,
The music of the world's accord,
Confessing Christ, the inward word!

That song shall swell from shore to shore,
One faith, one love, one hope restore
The seamless garb that Jesus wore!

— John Greenleaf Whittier. Used by permission of the authorized publishers, Houghton Mifflin Company.

Earth's crammed with heaven
And every common bush afire with God;
But only he who sees takes off his shoes,
The rest sit round it and pluck blackberries.

— Elizabeth Barrett Browning.

God's Promise

God hath not promised
Skies always blue,
Flower-strewn pathways,
All our lives through;
God hath not promised
Sun without rain,
Joy without sorrow,
Peace without pain.

But God hath promised
Strength for the day,
Rest for the labor,
Light for the way;
Grace for the trials,
Help from above,
Unfailing sympathy,
Undying love.

— Annie Johnson Flint. Copyright by Evangelical Publishers, Toronto, Canada. Used by permission.

Destiny

Pray, brothers, pray!
Destiny
Is stalking today
Along the way;
And in the fight for the right
We need keener sight, clearer light
Than yesterday.

— Laura Austin Dickinson. Used by permission of *Advance*.

The Christian Church

Let us have a Church that dares
Imitate the heroism of Jesus;
Seek inspiration as He sought it;
Judge the past as He;
Act on the present like Him;
Pray as He prayed;
Work as He wrought;
Live as He lived.

— Theodore Parker

Simon the Cyrenian Speaks

He never spoke a word to me,
And yet He called my name,
He never gave a sign to me,
And yet I knew and came.

At first I said, "I will not bear
His cross upon my back;
He only seeks to place it there
Because my skin is black."

But He was dying for a dream,
And He was very weak,
And in His eyes there shone a gleam
Men journey far to seek.

It was Himself my pity bought:
I did for Christ alone
What all of Rome could not have wrought
With bruise of lash or stone.

— Countee Cullen, in *Color*. Used by permission of Harper & Brothers, publishers.

The spirit of self-sacrifice
Stays not to count the price.

Christ did not of His mere abundance cast
Into the empty treasury of man's store:
The First and Last
Gave until even He could give no more;
His very living,
Such was Christ's giving.

— Anna E. Hamilton.

Grant Me This!

O God,
Through all the life that will fill today,
May I keep my head:
Never aloof from friends in work,
Nor lost to self in play,
Morning, night, and noon,
May I keep myself in authority.
May happiness be mine
But not at cost of sadness to another.
Let eagerness to learn
And willingness to meet responsibility,
And clean ambition, too,
Become my habits.
I would not be ruled by chance,
Or follow always where another leads the way;
But learn to steer my course
By compass points of reason.
And grant me this, my final,
My most earnest prayer of all:
Teach me to know my God.
Amen.

— James L. Waller.

The Winds of Fate

One ship drives east, another west,
With the selfsame winds that blow,
'Tis the set of the sails and not the gales
That tells them the way to go.

Like the winds of the sea are the winds of fate,
As we voyage along through life,
'Tis the set of the soul that decides the goal
And not the calm or the strife.

— Ella Wheeler Wilcox. Used by permission of W. B. Conkey Company, publisher.

God, I need Thee.
When morning crowds the night away
And tasks of waking seize my mind;
I need Thy poise.

God, I need Thee.
When love is hard to see
Amid the ugliness and slime,
I need Thy eyes.

God, I need Thee.
When clashes come with those
Who walk the way with me,
I need Thy smile.

God, I need Thee.
When the path to take before me lies
I see it . . . courage flees —
I need Thy faith.

God, I need Thee.
When the day's work is done,
Tired, discouraged, wasted,
I need Thy rest.

— Howard Thurman. Used by permission.

The Song of a Heathen

(Sojourning in Galilee, A.D. 32)

If Jesus Christ is a man —
And only a man, — I say
That of all mankind I cleave to Him
And to Him will I cleave alway.

If Jesus Christ is a god —
And the only God, — I swear
I will follow Him through heaven and hell,
The earth, the sea, and the air!

— Richard Watson Gilder. Used by permission of the authorized publishers, Houghton Mifflin Company.

Be True

Thou must be true thyself
If thou the truth wouldst teach;
Thy soul must overflow if thou
Another's soul wouldst reach!
It needs the overflow of heart
To give the lips full speech.

Think truly, and thy thoughts
Shall the world's famine feed;
Speak truly, and each word of thine
Shall be a fruitful seed;
Live truly, and thy life shall be
A great and noble creed.

— Horatius Bonar.

In men whom men condemn as ill
I find so much of goodness still,
In men whom men pronounce divine
I find so much of sin and blot,
I do not dare to draw a line
Between the two, where God has not.

— Joaquin Miller. Used by permission of Juanita Miller.

Man-Making

We are all blind, until we see
That in the human plan
Nothing is worth the making if
It does not make the man.

Why build these cities glorious
If man unbuilded goes?
In vain we build the work, unless
The builder also grows.

— Edwin Markham. Used by permission of Virgil Markham.

Is true Freedom but to break
Fetters for our own dear sake,
And, with leathern hearts, forget
That we owe mankind a debt?
No! true freedom is to share
All the chains our brothers wear,
And, with heart and hand, to be
Earnest to make others free!

They are slaves who fear to speak
For the fallen and the weak;
They are slaves who will not choose
Hatred, scoffing, and abuse,
Rather than in silence shrink
From the truth they needs must think;
They are slaves who dare not be
In the right with two or three.

— James Russell Lowell. Used by permission of the authorized publishers, Houghton Mifflin Company.

Thy Kingdom Come!

Thy Kingdom come!
And quickly, Lord!
For Life is a tempestuous sea,
Where storm-winds beat unceasingly
And drive us oft away from Thee.
So, day by day,
We ever pray —
"Thy Kingdom come!
Thy Kingdom come!"

Thy Kingdom come!
Lord, till it comes,
We are but voyagers who roam
With straining eyes amid the gloom,
And seek but cannot find our home.
So, day by day,
In faith we pray —
"Thy Kingdom come!
Thy Kingdom come!"

Thy Kingdom come!
For when it comes
Earth's crying wrongs will be redressed,
And man will make his chiefest quest
The Peace of God which giveth rest.
So, day by day,
In hope we pray —
"Thy Kingdom come!
Thy Kingdom come!"

Thy Kingdom come!
Ah, grant us, Lord,
To see the day when Thou shalt reign
Supreme within the hearts of men,
And Love shall dwell on earth again!
For that, Thy Day,
We ever pray —
"Thy Kingdom come!
Thy Kingdom come!"

— John Oxenham, in "*Gentlemen — The King!*"
Used by permission.

Prayer

I know not by what methods rare,
But this I know, God answers prayer.
I know not when He sends the word
That tells us fervent prayer is heard;
I know it cometh, soon or late,
Therefore we need to pray and wait.
I know not if the blessings sought
Will come in just the guise I thought.
I leave my prayer to Him alone
Whose will is wiser than my own.

— Eliza M. Hickok. Used by permission.

The Ways

To every man there openeth
A Way, and Ways, and a Way.
And the High Soul climbs the High Way,
And the Low Soul gropes the Low,
And in between, on the misty flats,
The rest drift to and fro.
But to every man there openeth
A High Way, and a Low.
And every man decideth
The Way his soul shall go.

— John Oxenham, in *Bees in Amber*.
Used by permission.

I read
In a book
That a man called
Christ
Went about doing good.

It is very disconcerting to me
That I am so easily
Satisfied
With just
Going about.

— George Small.

Not what we give, but what we share,
For the gift without the giver is bare;
Who gives himself with his alms feeds
three,
Himself, his hungering neighbor, and
Me.

— James Russell Lowell. Used by permission of the authorized publishers, Houghton Mifflin Company.

A Hungry Man Is at My Door

A hungry man is at my door,
What shall I do?
My fire is warm, my loaf is sweet,
And I have you,
Sufficient for my needs . . . but, oh,
The wind is cold.

A hungry man is at my door
And he is old;
And he is weary, waiting to be fed.
I cannot dine
Until I break in three this loaf
I thought was mine.
I cannot rest beside my fire
Unless I share
Its warmth with him, and find a cloak
That he can wear.
This done — and he upon his way
Along the street —
I find a warmer fire — my loaf
Grown doubly sweet.

— Grace Noll Crowell. Used by permission of *The Christian Advocate.*